Venkata Rangarao Kaluri

Direction Finding Algorithms for Practicing Engineers

With C and MATLAB Code

Springer

Venkata Rangarao Kaluri
Department of Computer Science (ICDT)
Ohio State University
Columbus, OH, USA

ISBN 978-3-032-06996-2 ISBN 978-3-032-06997-9 (eBook)
https://doi.org/10.1007/978-3-032-06997-9

This Springer imprint is published by the registered company Springer Nature Switzerland AG
The registered company address is: Gewerbestrasse 11, 6330 Cham, Switzerland

To my beloved wife, Lavanya Kaluri (née Pragada), whose unwavering support and quiet strength made the completion of this book possible.
To my children, Kadambari Kaluri and Kannan Srinivasan, and Soujanya Kaluri and Chandrasekar Goda, whose love and encouragement have always been a guiding light.
And to my cherished grandchildren, Abhay Ram, Shreya, Aarti, and Aria—the joy of our lives and the hope of our future.

Preface

With reverence and devotion, I bow to the Divine. The inspiration and strength to complete This book comes from that eternal source.

—Sankaracharya

At the very outset, I express my sincere gratitude to Prof. K. V. S. Hari, who generously supported this project during its formative stages despite his demanding schedule. I ask readers to kindly pardon any lapses in thought flow or language, as my primary focus has been on the algorithms—their demonstration and understanding. Throughout this book, I have aimed to present the key concepts of direction-finding methods and their associated algorithms with clarity. Yet, no explanation or mathematical detail can replace hands-on experience. To that end, I have provided accompanying C and MATLAB code to help readers deepen their understanding by actively working through the material. A working knowledge of MATLAB and access to a basic C compiler will be helpful; both tools are widely available and well supported. For convenience, each chapter concludes with a table listing the directories containing the relevant MATLAB and C code.

Nearly 30 years ago, I struggled to understand direction-finding literature as a hardware engineer, finding its abstractions often felt distant from practical needs. This experience inspired this book, which marks the culmination of a twelve-year Jupiter cycle of learning and reflection. A key influence was the 1996 *IEEE Signal Processing Magazine* article, "*Two Decades of Array Signal Processing*," emphasizing the evolving relevance of the field. Each figure in this book serves as an executable program, carefully crafted from actual code, and aims to clarify concepts without overwhelming readers with mathematical jargon. I encourage you not only to read but also to engage with the figures, run the code, and experiment with the algorithms for a deeper understanding. The book was developed over two years, primarily living in Princeton, an environment that fosters clarity and contemplation.

A distinctive feature of this book is its emphasis on implementation. Most algorithms are written in C, with MATLAB interfaces via MEX files. This "MEXing" approach allows high-performance C code to be called from within MATLAB, enabling efficient execution and fast Visualization. All figures were generated using these routines, often run in cloud environments. The complete source code, including C implementations and MATLAB wrappers, is available to book readers. Though not production-optimized, it provides a solid base for engineers to explore and build upon.

Since direction finding is an interdisciplinary field, variable names and notations may differ slightly between chapters. I have adopted conventions tailored to each domain for clarity. Although I have made efforts to maintain consistency, I kindly ask readers to excuse any notational inconsistencies that may arise. The variables are specific to their respective sections and are intended to be self-explanatory.

This book spans six chapters. Chapter 1 introduces the history and relevance of direction finding, tracing its origins from defense applications to its contemporary roles in radar, drones, and intelligent systems. Chapter 2 establishes the mathematical foundations, with an emphasis on matrix algebra and linear transformations. Chapter 3 focuses on Time Difference of Arrival (TDOA) methods, presenting both intuitive explanations and practical illustrations. Chapter 4 delves into subspace methods—including MUSIC, *gold*-MUSIC (a contribution from the author), *root* MUSIC, κMUSIC, and *easy* MUSIC tailored for wideband signals. Chapter 5 covers beamforming and beam steering techniques. Finally, Chap. 6 Presents case studies drawn from FMCW radar systems and voice-based applications.

Each chapter concludes with a structured table that lists the associated program files and their corresponding directories and the files necessary for creating MEX files, enabling readers to experiment directly with the Algorithms discussed.

My intent in writing this book is to bridge the gap between theory and practice. I hope it becomes a valuable and inspiring resource for engineers, students, and researchers. Working in radar, signal processing, communications, and related fields.

Readers can download the code for this book from the Springer Nature Code Inside repository on GitHub via the Access Source Code tab at https://link.springer.com/book/9783032069962

Belle Mead, NJ, USA
July 2025

Venkata Rangarao Kaluri

Acknowledgements I offer my salutations to Lord Ganesha, the remover of obstacles, and to Lord Shiva, the Supreme Almighty. It is only through their divine blessings that I have been able to bring this work to completion. I also extend my heartfelt thanks for the blessings of my parents and brothers, whose values and support have guided me throughout my life. I am especially grateful to my living brother, Narasingarao Kaluri, for his enduring encouragement and steadfast presence. I continue to seek Their grace for the successful dissemination and meaningful impact of this effort. My deepest gratitude goes to my family—my wife, children, and grandchildren—who played an indispensable role in making this work a reality. Their love, patience, and unwavering support have been the foundation of this journey. This work is lovingly dedicated to them.

The idea for this book took shape following my talk at IEEE, New Jersey, on *gold* methods, which planted the initial seed for this project. I am grateful to Dr. Ajay Poddar and Dr. U. M. S. Murty of Keysight Inc., USA, for their encouragement and support. I would also like to express my sincere thanks to Prof. Atul Negi, Dean of the School of Computer and Information Sciences at the University of Hyderabad, India, whose academic guidance has accompanied me through various phases of this journey. His camaraderie, insight, and thoughtful discussions have been a constant source of intellectual encouragement.

I would be failing in my duty if I did not express my sincere gratitude to Prof. Zhiqiang Lin, Distinguished Professor in the Department of Computer Science at The Ohio State University, for providing me with an academic umbrella under which this book could take shape, and to Prof. Eric Fosler-Lussier, Department Chair, for his unwavering support and encouragement. I am equally indebted to Prof. Anish Arora, Chairman of the Department of Computer Science, who graciously reviewed this book during my stay in Dublin, Ohio. My heartfelt thanks also go to my close walking companion and dear friend, Dhulipala Srinivasrao of Dublin, Ohio, with whom I often shared my stress during the writing process. His constant encouragement and presence have been a great source of strength throughout this journey.

A special thanks to Oruganti Gopalakrishna, who set the *muhurtam* (auspicious time) for starting this project, coordinating spiritual guidance with this academic effort. Professor Suman Kumar Tumuluri from the Department of Mathematics at the University of Hyderabad for their ongoing encouragement and support. I also thank my co-author from Ref. [1], Balaji Kanigicherla, and his team for their technical collaboration and support.

Santhosh Kumar and Chethan Kumar of Texas Instruments, Bengaluru, thank you for allowing me to use some of the images. Many well-wishers, friends, and mentors—both known and unknown—have supported and encouraged me in countless ways. Their unseen hands helped bring this professional and social initiative to life. Thank you, Grammarly! Your help has been invaluable in ensuring clarity and correctness in my writing.

Belle Mead, NJ, USA Venkata Rangarao Kaluri

Reference

1. Kaluri V. Rangarao and Balaji Kanigicherla, DOA Estimation via kMUSIC in FMCW Radar 793 Application, in Proc IEEE Aug ICSP2018, pp 903–908, Beijing, China

Competing Interests The author has no competing interests to declare that are relevant to the content of this manuscript.

Reserved Abbreviations and Symbols

Other than these symbols local to the context and defined for the purpose, they can be reused.

DF	Direction Finding
DOA	Direction of Arrival
DSP	Digital Signal Processing
LNA	Low Noise Amplifier
ULA	Uniform Linear Array
$\mathbf{x}$	Any Bold Face Lower case is a column vector
$\mathbf{x}^T$	Transpose of $\mathbf{x}$
$\mathbf{x}^{*T}$	Conjugate Transpose of $\mathbf{x}$
$\mathbf{X}$	Any Bold Face Upper case is a matrix
$\lvert\mathbf{X}\rvert$	Determinant of matrix $\mathbf{X}$ if it is a square
$\lVert\mathbf{x}\rVert$	Square root of $\mathbf{x}\mathbf{x}^{*T}$
φ	Phase of Narrow Band Signal
z	Delay operator or a complex variable
λ	Wavelength of the propagating wave or Eigen Values of the Matrix based on the context
c	Speed of the propagating wave
θ	DOA of the emitter
$\hat{\theta}$	Estimated DOA of the emitter
$\mu(\mathbf{x})$	$\frac{\sum_i x_i}{n}$ mean of the argument x and n length($\mathbf{x}$)
$\sigma^2(\mathrm{x})$	$\frac{\sum_i (x_i-\mu)^2}{n-1}$ variance of the argument $\mathbf{x}$ and n length($\mathbf{x}$)
$\sigma(\mathbf{x})$	Standard Deviation of the argument $\sqrt{\left[\sigma^2(\mathbf{x})\right]}$
π	A mathematical constant, the ratio of a circle perimeter to diameter
j	A mathematical constant $\sqrt{-1}$
t	Continuous time, a real number
k	Discrete time, an integer
δt	A real number related as $t = k\delta t$
f	Frequency of the wave with or without subscripts or superscripts

$x_k^{\frac{\pi}{2}}$ Time series x_k shifted by 90°
$J(.)$ An objective function with an argument scalar or a vector

Contents

List of Figures

Chapter 1
History and Need

This opening chapter will explore the historical significance and development of direction-finding (DF) systems. We will explain the various applications of DF across different sectors of society and provide estimates of their usage. Additionally, we will offer a brief overview of the algorithms [1] used in DF systems and discuss their evolution. Ultimately, we will give a glimpse into DF for wideband signals, with more detailed information reserved for future chapters. We will introduce the fundamental principles of DF systems to ensure that readers are well-prepared for the chapters that follow. Furthermore, we will examine the impact of high-speed computing and the advancements in high-speed analog-to-digital converters. Finally, we will discuss the transition from the analog to the digital domain and its influence on the field of direction finding.

1.1 Purpose

This subject of DF is interdisciplinary, and the author would like to cover all the required mathematics that is needed for DF algorithms in this book. As a result, this book serves as a self-contained reference guide that any practicing engineer can rely on. One crucial aspect is that engineers often struggle with implementing the algorithms in real-world situations. To address this issue, we have provided C code integrated with MATLAB for all the algorithms in the book. These codes can be compiled, executed, and tested to instill reasonable confidence.

V. R. Kaluri, *Direction Finding Algorithms for Practicing Engineers*,
https://doi.org/10.1007/978-3-032-06997-9_1

1.2 History of Direction Finding (DF)

Humans have long relied on directional awareness for survival and navigation. Biologically, this is enabled by the spatial separation of sensors our two ears for detecting *acoustic* signals and our two eyes for sensing *electromagnetic* signals in the visual spectrum. This spatial diversity allows the brain to estimate the direction of incoming signals with remarkable precision, forming a natural and effective direction-finding system.

Inspired by this principle, scientific efforts to mechanically and electronically determine the direction of signal sources began in the late nineteenth century. Notably, Smith-Rose and Hopkins [2–4] documented early attempts to determine the direction of ultra-short electromagnetic waves, tracing these developments back to the foundational experiments of Hertz in the 1880s.

These early investigations laid the groundwork for the invention of practical direction-finding systems. Over time, technologies such as rotatable antenna beams were developed, enabling the detection and tracking of signal sources with higher accuracy. These advancements ultimately led to the commercial implementation of course-indicating beacons and landing beam systems—critical technologies still used today in modern aviation for guiding aircraft [5].

1.2.1 The Need

The ability to locate objects in space is essential in various fields. Different technologies are used to locate objects above and below water, but the underlying algorithms remain the same. Ferdinand Magellan's navigation achievement, which helped locate new land masses, is an excellent historical reference for understanding the importance of direction-finding. During World War II, there was a significant push to develop direction-finding algorithms for military applications, which later found their way into civilian applications.

1.3 Direction Finding System (DF)

The DF System is complex, with various sensing elements and other associated hardware. The physical size depends on the *wavelength* and propagation velocity of the wave. Underwater systems have complexities and problems that differ from RF systems above water. The fundamental principle of direction finding (DF) is to sample signals in space. This is essential to determine the direction of the source. It's similar to how two ears on a human head work together to sample sounds in space. Digital Signal Processing (DSP) has dramatically impacted various DF applications with the advancement of digital technology. For instance, electronic beam steering has often replaced mechanical systems [6].

1.3.1 Generic View

Figure 1.1 shows a simplistic but accurate view of a *generic* direction-finding system. There are two primary components: the sensor and the processing component, which executes the algorithm and outputs direction. The direction obtained is a random variable $\hat{\theta}$.

1.3.2 Cardinals of DF

Ross's paper [3] discusses the challenges of direction-finding in high-frequency environments, which can be grouped into three categories. First, the sensing system, such as an antenna or sensor, must be appropriate for the type of energy being detected. Second, the algorithm used to estimate the source direction must account for challenges in wave propagation, such as multi-path propagation. Finally, the bearings obtained from readings must be correctly interpreted. In the figure labeled as Fig. 1.1, you can see three blocks: Geometry, Algorithm, and Output. The textbook provides detailed explanations of the blocks, along with an interpretation of the output parameter $\hat{\theta}$, which is an estimate of the direction of arrival (DOA) θ. Under ideal conditions, the residue $e_k = \theta - \hat{\theta}_k$ has zero energy. The variance of e_k, denoted as $\sigma^2_{e_k}$ or simply σ^2, is a good measure of the energy of this residue. Many factors contribute to the variance, including noise, unwanted modulations, channel imperfections, design tolerances, component imperfections, and sometimes hostile intentional jammers. These factors contribute to an increase in variance. Good algorithms *minimize* this σ^2 and make a mean of $\hat{\theta}_k$ asymptotically close to the unknown value θ.

1.3.2.1 Geometry

Over the years, the antenna system has undergone several changes. It has evolved from Adcock's [7] use of spaced vertical aerials to different practical spaced-loop direction-finders, as well as to systems of wide-aperture and synthetic-aperture systems. The various geometries assumed vary from Uniform Linear Array (ULA) Uniform Circular Array (UCA) [8, 9], and Hexagonal Array [10], among others. DSP technology has introduced new concepts, leading to changes in arrays and paving the way for interpolated or synthetic arrays. Sufficient work has been reported [11–13] and discussed in this area.

1.3.2.2 Algorithms

Direction finding has evolved from mechanical systems to analog electronics and digital systems. Nowadays, antenna arrays [8, 9, 14] or smart antennas [15, 16] are used for this purpose. The methods used for direction finding are related to Digital Signal Processing (DSP) and Control and Estimation Theory. Willsky [17] has explained these relationships in detail. Modern algorithms [1] for direction finding involve accurate phase measurement [18–20], gold-MUSIC [21], time delay estimate [22, 23], and the use of the *Kalman Filter Approach* [24]. These methods assume an array of antennas and a collection of snapshots, which means simultaneous measurements of signals at the antennas. The different types of methods and related papers have been outlined, and important references are provided.

1.3.2.3 Output

The Direction of Arrival (DOA) estimate, denoted by $\hat{\theta}$, is a random variable whose probability density function (PDF) reflects the Statistical variability of the estimator. This PDF is illustrated in the accompanying Fig. 1.1. The accuracy of the DOA estimate is typically characterized by its standard deviation σ. The mean of multiple realizations of $\hat{\theta}$ provides the best unbiased estimate of the true DOA.

Several analyses of DOA estimation accuracy have been reported in the literature. The *Cramér-Rao Bound (CRB)* sets a theoretical lower bound on the variance of any. unbiased estimator, offering a benchmark for the best possible performance under a Given statistical model. The CRB depends on the signal and noise model, but not on the specific. Estimation algorithm. While the bound may not always be easy to derive in general settings, it is obtainable for certain well-defined cases. Detailed CRB analyses relevant to DOA estimation are available in several studies [25–28].

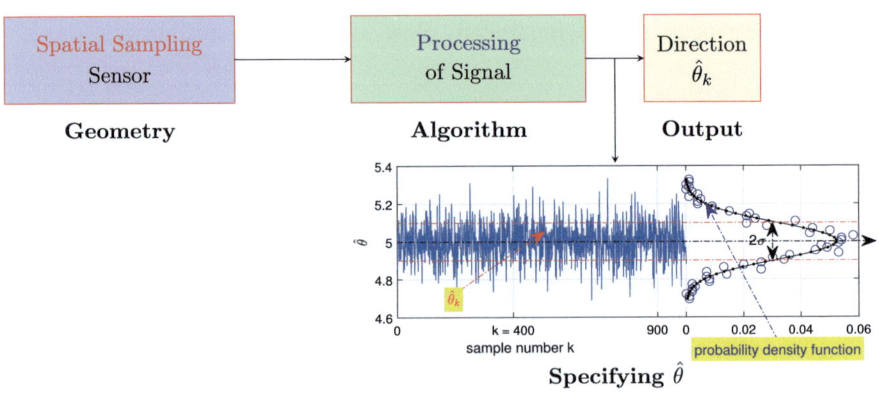

Fig. 1.1 Direction finding overview

1.4 DF Domains

Direction Finding (DF) systems are sophisticated technologies that have become ubiquitous in modern society. These systems serve various purposes and can be classified into three main domains: communication, radar, and acoustics. Figure 1.2 shows authors' viewpoint usage trends in domains and their sub-domains. DF systems used in communication help identify the location of a radio transmitter or receiver. They are commonly used in mobile phones, walkie-talkies, and other communication devices. Radar-based DF systems, on the other hand, are widely used in aviation, military, and weather forecasting. These systems utilize radio waves to determine the locations of objects and calculate their speed and direction of movement. Lastly, DF systems used in acoustics are most commonly found in navigation and underwater communication systems. Submarines and marine researchers often use sound waves to locate underwater objects. Above-water applications include speaker direction, robot cleaners, and ultrasonic applications in medical and other allied areas. DF systems play a significant role in our daily lives, improving communication, transportation, and safety.

1.5 Mathematical Back Ground

Direction Finding (DF) is a specialized field with numerous practical applications in various industries. Initially, analog signal processing was the prominent technique used in this field, utilizing communication engineering, linear systems, statistics, circuits, and devices, as well as detection and estimation. For instance, the Butler

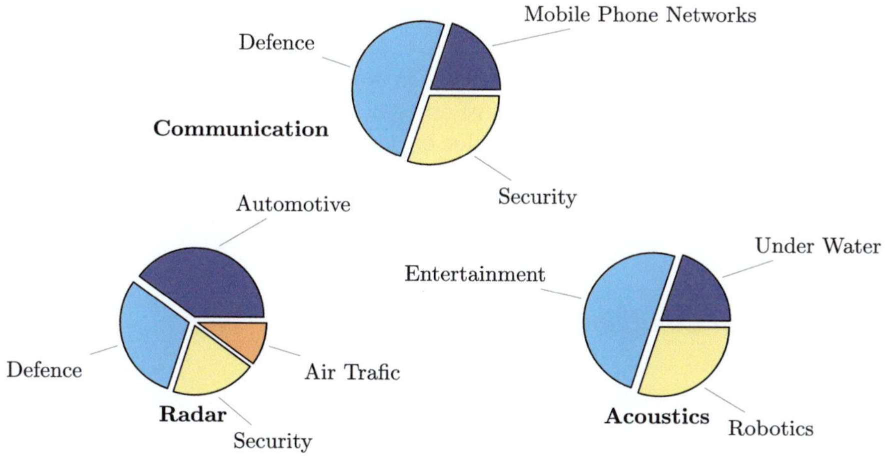

Fig. 1.2 Direction finding domains

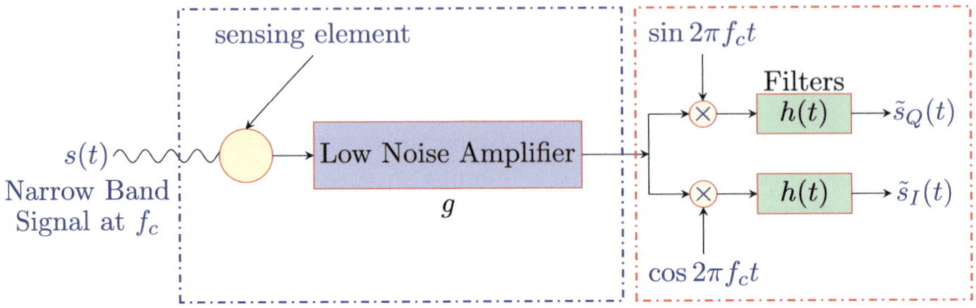

Fig. 1.3 Signal conditioning at direction finding

matrix is a typical example of how the Fourier transform is implemented using analog components, which requires demanding device specifications. Therefore, a thorough understanding of DF requires a comprehensive grasp of the areas above. The field of direction finding has made significant progress with the introduction of signal digitization. This progress has resulted in the integration of various statistical methods, multivariate optimizations, and linear algebra concepts, making direction-finding more efficient and versatile. Acoustic and radar imaging are among the new areas enabled by high-accuracy direction-finding technology. As a result, having a deeper understanding of control, estimation, and digital signal processing has become necessary, and it has opened up new avenues in direction finding. The author has taken a keen interest in presenting this chapter to help beginners quickly grasp the principles and apply them to create novel algorithms or methods.

1.6 Sensor Geometries

DF systems rely on the geometry of the sensor used. Different geometries are used, and Figs. 1.4 and 1.5 present some examples in both the analog and digital domains. It is important to note that the emitter or reflector, indicated as a red-filled circle, is at a distance of R. Assuming that the value of $\left[\tan^{-1}\left(\frac{d}{R}\right) \times \frac{180}{\pi}\right]$ is less than or equal to 1 in Figs. 1.4 and 1.5 ensures that the value of θ is the same at all elements. This empirical condition is crucial.

1.6.1 Signal Conditioning

It is essential to understand that each sensor element must be associated with a corresponding hardware component before a signal can be obtained, whether in the analog or digital domain. The received signals vary with time, denoted by t, and in the discrete case, we define a relation as $t = \delta t \times k$, where δt is a constant, and k is

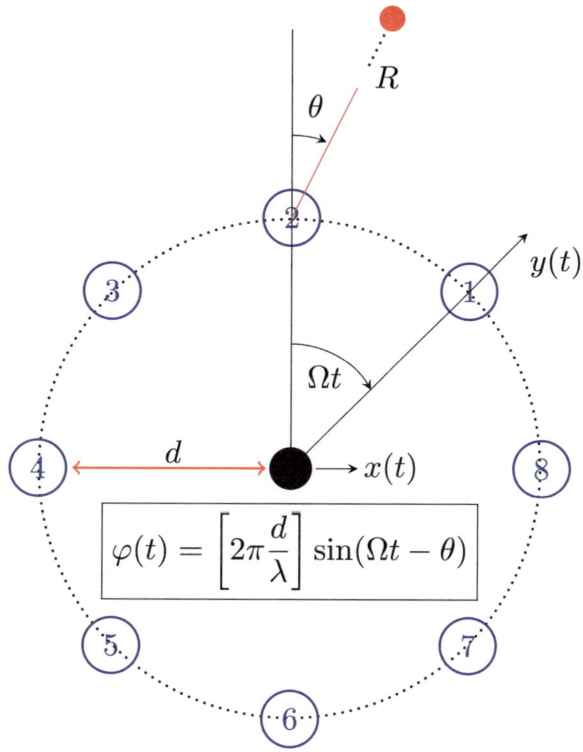

Fig. 1.4 Uniform Circular Array (UCA) geometry

an integer. The number of elements chosen in both circular and linear arrangements is arbitrary and is fixed relative to each other.

Upon receiving a signal, it is crucial to bring it down to an Intermediate Frequency (IF) output. The IF output is the frequency at which the signal is processed further. The received signal is passed through a Low Noise Amplifier (LNA) and a receiver, which amplifies and cleans up the signal. The Low Noise Amplifier (LNA) is a crucial component that amplifies the signal while maintaining a low noise level. The LNA is typically placed close to the antenna element to prevent the noise from entering the system. The receiver, on the other hand, is responsible for detecting the signal. Understanding the role of each component in the sensor geometry is vital to creating a compelling direction-finding (DF) system. The signal source's direction can be accurately determined by carefully optimizing the positioning and configuration of the antenna elements, LNAs, and receivers.

1.6.2 *Basic Hardware*

DF systems require basic components that must be outlined. One such component is an antenna element or an acoustic sensor, followed by a low-noise amplifier (LNA). This is followed by a receiver chain, illustrated in Fig. 1.3 in the red box. The narrow band signal $s(t)$ received at the sensing element and LNA with gain g is shown in the blue box. The receiver chain essentially performs a faithful frequency translation and resolves as two *orthogonal components* represented as

$$\boxed{s(t) \longrightarrow \tilde{s}_I(t) + j\tilde{s}_Q(t)} \text{ and } \boxed{f_c \longrightarrow f_{IF}}$$

which are denoted as $\tilde{s}_I(t)$ and $\tilde{s}_Q(t)$.

In Fig. 1.3, the receiver chain is enclosed in a red box. This chain comprises two crucial components, namely a filter and a mixer. The filter has an impulse response of $h(t)$ or a frequency characteristic of $H(f)$. It's essential to note that most components in this chain introduce a phase shift, which is particularly significant in direction-finding (DF) systems. These shifts should ideally remain constant for all elements to ensure accurate determination of the DF. Therefore, designing these systems requires careful attention as this significantly affects the DF error budget. However, by switching to digital receivers, we can predict and compensate for all phase errors, guaranteeing phase matching at all elements. Consequently, the accuracy of these systems is limited only by the algorithms used.

1.6.2.1 Analog

In the early 1980s, Direction Finding (DF) systems typically used a circular array, as shown in Fig. 1.4. The array consisted of a reference antenna at the center, surrounded by other antenna elements arranged in a circular path at a distance of d. The omnidirectional antenna, located at the center of the system, collects the narrow band reference signal $x(t)$ at a frequency of f_c with an inherent phase modulation $\phi(t)$, given as

$$x(t) = B\cos[2\pi f_c t + \phi(t)] \tag{1.1}$$

Δ denotes the elevation angle of the signal, while the direction of arrival (DOA) is denoted by θ. The velocity of propagation c is related by $c = \lambda f_c$. To achieve the Doppler effect, the antenna elements were switched clockwise or anticlockwise at a speed of Ω radians per second. The signal received at each element on the circular path is $y(t)$. The resulting multiplexed signal $\tilde{y}(t)$, obtained through this switching arrangement, can be expressed as follows.

$$\tilde{y}(t) = A\cos\left[2\pi f_c t + \phi(t) + \cos\Delta\varphi(t)\right] \text{ where } \boxed{\varphi(t) = \left[2\pi\frac{d}{\lambda}\right]\sin(\Omega t - \theta)} \tag{1.2}$$

Analog methods are utilized to extract phase modulation $\varphi(t)$ and DOA θ from signals $x(t)$ and $\tilde{y}(t)$. Cheol-Sun Park and Kim [29] provided a comprehensive account and derived the CR-Rao bounds, as well as the variance of DOA for a digital equivalent.

$$\sigma^2_{DOA} = \frac{1}{2N\,(\text{snr})\,\frac{\pi D^2}{\lambda}\frac{m}{2}} \tag{1.3}$$

where N is number of snapshots and m is number of elements and snr is signal-to-noise ratio. The aperture of the antenna system is $D = 2d$.

1.6.2.2 Digital

The Uniform Linear Array (ULA) structure is commonly used in formulating algorithms for many digital signal processing (DSP) applications in DF systems. The structure is depicted in Fig. 1.5. In the digital domain, a narrow band, the analog signal $s(t)$, is converted using a high-speed analog-to-digital converter. The converter outputs a signal labeled as s_k with an arbitrary phase. At a specific sensor point, such as antenna element (2), the narrow-band signal $s_k^{(2)}$ splits into two orthogonal signals [30]. These signals are an ordered pair $[x_k^{(2)}, y_k^{(2)}]$.

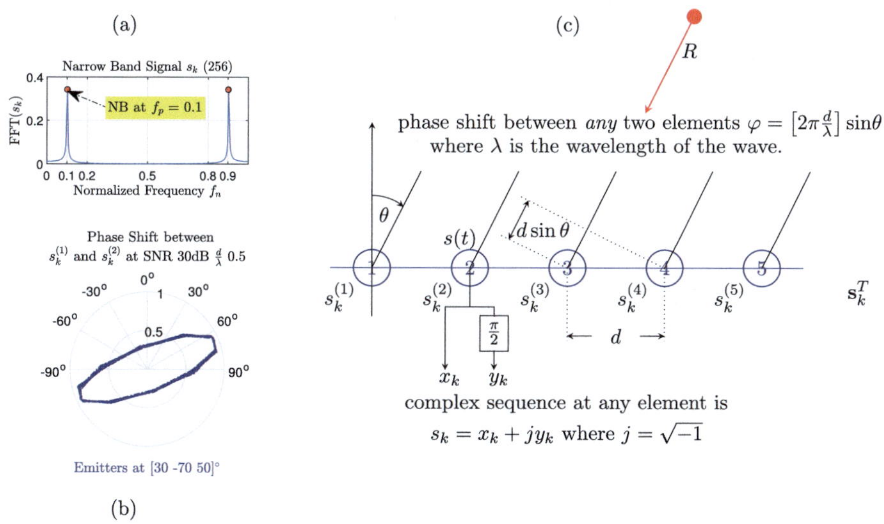

Fig. 1.5 Uniform linear array in direction finding

$$x_k = a\cos(2\pi f_c \delta t k + \varphi) + \gamma_k \tag{1.4}$$
$$y_k = b\sin(2\pi f_c \delta t k + \varphi) + \gamma_k \tag{1.5}$$

where γ_k is of arbitrary *statistics*. The signals x_k and y_k are orthogonal to each other. We can represent them as $s_k = x_k + jy_k$, where $j = \sqrt{-1}$. When the narrow band signals become *monochromatic*, they become a *phasor* and can be written as

$$s_k^{(2)} = \sqrt{(a^2 + b^2)} \times e^{j(2\pi f_c \delta t k + tan^{-1}\frac{b}{a} + \varphi)} \tag{1.6}$$

The complex narrow band sequence at antenna element (2), denoted by $s_k^{(2)}$ in Eq. 1.6, can be expressed in compact form by using the variables $A = \sqrt{(a^2 + b^2)}$ and $\phi = \tan^{-1}\frac{b}{a}$, where A and ϕ are constants. These values are consistent across all antenna elements, and the new equation is given by

$$s_k^{(2)} = Ae^{j(2\pi f_c \delta t k + \phi + \varphi)} = s_k^{(1)} e^{j\varphi} \tag{1.7}$$

We can obtain a crucial recursive relation by denoting $z = e^{-j\varphi}$ in Eq. 1.7.

$$s_k^{(2)} = s_k^{(1)} z^{-1} \tag{1.8}$$

The notation

$$z = e^{-j\varphi}, \text{ where } \varphi = \left[2\pi \frac{d}{\lambda}\right] \sin\theta \tag{1.9}$$

It is a functional algebraic notation that will be useful later in the following chapters. We define a row vector called a *snapshot*, denoted as

$$\mathbf{s}_k^T = \{s_k^{(1)}, s_k^{(2)} \ldots, s_k^{(m)}\}, \text{ where } m \text{ is the number of antenna elements in an ULA.} \tag{1.10}$$

Or switching to matrix indexing notation with index k for each signal, we write as

$$\mathbf{s}_k^T = [s_{k1}, s_{k2} \ldots, s_{km}] \text{using Eq. 1.8 rewrite as } \mathbf{s}_k^T = s_{1k}[1, z^{-1} \ldots, z^{-(m-1)}] \tag{1.11}$$

For notational clarity, we rewrite Eq. 1.11

$$\boxed{\text{Defining } \mathbf{h}^T = [1, z^{-1} \ldots z^{-(m-1)}] \text{and the polynomial } h_k(z) = \mathbf{s}_k^T \mathbf{h}} \tag{1.12}$$

It's important to remember that the signal we're dealing with is narrowband and originates from a ULA. Next, we introduce a data matrix known as a *look matrix*, denoted by

$$\mathbf{S}^T = [\mathbf{s}_1, \mathbf{s}_2 \ldots \mathbf{s}_k \ldots \mathbf{s}_N] \text{ note } \mathbf{s}_k \text{is } k\text{th column vector of } m \text{ rows.} \tag{1.13}$$

The *look matrix* $\mathbf{S}$ consists of N snapshots and is an $N \times m$ matrix as shown in *picture* Eq. 1.14, where the red filled circles represent the m sensors indicating spatial sampling.

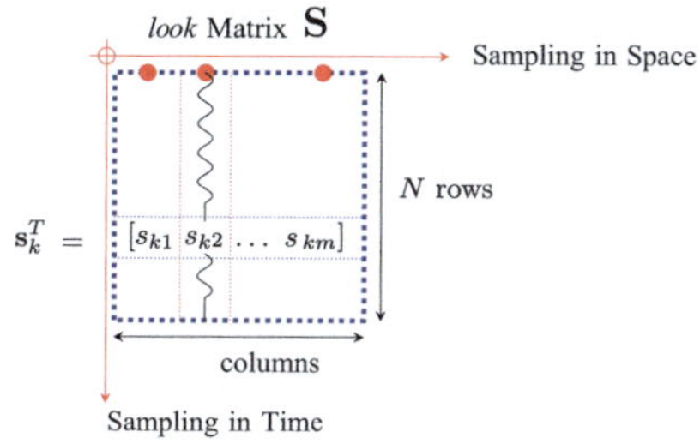

(1.14)

The rows in this look matrix represent spatially sampled data, while each column represents temporally sampled data, as depicted in column 2 of *picture* Eq. 1.14. There are various techniques available to process either $\mathbf{s}_k$ or $\mathbf{S}$, resulting in a range of algorithms that are suitable for specific applications or domains. One important formulation is the *look* matrix is visualized as *weighted* sum of *sliced look* matrices nicely depicted by Harry [31] in his paper in Fig. 1, $\tilde{\mathbf{S}}_i$ of $N \times m$ as

$$\mathbf{S} = \sum_{i=1}^{m} \lambda_i \tilde{\mathbf{S}}_i \text{ where } \lambda_i \text{ is a real constant} \tag{1.15}$$

The idea in Eq. 1.15 is a fundamental concept that we will discuss in the chapter on matrix algebra. There are established methods available to obtain λ_i and the corresponding $\tilde{\mathbf{S}}_i$.

1.7 Earlier Methods

Various techniques are available to estimate a signal's Direction of Arrival (DOA), and the choice of method depends on the technology being used. In the past, interferometer methods [32, 33] and trigonometric interpolation [34] were commonly employed. To estimate DOA, the interferometer method measures and processes the relative phase delay between two adjacent antenna elements. To resolve quadrant ambiguity, we use the topology of pairs of elements such as circular or cross. We can obtain the relative phase difference information from any adjacent antenna elements. We can compute this information using analog or digital methods when dealing with planar array sensors.

1.8 Time Difference of Arrival (TDOA) Method

One of the earliest and most efficient methods for finding direction is to estimate the Time Difference of Arrival (TDOA). This method is highly accurate for pulsed or coded waveforms since detecting signals is very efficient. In Fig. 1.6a, you can see the arrangement of the sensors and the emitter's orientation required to create the delay τ. A and B sensors are spaced apart to generate a delay. There are several ways to measure the delay τ between two received signals, as discussed in [22, 35]. By determining this delay, we can estimate the signal's Direction of Arrival (DOA). The delay depends on the angle of arrival θ, the inter-element spacing d, and the wave's propagation velocity c. To compute the DOA from the delay, we use the following formula where: τ units of time in seconds, c units of meters per second, and d has the units of meters.

$$\sin\theta = \left[\frac{c\tau}{d}\right] \text{this implies } c\tau < d \text{ since } |\sin\theta| \leq 1 \text{ the solution range is } -\frac{\pi}{2} < \theta < \frac{\pi}{2} \tag{1.16}$$

1.8.1 Topology

To understand how sensors are positioned and the constraints used in Direction Finding, we need to examine some specifics with the help of Fig. 1.6 and Eq. 1.16. The DOA estimate with a two-element topology can only be obtained between $-\frac{\pi}{2}$ and $-\frac{\pi}{2}$. Therefore, when designing a direction-finding system, the choice of d, the number of sensor elements, and their geometry are crucial to overcome these limitations. One example is a 3 element configuration [22] with $d = \frac{\lambda}{2}$.

1.8.2 Estimating the Delay

In this method [22], an algorithm is described for estimating the time delay τ between two time series x_A and x_B collected by the antenna elements A and B, which are spatially separated as shown in Fig. 1.6a. In this setup, the signal received at B, x_B, will be delayed compared to the signal received at A, x_A. The delay is depicted in the diagram of Fig. 1.6c, where the signal x_B is shown in blue and lags behind the signal x_A, shown in red, by τ. We use normalized units in cycles, where one cycle has $\tilde{N}$ samples and $f_n = \frac{1}{\tilde{N}}$ is the normalized frequency, expressed as samples per cycle. The signals x_A and x_B are sampled at $\tilde{N}$ samples per cycle, and we define phase shift due to one sample $\delta\phi = \frac{2\pi}{\tilde{N}}$ radians. This method establishes the delay τ as the sum of two components, as

$$\tau = \tau_c + \tau_f \text{ where } \tau_c = n\delta\phi \text{ and } \tau_f = \epsilon\delta\phi \text{ where } n \text{ is an integer and } \epsilon \text{ is a real number.} \quad (1.17)$$

There are three distinct steps. The first step is to determine the detection window (72.5 to 96.3 cycles), as illustrated in Fig. 1.6c. The other two steps are finding the coarse delay τ_c and the fine delay τ_f. Figure 1.6c diagram shows the value of $n = 27$ samples and the shifted waveform as $x_B \longrightarrow \tilde{x}_B$. Figure 1.6b diagram shows that the waveform $\tilde{x}_B$ is passed through an *all pass filter* to obtain $\hat{x}_B$, to obtain a fine delay ϵ of -2.48 samples. In this example, the delay $\hat{\tau} = (n + \epsilon) f_n$ is 4.0867 cycles. It's important to remember that the distance between the two sensors, A and B, must conform with the constraint given in Eq. 1.16. The detailed algorithm is given in the following chapters.

1.8.2.1 Detection Window

To estimate delay τ, we need to determine the detection window, represented by a dotted line in the top diagram of Figure 1.6a. The Signal-to-Noise Ratio (SNR) is a crucial parameter that affects detection ability. Specialized algorithms determine the detection time envelope that contains the signals x_A and x_B. The lower diagram in Fig. 1.6a shows the detected signals x_A and x_B, color-coded for easy identification. Additionally, this diagram displays the estimated delay $\hat{\tau}$ and the estimated signal $\hat{x}_B$.

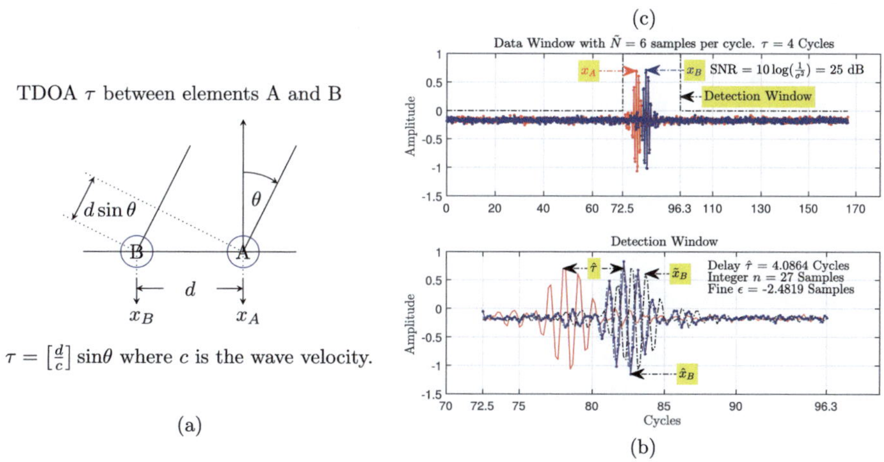

Fig. 1.6 Signals received at two elements A and B

```
% ... copyright protected Dr Kaluri V Ranga Rao
% ... kaluri@ieee.org
clc; clear all;
close all;
% .... Input Parameters ..
N = 6; Tau = 4; Cycles = 10.0; nSize = 1000; SNR = 25.0;
% .... Matlab callable C code ..
[a,b,c,f,tou]=delayT(N,Tau,Cycles,nSize,SNR);   mex command
t = a(1,:); x1 = a(2,:); x2 = a(3,:);
T = b(1,:); y1 = b(2,:); y2 = b(3,:);
% .... detection window ..
X = [t(1) T(1) T(1) T(length(T)) T(length(T)) t(length(t))
Y = [0     0    1      1              0   0];
% .... data plot with detection window ..
subplot(211); plot(t,x1,'.-r',t,x2,'.-b',X,Y,'-.k');grid;
title([' Data Window with $\tilde{N} =$ ' num2str(N) ...
' samples per cycle. $\tau$ = ',...
num2str(tou(5)) ' Cycles'],'interpreter', 'latex');
ylabel(' Amplitude ','interpreter', 'latex');
label211(x1,x2,T,t,SNR);
% .... Waveforms and Delay Estimation ..
subplot(212); plot(T,y1,'r',T,y2,'-.b',T,c,'-.k',T,f,'.-b'
grid;
xlabel(' Cycles ','interpreter', 'latex');
ylabel(' Amplitude ','interpreter', 'latex');
title('Detection Window','interpreter', 'latex');
label212(f,T,y1,c,tou,N);
```

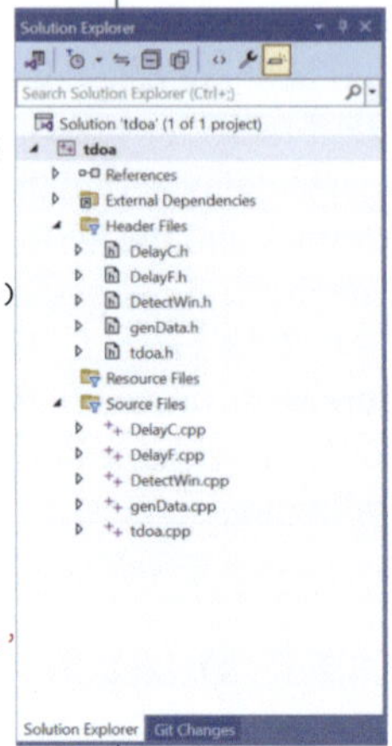

Fig. 1.7 Embedded C in MATLAB for TDOA

1.8.2.2 Embedded C in MATLAB

In Fig. 1.7, the MATLAB code with the MEX command is highlighted in yellow. This code was developed in C using Visual Studio and integrated with MATLAB. You can refer to upcoming chapters for a detailed explanation of the code and use it to create your algorithm. The outcome of this code, along with the delay estimation, is shown in Fig. 1.7 with the corresponding waveforms in Fig. 1.6a. In Fig. 1.7, a companion code includes five modules. This code comprises approximately 4,000 lines of C code, and modules are displayed in the solution panel for the reader's convenience. The C code is password-protected and can be accessed on Git.

1.8.2.3 Direction of Arrival

Figure 1.6a displays the complete results. On estimating the delay $\hat{\tau}$ using Eq. 1.16, the DOA $\hat{\theta}$ is estimated. Quadrant ambiguity is addressed by the DF system, which employs an algorithm that comprises *three* elements providing coverage of the entire azimuth plane. The algorithm details are included, and the results are presented for various signal-to-noise (SNR) conditions. The DF system achieves an accuracy of 1° or better for SNR less than 4 dB, as determined by the standard deviation (σ). The subsequent chapters provide a detailed explanation of the algorithms used for TDOA estimations and their respective performance. It is worth noting that other

TDOA methods, such as those presented in [36–40], utilize beamforming or beam steering techniques to obtain TDOA.

1.9 Beam-Forming and Beam-Steering

In arrays, the beam represents the array's response in the azimuth and or elevation planes. Notionally, it is like a linear time-invariant filter's magnitude *frequency response*. Several techniques are available to manage this response. One of these methods is beamforming and beam-steering, which are available for narrowband signals. These ideas took a paradigm shift in the context of Direction Finding. Signals from Uniform Linear Array (ULA) are represented by vector $\mathbf{s}_k^T$ in Eqs. (1.7), (1.8), (1.10), (1.11) as shown in Fig. 1.5. An antenna array, such as the ULA shown in Fig. 1.5, captures combined and weighted signals to produce a single output. Using Eq. 1.12, this output is called the objective function $J(\varphi)$ is defined as

$$J(\varphi) = |\mathbf{s}_k^T \mathbf{W}\mathbf{h}| \text{ where } \mathbf{W} \text{ is a diagonal matrix} \tag{1.18}$$

with diagonal as $[w_1, w_2 \ldots, w_m] = \mathbf{w}^T$ are the weights mostly complex. Other formulations, such as g-MUSIC [21] and methods, use this form.

$$J(\varphi) = \frac{1}{\left(\sum_{i=1}^{m-1} \underbrace{s_1|\mathbf{w}_i^T\mathbf{h}|}_{|a_i(z)|}\right)} = \frac{1}{\sum_{i=1}^{m-1}(|a_i(z)|)} \tag{1.19}$$

Equation 1.18 can be written elegantly as $|s_1\mathbf{w}^T\mathbf{h}|$ with the notation described in Eq. 1.12. We can drop the variable s_1 as it does not contribute to φ. The objective function can be written as

$$J(\varphi) = \frac{\overbrace{|(w_1 + w_2 z^{-1} + w_3 z^{-2} \ldots + w_m z^{m-1})|}}{|b(z)|} \tag{1.20}$$

other formulations like in Eq. 1.19 we describe the objective function as

$$J(\varphi) = \frac{1}{\sum_{i=1}^{m-1}(|a_i(z)|)} \tag{1.21}$$

in which $z = e^{-j\varphi}$ where $\varphi = \left[2\pi \frac{d}{\lambda}\right] \sin\theta$, relates the *phase* with the spatial angle θ using the properties of the wave. We can rewrite the objective function as

$$\boxed{J(\varphi) = |b(z)| \text{ as in Eq. 1.20 or } J(\varphi) = \frac{1}{\sum_i (|a_i(z)|)} \text{ as in Eq. 1.21}} \quad (1.22)$$

The polynomials $b(z)$ or $a_i(z)$ in Eq. 1.22 are known as the *spatial filter*. Depending on the chosen method, we must either maximize or minimize the objective function. Most concepts and calculations in this field are based on linear filters from the time domain.

In this context, it is essential to note that finding the Direction of Arrival (DOA) involves estimating $b(z)$ or $a(z)$. Solving for these *spatial filter* is equivalent to spectral estimation solutions. All the methods from that domain are applicable. Understanding the equations labeled as (1.20) and (1.21) is crucial for properly comprehending the DF system. In this context, examining the impact of the spatial sampling number $\frac{d}{\lambda}$ is essential. This is similar to the normalized frequency($\frac{\delta t}{T}$) in the time domain. In the time domain, the Nyquist theorem connects the signal's sampling rate and the maximum frequency content present in the signal. If $\frac{d}{\lambda} > 0.5$, the *grating lobe* phenomenon occurs, which is similar to the aliasing error in the time domain. The relationship between the phase φ and the DOA θ is non-linear and varies with $\frac{d}{\lambda}$. This is shown in Fig. 1.8 for two values of $\frac{d}{\lambda} \leq 0.5$ as two separate diagrams in the exact figure. For $\frac{d}{\lambda} = 0.5$, the phase angle φ covers the entire range between $-\pi$ to π, and the spatial angle θ is spans $-\frac{\pi}{2}$ and $\frac{\pi}{2}$. The blue-red plot illustrates the relationship in the top diagram of Fig. 1.8. The linear portion of the φ relation, within the range of $-\frac{\pi}{2}$ to $\frac{\pi}{2}$, is depicted in red. It was obtained by conducting a linear regression and is represented by the equation $\theta \approx 0.33\varphi$. In the lower diagram of Fig. 1.8, it is essential to note that when the spatial sampling number $\frac{d}{\lambda}$ is 0.3, the usable phase span is reduced, as shown in the black-green plot. The unavailable phase is also shown while covering the same DOA range. Additionally, the linear part is $\theta \approx 0.55\varphi$, with a steeper slope. Beam steering and beamforming are two standard methods that are used in practice. Using the beam steering technique, the weights are adjusted adaptively to estimate the Direction of Arrival (DOA). In contrast, in beamforming, the weights are fixed by design to create a specific beam shape. To gain a better understanding of both techniques, you can take a look at Figs. 1.9 and 1.10.

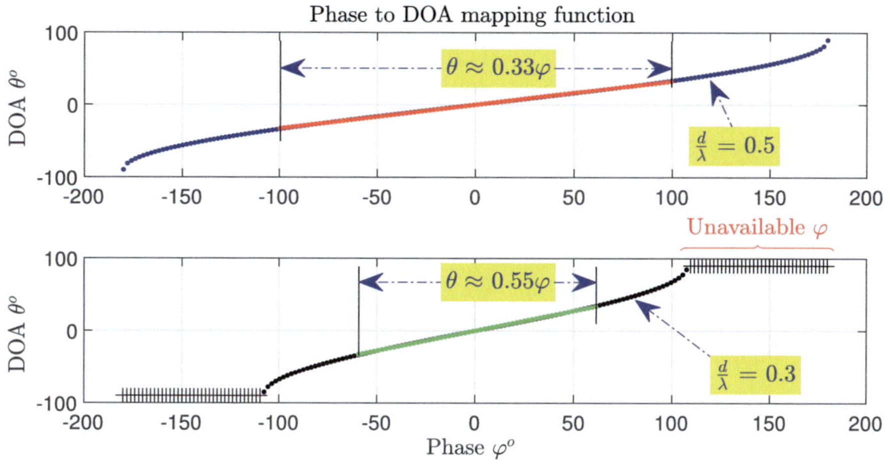

Fig. 1.8 Phase to DOA mapping function

1.9.1 Beam Forming

In this technique, the response is constant and the pattern is based on the domain of application. One of the earliest techniques used to detect and locate emitters is beamforming. Guy and Davies describe direction finding using the Butler Matrix technique [41], which provides amplitude and phase distributions for generating phase modes that are orthogonal to each other. The phase difference between the signals received on two modes allows for direct measurement of the signal's angle of arrival for a single far-field source. Chan et al. [42] presents a digital, frequency-domain implementation of the Adcock-Butler Matrix [43] for direction finding. Littlefield and team [44] discuss the use of analog-to-digital converters (ADCs) and Digital Signal Processing (DSP) for digital Radio Frequency (RF) beamforming in phased arrays for MILSATCOM. In radar, a conical scan radar was used where the *squint* beam was rotated along the axis of the radar, creating a modulation that was used to estimate the direction of arrival (DOA).

In the case of fixed beams, the beam axis usually passes through the maxima of beam response, known as *electrical* axis. An axis normal to ULA is called *mechanical* or *bore* axis at zero degrees as shown in Fig. 1.9. The angle between *bore* axis and *electrical* axis is known as *squint* angle θ_q. We have generated two *squint* beams involving the Uniform Linear Array (ULA) in this example. In this illustration, we need to compute the vector **w** or polynomial $h(z)$, as shown in Eq. 1.20 for generating beam response $J(\varphi)$. The number of sensor elements, denoted as m, is chosen as 5. The following Eq. 1.23 defines w_i, where a value of 0.5 is used for $\frac{d}{\lambda}$, and the index i varies from 1 to 5.

$$w_i = e^{i \times \left(j2\pi \frac{d}{\lambda} \sin\theta_q\right)} \text{where } \theta_q \text{is squint angle of the beam} \tag{1.23}$$

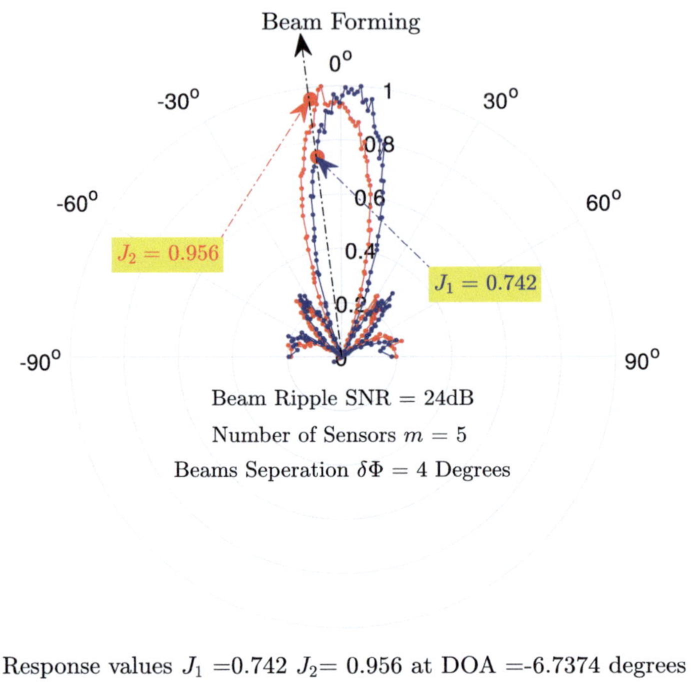

Fig. 1.9 DOA via beam forming

Two beams, $J(\varphi)$, are generated using Eq. 1.23 with $\theta_q = \pm 2^\circ \times \frac{\pi}{180}$ for computing the weights w_i in the vector $\mathbf{w}$. The two fixed beams (red and blue) have electrical axes separated by $\delta\Phi$ (which is $2\theta_q = 4^\circ$), as shown in Fig. 1.9. The beam patterns are measured in an anechoic chamber as $J_m(\varphi)$. The beam ripple in dB is defined as dropping the argument φ for ease of calculation.

$$10 \log_{10} \left[\frac{\sigma^2(J)}{\sigma^2(J_m - J)} \right] \text{ where } \sigma^2(.) \text{ is variance operator} \tag{1.24}$$

The beam ripple is shown in Fig. 1.9 as 24 dB computed using Eq. 1.24. This is one of the error contributors in the DOA method. From the same figure, we see the response of the two beams at an angle of -6.73°, with $J_1 = 0.785$ and $J_2 = 0.934$. Beforehand, a table of J_1 and J_2 for various values θ (DOA) is created since the beams are fixed. This table is a mapping function denoted as $(J_1, J_2) \longrightarrow \theta$. This method involves two steps: detection and DOA estimation. The value of θ is estimated using a table or mapping function for a given detected pair of (J_1, J_2). A detailed algorithm is described in the following chapters.

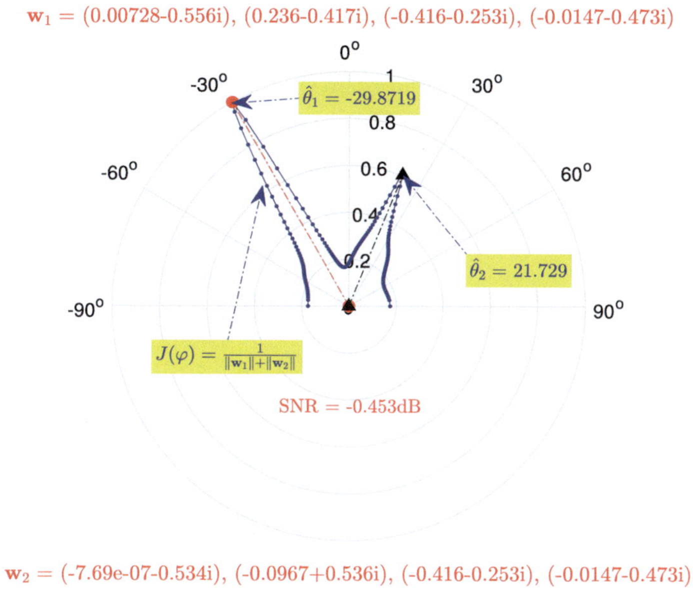

Fig. 1.10 DOA via beam steering

1.9.2 Beam Steering

Leiner [45] offers a general comparison of direction-finding systems. In their study, Benjamin and colleagues [46] introduce a phased array that can adaptively steer beams. Gabriel introduces adaptive beamforming [6], and Griffiths [47] presents a simple algorithm for real-time antenna array processing. Berni [48] presents a direction-finding technique that uses an adaptive antenna array. Other recent papers [49, 50] also discuss this subject.

1.9.2.1 Tweaking of Weights

To adjust the focus of the beam on the targets, the weights in the vector **w** in Eqs. (1.19) or (1.20) can be modified. This vector is referred to as the steering vector, which can typically be represented as a matrix. In the context of adaptive beamforming, an objective function such as $J(\varphi) = |b(z)|$ or $\frac{1}{\sum_i(|a_i(z)|)}$ as given in Eq. 1.22 can be used to optimize the beam's response by adjusting these weights, which are coefficients of the polynomial $b(z)$ or $a_i(z)$. The steering vector is obtained by optimizing $J(\varphi)$. The *snapshots* in Eqs. 1.10 and 1.11, or the *look* matrix in Eq. 1.13, will guide the optimization process. This function is often the beam response itself. In this example, we choose to maximize and $J(\varphi) = \frac{1}{|\mathbf{w}_1^T\mathbf{h}|+|\mathbf{w}_2^T\mathbf{h}|}$ and the optimal function is shown in Fig. 1.10. The two peaks are depicted as a solid red circle and a black triangle, along

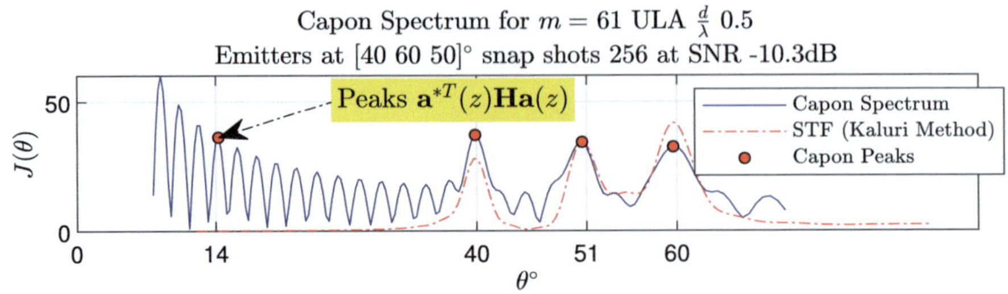

Fig. 1.11 Capon spectrum and STF details are given in Chap. 5

with the optimal vectors, in Fig. 1.10. In this example, the Signal-to-Noise Ratio (SNR) of the *look* matrix, a critical factor in the beam steering process, is -0.453 dB. A more detailed explanation is needed to understand how these steering vectors were obtained, and we will provide this information in the upcoming chapters. For clarity, Fig. 1.10 shows the $J(\varphi)$ and numerical values (peaks). These peaks indicate the target's or emitters' Direction of Arrival (DOA). In this section, we demonstrate beam steering using two steering vectors, $\mathbf{w}_1$, and $\mathbf{w}_2$, to estimate the DOAs as θ_1 and θ_2. In the following chapters, we will explain the methods and provide details on calculating these steering vectors, along with the corresponding C code. One recent development is spatial tuning (Radar).

1.9.2.2 Spatial Tuned Filtering and Capons Method

An innovative and award-winning method, Kaluri et al. [23] for estimating the direction of arrival (DOA) of narrowband signals using the beam-steering by *spatial tuning technique*. This method performs better than Capon's method, while tolerating poor SNR conditions. The beam steering coefficients $\mathbf{w}$ are calculated using a second-order autoregressive (AR) narrow-band filter. The reader may please revisit 1.9 highlighted mini page. However, mapping an AR(2) process into a spatial domain is not feasible (Fig. 1.11). To overcome this problem, an equivalent FIR filter is obtained, representing a uniform linear array (ULA). The paper derives a closed-form solution for these FIR filter coefficients. The DOA is estimated by performing beam-steering using these coefficients. The estimation of DOA is considered a min-max problem, where minimization is performed using a simple golden-section univariate minimization technique without gradients. Details are provided in the chapters that follow.

1.10 Model-Based Methods

The fundamental concept behind direction-finding is to estimate the polynomial $h(z)$ as described in Eq. (1.22), which is derived from spectral estimation. A comprehensive review of this topic can be found in the paper by Kay and Marple [51]. Marple's tutorial [52] provides a straightforward introduction to Prony's Method and the Pisarenko Harmonic Decomposition Method [53].

1.10.1 Prony's Method

In this method, we assume the time series signal x_k is noise-free and is a sum of several damped sinusoids, dating back to 1795. A prior knowledge of the number of frequencies is assumed; it is like a known model order

$$
\begin{aligned}
\sin(\omega k) &= 2\cos\omega \sin(\omega(k-1)) - \sin(\omega(k-2))\text{the trignometric identity can be written as} \\
x_k &= r\left[2\cos\left(2\pi\frac{\varphi^\circ}{360}\right)\right]x_{k-1} - r^2 x_{k-2}\text{is an AR(2) process [54, 55] with poles at } (r,\varphi) \\
y_k &= \mathbf{x}_k^T\mathbf{p}\text{where } y_k = x_k \text{and } \mathbf{x}_k^T = [x_{k-1}\ x_{k-2}]\text{and } \mathbf{p}^T = [a_1\ a_2]
\end{aligned} \tag{1.25}
$$

We have the transversal filter $h(z) = [1\ a_1 z^{-1}\ a_2 z^{-2}]$. Using least squares (LSQ), we solve Eq. 1.25 and obtain the coefficient of x_{k-1}. In case of spectral estimation the parameter $\frac{\varphi^\circ}{360}$ gives the normalized frequency and in case DOA (θ) estimation $\varphi = 2\pi\frac{d}{\lambda}\sin\theta$. Generally, the roots of the polynomial $h(z)$ or the peaks of the frequency response would indicate the frequency for time series analysis. We discussed subspace methods in Chap. 4. This method is less tolerant of noise and biased in case of noise.

1.10.2 Pisarenko Harmonic Decomposition Method (PHD)

We have seen in the Prony method that x_k must be noise-free, and this is a strict restriction. The least squares solution uses the covariance matrix as

$$
\mathbf{H} = \sum_{i=1}^{N}\mathbf{x}_i\mathbf{x}_i^T \text{where } \mathbf{x}_k^T = [x_{k-1}\ x_{k-2}\ldots x_{k-m}] \tag{1.26}
$$

The presence of noise in the LSQ solution for Eq. 1.25 is biased, and several methods are available to address this issue. One of the popular methods is the MUSIC-like method. In this method, the smallest eigenvalue λ_{min} of the covariance matrix is taken and the corresponding eigenvector is used as the transversal filter $h(z)$ and the frequency is estimated.

1.10.3 Other Accurate Methods

In the past, some approaches to direction-finding relied on specific process models for the signals, such as Auto-Regressive (AR) or Auto-Regressive Moving Average (ARMA) models. However, a recent method developed by Mallik and Kaluri [24] represents another example of direction-finding that focuses on estimating model parameters.

There are numerous other methods in this field, including the instrumental variable methods described by Wong and Polak [56, 57]. Akaike has addressed the statistical aspects of model identification [58, 59] and hypothesis testing. Additionally, Capon's Maximum Likelihood method [60] and Burg's Maximum Entropy method [61] belong to the same category of techniques. Both Pisarenko's method and other eigenanalysis-based approaches are model-based methods. All these techniques utilize covariance, or second-order statistics, of the measurements, which are also used in power density spectrum estimation. Schmidt and other references explain how simple beamforming can be understood as a model-based method using a covariance matrix.

1.11 Eigenanalysis Based Methods

The method of estimating the direction of arrival (DOA) involves the eigendecomposition of the covariance matrix $\mathbf{SS}^T$. The matrix $\mathbf{S}$ is obtained from signal measurements and is defined in Eq. 1.13. The eigenvectors are divided into a noise subspace and a signal subspace. One of this class's earliest and most effective methods is the Multiple Signal Classification (MUSIC) algorithm. Further details and case studies will be discussed in the following chapters. The performance of the *gold*-MUSIC [21] algorithm, including its benefits and a comparison of the time complexities for MUSIC and Root-MUSIC, is described. It's important to note that the MUSIC algorithm by Schmidt [62] was developed after model-based methods.

1.11.1 Multiple Signal Classification (MUSIC)

The application of MUSIC is incredibly versatile, as it can be used with all planar geometries. When dealing with a fixed array geometry, the angle of direction of arrival (DOA) is well-defined. The MUSIC algorithm for DOA estimation evaluates the MUSIC spectrum for various angles and chooses the maxima or peaks as the angles of arrival. The accuracy of values obtained depends on the interval at which the MUSIC spectrum is evaluated. This issue was resolved using the numerically efficient *gold* -MUSIC method.

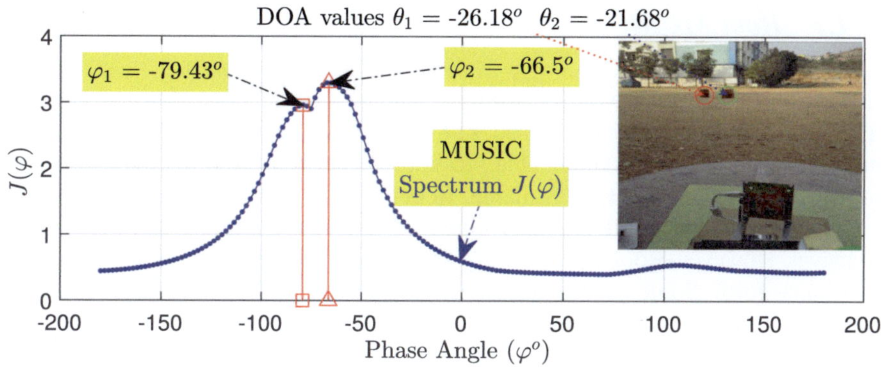

Fig. 1.12 MUSIC spectrum

This is expressed by the complex vector function of the phase angle φ as given in Eq. 1.19, referred to as the MUSIC spectrum, depicted in Fig. 1.12. To estimate DOA, we can plot the inverse square of the distance between the array manifold and the noise subspace labeled as $J(\varphi)$. Peaks can be observed in the plot shown in Fig. 1.12. These peaks correspond to the angle spectrum and phase angles of $(-79.4276°, -66.4974°)$ degrees. By utilizing these phase angles, we can determine the direction of arrival (DOA) as $(-26.1846°, -21.6805°)$ degrees using the formula $\varphi = 2\pi\frac{d}{\lambda}\sin\theta$. The picture inset in Fig. 1.12 highlights the two circled targets. Typically, $\frac{d}{\lambda}$ is 0.5. Assuming φ is in degrees, we can calculate $\hat{\theta}$ using the following equation:

$$\hat{\theta} = \left(\sin^{-1}\left[\frac{\varphi^\circ}{180}\right]\right) \times \frac{180}{\pi} \text{in degrees where } -180 < \varphi < 180 \tag{1.27}$$

The MUSIC spectrum $J(\varphi)$ is shown in Fig. 1.12, along with the phase peaks and their values. The Direction of Arrival (DOA) values, calculated using Eq. 1.27, are also presented. Examining the relationship between φ and the direction of arrival (DOA) in Fig. 1.8 could be interesting, as it provides a linear formula. Pisarenko's method is similar to MUSIC in that it uses eigenanalysis, but it employs only one eigenvalue and the corresponding noise eigenvector. MUSIC and a related constrained MUSIC algorithm are clearly explained in [16]. Constrained MUSIC requires knowledge of some direction of arrival (DOA) sources. This information can be used to remove the components of these known sources from the data vector, and the remaining matrix can be used to estimate the DOA.

1.11.2 Root MUSIC

This text discusses the use of Spectrum to estimate the directions of arrival (DOAs) of narrowband signals. It can be used with any smart antenna geometry and for any purpose where MUSIC is applicable. To improve accuracy and not depend on the interval, Root-MUSIC [63] is available. Root-MUSIC involves finding the roots of a polynomial created using the noise eigenvectors, whose solution gives the angles of arrival. However, Root-MUSIC only applies to uniform linear arrays (ULA) in its original form. Some papers discuss the performance [64] of Root-MUSIC, and some give improvements in speed [65–68]. Root-MUSIC is directly applicable only for ULA, but the algorithm is extended using an interpolation technique to a larger class of arrays [63].

1.11.3 gold-MUSIC

The MUSIC algorithm has evolved, branching into Root-MUSIC and a more efficient algorithm called *gold* MUSIC. This numerically efficient algorithm outperforms Root-MUSIC with the same accuracy and greater efficiency. The steps are the same until eigendecomposition. The gold-MUSIC algorithm is a two-stage process. The first stage evaluates the objective function at coarse intervals. It determines peaks followed by an iterative approach based on gold-section univariate (GSU) minimization [69] to find accurate values of the peaks. The algorithm stops with this first stage if the number of peaks found so far equals the number of estimated peaks. The second stage is an iterative step for achieving an acceptable resolution, using finer intervals around the previously identified peaks to pinpoint those that were previously missed. This includes a method based on a partitioning algorithm for estimating the number of emitters. This algorithm gives good results even when the number of snapshots is small. This gives it an additional computational advantage. It does not compromise on the resolving power of MUSIC.

1.11.4 ESPRIT

For MUSIC, the number of signals D is constrained by the number of sensor elements M by $D < m$, whereas for ESPRIT, it is $D < 2m - 1$. However, ESPRIT is more computationally efficient. A clever combination of ESPRIT and MUSIC is shown in [10], where a hexagonal array is used to determine up to $m - 1$ DOAs using M elements. ESPRIT [70–73] a method based on the eigendecomposition of the covariance matrix. It assumes two identical subarrays are spaced with a constant displacement between corresponding sensor elements. Knowledge of the array manifold is not required for this method. The DOA is obtained after several eigen-decompositions/eigenanalyses. There have also been performance improvements to ESPRIT regarding computation as in Unitary ESPRIT [74]. The relative performance of MUSIC, ESPRIT, and Moving Window is given in [75]. Mewes et al. [76, 77] presented experimental results comparing these *high or super resolution* algorithms. Featherstone et al. [78] give simulation results for channel conditions specific to the HF band.

1.12 Direction Finding for Wide-Band

Interest in direction finding for Wide-Band signals is more recent. Spread spectrum techniques have been widely used in recent radio telecommunication. There are a number of papers on this subject: [11, 79–86]. Most of them divide the wide band into several narrow-band signals and apply existing techniques, such as MUSIC and ESPRIT. As an introduction, an FMCW radar is taken as an example of a wideband signal.

A single board FMCW radar [87] sensor like AWR1642 of Texas Instruments is a millimetric wave radar operating at 77GHz ISM band, which is used for illustration and shown in the inset of Fig. 1.13. This uses a ULA with four elements and $\frac{d}{\lambda} = 0.5$. A typical wideband signal spectrum of time series s_k is shown in Fig. 1.13 using normalized frequency. Each spectral peak represents a narrow-band signal corresponding to a specific target. This figure shows distinct narrow band signals as peaks, with a couple of red square markers at the top two amplitude peaks. These two peaks correspond to two copper bottles in the inset of Fig. 1.13. It can be seen that it is the sum of many, say, n narrow band signals representing a target at each peak frequency f_i. In Fig. 1.13, the top right corner inset shows the environment scanned by an FMCW radar. For illustration, a narrow-band (NB) signal at peak frequency $f_i = 0.11742$ is considered and presented.

$$s_k = \sum_{i=1}^{n} \underbrace{A_i e^{j(2\pi f_i k)}}_{\text{NB complex signal}} \quad \text{where } f_i \text{is peak frequency} \tag{1.28}$$

One important application is in the automotive industry, where FMCW Radars are employed. Recent developments in DF are κMUSIC [19] for broadband signals. This method fares well [18] compared to MUSIC and other established methods. We will briefly outline this method, reserving the more detailed information for the subsequent chapters.

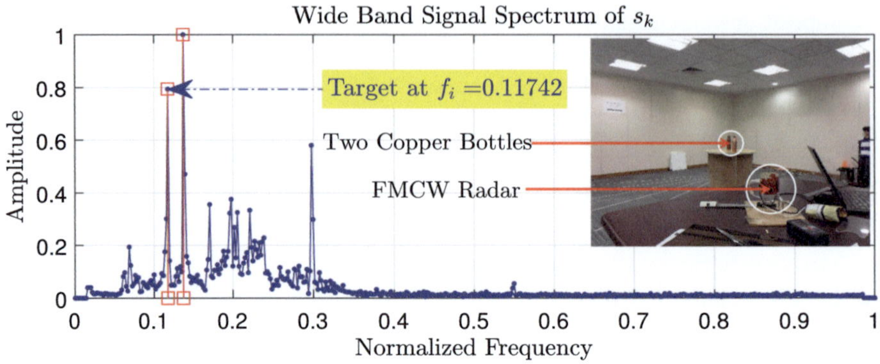

Fig. 1.13 Wide band spectrum

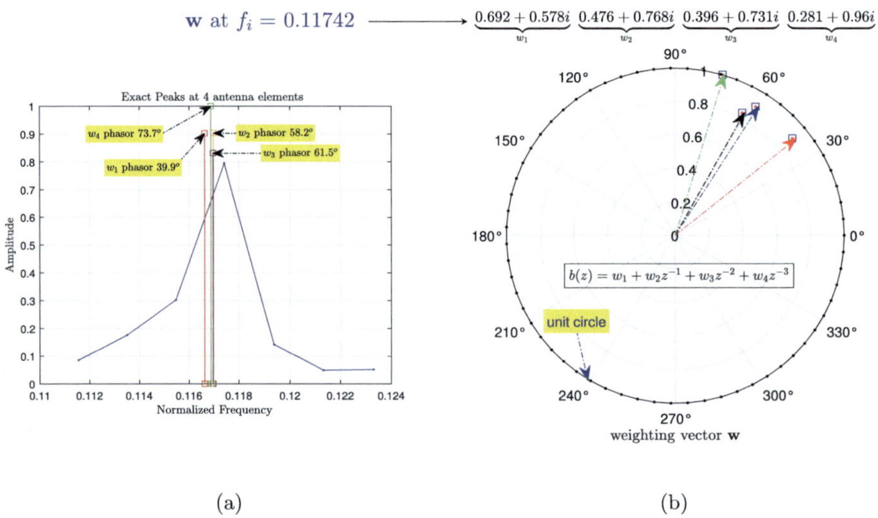

Fig. 1.14 Steering Vector **w** for wide band signals

1.12.1 κMUSIC

This new method is a novel approach to estimating the Direction of Arrival (DOA) for Classifying Multiple Signals (κMUSIC) [19]. It works by reducing the wide-band spectrum to the sum of pure tones at all the dominant peaks of the spectrum at each sensor element, enabling the estimation of the phase at each spatially separated sensor.

We utilize the gold-Fourier-Kaluri (gFK) method to obtain pure tones (phasors) around each spectral peak f_i at all four sensing elements. In Fig. 1.14a, we can observe four distinct spectral peaks at each antenna element, marked by a square and accompanied by the phase angle. Ideally, these angles ([39.9°, 58.2°, 61.5°, 73.7°])

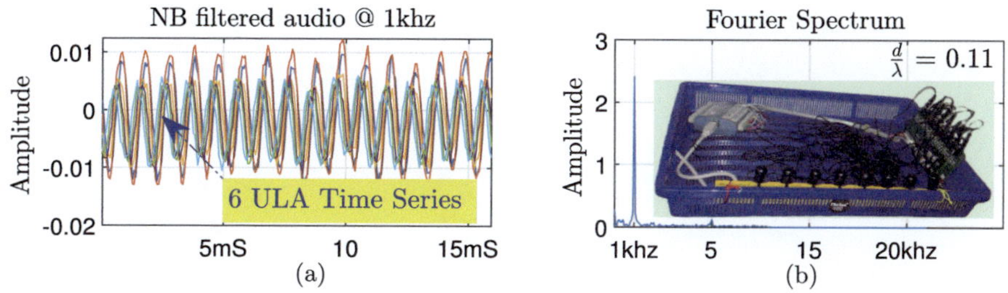

Fig. 1.15 Experimental Setup

should show a linear increase. However, the amplitude variations in $b(z)$ compensate for the non-linear angle variations and provide an accurate Direction of Arrival (DOA), a key metric in our analysis. The corresponding phasor for each antenna's peak frequency, depicted in Fig. 1.14b, is a complex number w_i in the Argand plane. This graphical representation facilitates an understanding of the behavior of these phasors. We then generate a complex beam steering vector $\mathbf{w}$ or $b(z)$ to determine the direction of arrival (DOA), as depicted in Eqs. 1.18 and 1.20. Results are presented and compared with standard MUSIC for reference. They were tested with field data for performance. ADC samples of $M = 128$ were used to reduce computing effort without sacrificing performance. Readers can look forward to more details in the upcoming chapters.

1.12.1.1 Performance

This algorithm provides DOA of $\sigma_\theta = 0.15^\circ$ and $\sigma_r = 0.2\,\text{mm}$ for range, with *lean* computing. The results are comparable with those of standard MUSIC, which is computationally expensive and has other limitations. Current algorithm κMUSIC is $\approx$11 times faster than MUSIC. The angular accuracies are of the order of a fraction of a degree. This is intended to demonstrate a new approach to DOA and the range.

1.12.2 Audio

One frequently encountered signal is the acoustic signal. In this example, we consider the human voice as a wide-band signal. Pitch variations occur continuously as humans communicate, talk, or sing. The point of this section is to show that processing of the *look matrix* $\mathbf{S}$ stays the same. The anatomy of this matrix is shown in picture Eq. 1.14 and is well described in Sect. 1.6.2.2. The structure remains the same regardless of the sensor used to acquire it. The sensor consists of a ULA with six microphones in the audio range [88], as shown in the inset of Fig. 1.15b.

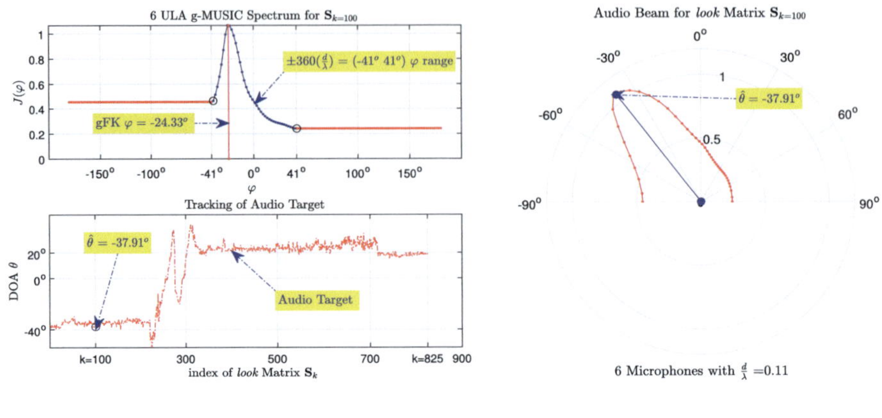

(a) (b)

Fig. 1.16 Tracking audio target via beam steering

The audio signal output is acquired through data acquisition hardware and is filtered using a 1 kHz narrow-band 6th-order digital Butterworth filter. The filtered signal is displayed in Fig. 1.15a, and the Fourier spectrum of the signal is presented in Fig. 1.15b, showing a distinct spectral line at 1 kHz. The speed of sound in air is $\approx 343\frac{m}{sec}$, and the frequency is 1000 $\frac{cycles}{sec}$, and the wavelength λ is 34.3 cm. Microphones are kept 3.8 cm apart for practical reasons, making the array of 8 not too long, and are designed to accommodate a 12-inch wooden foot ruler. This makes the $\frac{d}{\lambda} = 0.11$. Out of the eight microphones available, only six were used in this context.

1.12.2.1 Tracking of Audio Target

Real-time matrices $\mathbf{S}_k$ with a size of 256×6 are obtained, and the DF algorithm *gold*-MUSIC is used to determine the direction of the audio target. In this case, the objective function $J(\varphi)$ is given by the equation $J(\varphi) = \frac{1}{\sum_i (|a_i(z)|)}$ as shown in Eq. 1.22. The optimal response of the beam is determined by calculating weights, which are coefficients of the polynomial $a_i(z)$ produced for each *look matrix* $\mathbf{S}_k$. The relationship between the phase φ and the direction of arrival (DOA) θ is non-linear and changes with $\frac{d}{\lambda}$, as illustrated in Fig. 1.8. In this scenario, the value of $\frac{d}{\lambda}$ is 0.11, which limits the usable range of φ. This limitation is depicted as blue curve in Fig. 1.16a's top diagram. The usable phase is constrained to $\pm 360^\circ \left(\frac{d}{\lambda}\right)$ which is (-41° to 41°) while still maintaining the full range of DOA from -90° to 90°. For $k = 100$, the audio beam spanning -90° to 90° is shown as a polar diagram in Fig. 1.16b, where the audio target is at -37.91°, which is beam peak. The DOA is computed and plotted for various values of $\mathbf{S}_k$ in the bottom diagram of Fig. 1.16a. The top diagram shows the objective function, also known as the MUSIC spectrum, for $k = 100$.

We observe a few things from Fig. 1.16; the target has moved -40° to 20°, depicting the audio target tracking. The audio beam must have been much sharper for a 6-ULA. The deviation is probably due to SNR conditions and the value of $\frac{d}{\lambda}$. We will delve into more details in upcoming chapters of the book, providing further information on obtaining the coefficients and understanding other aspects.

1.13 Analog-Digital Evolution

The transition from analog to digital signal processing has significantly impacted the field of direction finding. While early analog systems laid the groundwork, they were limited by hardware variability, susceptibility to noise, and inflexible designs. The shift to digital techniques introduced considerable advantages in algorithmic flexibility, calibration, and data handling.

A significant factor driving this transformation has been the remarkable improvement in Analog-to-Digital Converters (ADCs). Over the past two decades, ADCs have undergone substantial improvements in both speed and resolution. Modern high-speed ADCs can achieve sampling rates in the gigasample-per-second (GSPS) range, with resolutions ranging from 12 to 16 bits. This capability allows for precise digitization of wideband signals with minimal distortion. As a result, digital systems can capture finer details of signals and implement high-resolution direction-finding algorithms' such as MUSIC, *gold*-MUSIC, ESPRIT, and *root*-MUSIC techniques with greater accuracy and reliability.

As a consequence, contemporary digital direction-finding systems offer superior performance, real-time adaptability, and integration with machine learning and advanced statistical methods. These features make them indispensable in various applications, including electronic warfare and autonomous navigation.

1.13.1 Evolution of ADC Specifications (2000–2020)

The table below summarizes the development of Analog-to-Digital Converters (ADCs) over the past twenty years, emphasizing key advancements in maximum sampling rates, resolution, and signal-to-noise ratio (SNR). In the early 2000s, ADCs typically featured a resolution of 8 to 10 bits and sampling rates of less than 100 million samples per second (MSPS). By 2010, the standard had shifted to 12-bit ADCs that operated with sampling speeds nearing one gigasample per second (GS/s), which became prevalent in RF systems (Table 1.1).

By 2020, the market had advanced ADCs capable of operating at speeds ranging from 5 to 10 GS/s, with resolutions of up to 16 bits. This evolution has significantly enhanced the accuracy and speed of digital direction-finding applications.

Table 1.1 Evolution of ADC over two decades

Year	Sampling rate	Resolution	SNR	Example models
2000	∼100 MSPS	8–10 bits	∼50 dB	Analog Devices AD9042 (12-bit, 41 MSPS), TI ADS804
2010	500 MSPS–1 GSPS	12 bits	60–65 dB	TI ADS5400 (12-bit, 1 GSPS), AD9446
2020	3–10 GSPS	12–16 bits	65–75 dB	TI ADC12DJ5200RF (12-bit, 5.2 GSPS), AD9208 (14-bit, 3 GSPS)

1.14 Summary

This introductory chapter for the book examines the development and significance of Direction Finding (DF) systems, detailing their purpose and historical evolution. It outlines the fundamental need for DF, basic components, system geometry, core algorithms, and output formats. The discussion covers various applications of DF systems and provides an overview of the mathematical principles and sensor geometries involved. Key hardware components, including analog and digital systems, as well as signal conditioning requirements, are reviewed. The chapter also explores earlier DF techniques and progresses to the Time Difference of Arrival (TDOA) method, detailing system setup, delay estimation methods, and MATLAB implementation with embedded C code.

The chapter explores beamforming and beam-steering techniques, including methods such as weight adjustment and spatial filtering, as well as Capon's method. It presents model-based approaches, such as Prony's and Pisarenko Harmonic Decomposition (PHD), along with more accurate methods. Eigenanalysis techniques are discussed, including MUSIC, Root MUSIC, *gold*-MUSIC, and ESPRIT. It concludes with wideband DF techniques, such as κMUSIC and audio-based methods, emphasizing audio target tracking.

1.14.1 MEX File Generation

The table below provides the location of the source code that can be used to generate MATLAB executable code using the command specified in the third column. The second column provides the location of the source code. The C source files and MATLAB scripts used to generate MEX files in Chaps. 3 through 6 They are distributed across several directories, including `chap3\figures\timeDelay\timeDelay`, `chap4\figures\musicAndGmu\musicAndGmu`, `chap4\figures\myMexGetRgD`, `chap4\figures\myMexInitR`, `chap5\figures\stfMexCode`, and

Chapter 1 C Files for MEX		
MEX File	Location of C Files	Command
gMusik.mexw64	chap6\figures\dOfVoice\dOfVoice	mexGmusik.m
gMusic.mexw64	chap4\figures\musicAndGmu\musicAndGmu	mexGmusic.m
getRgD.mexw64	chap4\figures\myMexGetRgD	myMexGetRgD.m
initR.mexw64	chap4\figures\myMexInitR	myMexInitR.m
delayT.mexw64	chap3\figures\timeDelay\timeDelay	mexDelayT.m
abcUla.mexw64	chap5\figures\stfMexCode	myMexAbcUla.m

`chap6\figures\dOfVoice\dOfVoice`. Each of the MATLAB `.m` files listed contains a `mex` compile directive. That links the relevant C source file and generates a corresponding platform-specific MEX file. The following table presents the generated `.mex` files in the first column, the corresponding file locations in the second column, and the MATLAB `.m` Files containing the `mex` command in the third column.

1.14.2 File Organization

This subsection provides a list of program files associated with the introductory chapter *History Need & Purpose*. The files are organized into eight directories, presented in a single table. Each directory name is highlighted in yellow at the top of its respective column for easy identification.

Chapter 1 Program Files					
figAudio	figBeam	figDoa	figAudio	figAudio	figMusic
Ar2Ai.mexw64	Beams2.eps	ds2nfu.m	ula.mat	ula21.mat	closeDoa.jpg
ds2nfu.m	beamStr.eps	pdf_y.m	ula1.mat	ula22.mat	closeDoa.txt
figAuBm.eps	closeDoa.txt	rvDoa.m	ula10.mat	ula23.mat	ds2nfu.m
figAudio.eps	ds2nfu.m		ula11.mat	ula24.mat	figMuSpk.m
figAuMu.eps	easyMusic.m	figKmusic	ula12.mat	ula25.mat	getRgD.mexw64
figAudio.m	figBeam.m	A0803.txt	ula13.mat	ula26.mat	initR.mexw64
gMusik.mexw64	fixedBeam.m	ds2nfu.m	ula14.mat	ula27.mat	input-2cr-15M-N25deg-10M-N27deg.txt
label211.m	getRgD.mexw64	figKMuSpk.m	ula15.mat	ula28.mat	iRdrJan.asv
label321.m	gMusic.mexw64	getRgD.mexw64	ula16.mat	ula29.mat	labelMu211.m
labelPolar.m	initR.mexw64	initR.mexw64	ula17.mat	ula3.mat	muspk.eps
obj.csv	iRdrFoot.jpg	iRdrJan.asv	ula18.mat	ula30.mat	rcon.txt
polarDS2nfu.m	labelFigBeam.m	kMusic.eps	ula19.mat	ula31.mat	
setUP.jpg	labelFxBm.m	labelgFKpeaks.m	ula2.mat	ula32.mat	figPhi2Theta
ulaAu6.jpg	polarDS2nfu.m	labelPhasors.m	ula20.mat	ula33.mat	ds2nfu.m
	rcon.txt	muspk.eps	ula5.mat	ula34.mat	label311.m
figTdoa	twoCr.txt	phasor.eps	ula6.mat	ula35.mat	label312.m
delayT.mexw64	x8M350Hz.mat	polarDS2nfu.m	ula7.mat	ula36.mat	phi2theta.eps
ds2nfu.m		rcon.txt	ula8.mat	ula37.mat	phi2theta.m
JkC.csv	figUlaPhase	twoBot.jpg	ula9.mat	ula38.mat	
label211.m	abcUla.mexw64	wbSpk.eps		ula39.mat	
label212.m	ds2nfu.m	wbSpk.m		ula4.mat	
Shift.csv	figUlaPhase.eps			ula40.mat	
tdoa.eps	figUlaPhase.m				
tdoa.m	labelUla.m				
tdoaC.jpg					

The code itself is provided separately in the repository and is not embedded in this document.

Disclaimer
These demo programs are intended solely for academic and illustrative purposes in connection with the book *Direction Finding Algorithms for Practicing Engineers*, published by Springer Nature. Authored by Dr. Venkata Ranga Rao Kaluri (kaluri@ieee.org) this material is protected under copyright © 2025. All rights are reserved. Unauthorized reproduction, distribution, or use of the code in any form is strictly prohibited without prior written permission. The author assumes no responsibility or liability for any outcomes resulting from the use of this code.

References

1. H. Krim and M. Viberg, *Two decades of array signal processing research*, IEEE Signal Processing Magazine, vol. 13, no. 4, pp. 67-94, 1996.
2. R. L. Smith-Rose, *Discussion on Radio Direction-Finding by Transmission and Reception* in Proceedings of the Institute of Radio Engineers, vol. 17, no. 10, pp. 1897-1898, 1929.
3. W. Ross, *Fundamental Problems In Radio Direction-Finding at High Frequencies(3-30Mc/s)*,(1947).
4. R. L. Smith-Rose and H. G. Hopkins; *Radio Direction-Finding On Wavelengths Between 6 and 10 meters(Frequencies 50 to 30 Mc./Sec.)*, Sep 1938, Institution of Electrical Engineers - Proceedings of the Wireless Section, Volume 13, Issue 39.
5. C. T. Solt, *The Development and Application of Marine Radio Direction Finding Equipment by the United States Coast Guard*, in Proceedings of the Institute of Radio Engineers, vol. 20, no. 2, pp. 228-260, 1932.
6. William F. Gabriel; *Adaptive Arrays-An Introduction*, Proceedings of the IEEE, Vol. 64, No. 2, February 1976 pp 239-272.
7. P. G. Redgment, W. Struszynski and G. J. Phillips; *An Analysis of the Performance of Multi-Aerial Adcock Direction-Finding Systems*. Journal of the Institution of Electrical Engineers - Part IIIA: Radiocommunication, Volume 94, Issue 15,(1947).
8. M. D. Zoltowski and C. P. Mathews, *Direction finding with uniform circular arrays via phase mode excitation and beamspace root-MUSIC*, [Proceedings] ICASSP-92: 1992 IEEE International Conference on Acoustics, Speech, and Signal Processing, San Francisco, CA, USA, 1992, pp. 245-248 vol.5.
9. L. Xiang, Z. Ye, X. Xu, C. Chang, W. Xu and Y. S. Hung; *Direction Of Arrival Estimation for Uniform Circular Array based on Fourth-order cumulants*, Antennas propag, IEEE 2008, Vol. 2, No. 3.
10. Eddy Taillefer,Jun Cheng and Yoichiro Watanabe; *Full Azimuth Direction-of-Arrival Estimation with Successive-Selection Technique*, IEEE Transactions on Signal Processing, Vol. 56, No. 12, December 2008.
11. Benjamin Friedlander and Anthony J. Weiss; *Direction Finding for Wide-Band Signals Using an Interpolated Array*, IEEE Transactions on Signal Processing. Vol. 41, No. 4, April 1993.
12. Ali Broumandan, John Nielsen and Gerard Lachapelle; *TOA Estimation Enhancement based on Blind Calibration of Synthetic Arrays*, 978-1-4244-1722-3/08 ©2008 IEEE.

13. A. Broumandan, J. Nielsen and G. Lachapelle, *Practical Results of High Resolution AOA Estimation by the Synthetic Array*, 2008 IEEE 68th Vehicular Technology Conference, Calgary, AB, Canada, 2008, pp. 1-5.
14. M. Cvetkovic, D. E. N. Davies, H. D. Griffiths and B. S. Collins, *An HF direction finding and null steering system employing a four element circular array*, 1988 Fourth International Conference on HF Radio Systems and Techniques, London, UK, 1988, pp. 221-225.
15. Fengzhen Wang, T. Lo, J. Litva and W. Reed, *High accuracy direction finding antenna array system*, Proceedings of IEEE Antennas and Propagation Society International Symposium and URSI National Radio Science Meeting, Seattle, WA, USA, 1994, pp. 1544-1547 vol.3.
16. R. S. Kawitkar, D. G. Wakde; *An Approach for MUSIC Algorithm in Smart Antenna System*, IEEE International Workshop on Antenna Technology: Small Antennas and Novel Metamaterials, pp 403-406, 2005. https://doi.org/10.1109/IWAT.2005.1461102.
17. Alan S. Willsky; *Relationships Between Digital Signal Processing and Control and Estimation Theory*, Proceedings of the IEEE, Vol. 66, No. 9, September 1978 pp 996-1016.
18. Kaluri V. Rangarao, Atul Negi, *A Perception Engine in Automotive FMCW Radar*, 2023 IEEE International Workshop on Technologies for Defense and Security (TechDefense), Rome, Italy, 2023, pp. 234-239.
19. V. Rangarao and Balaji Kanigicherla, *DOA Estimation via kMUSIC in FMCW Radar Application*, in Proc IEEE Aug ICSP2018, pp 903-908, Beijing, China
20. Kaluri V. Rangarao, and Venugopal A, *gold-Fourier Kaluri Method for Estimating Vortex Shedding Frequency*, in Proc IEEE R10 2016 Symposium (TENSYMP), pp 379-383, Bali, Indonesia
21. Kaluri V. Rangarao and Shridhar V. Narasimhan *gold-MUSIC: A variation on MUSIC to accurately determine peaks of the spectrum*, IEEE Trans Antenna and Propagation Vol 61 issue 4, April 2013 pp 2263-2268
22. Kaluri V. Rangarao and Shridhar V. *An Accurate Numerical Method for Estimating the Delay Between Two Omni-Directional Receiving Elements*, IEEE 30th Digital Avionics Systems Conference 2011, Seattle, Washington, U.S.A., October 2011, pp 8C3-4-8C3-7
23. Kaluri V. Rangarao et al *Estimating the Directions of Arrival of Narrow Band Signals using Spatial Tuned Filter*, IEEE International Conference on Radar Oct 24-27 2011, Chengdu, CHINA
24. Ranjan.K. Mallik, K V Rangarao and U.M.S. Murty, *DOA estimation by least squares approach, Electronics Letters*, vol. 34, no. 12, pp. 1187-1189, June 11 1998
25. Benjamin Friedlander; *On the Computation of the Cramer-Rao Bound for ARMA Parameter Estimation*, IEEE Transactions on Acoustics, Speech, and Signal Processing, Vol. ASSP-32, No. 4, August 1984.
26. Fernando Giannella; *C-R Bounds for AR Parameter Estimation as a function of the Data Length*, IEEE Transactions on Acoustics, Speech and Signal Processing, Vol. ASSP-34, No. 4, August 1986.
27. A. Satish and R. L. Kashyap, *Cramer-Rao bounds and estimation of direction of arrival for narrowband signals*, 1993 IEEE International Conference on Acoustics, Speech, and Signal Processing, Minneapolis, MN, USA, 1993, pp. 532-535 vol.4.
28. Jean-Pierre Delmas and Habti Abeida; *Cramer-Rao Bounds of DOA Estimates for BPSK and QPSK Modulated Signals*, IEEE Transactions on Signal Processing, Vol. 54, No. 1, January 2006 117.
29. Park, Cheol-sun and Kim, Dae-young, *The Fast Correlative Interferometer Direction Finder using I/Q Demodulator*, IEEE Proceedings Asia-Pacific Conference on Communications 2006 pp 1-5, doi 10.1109/APCC.2006.255915
30. Kaluri V. Rangarao et al. *A Robust BFSK Signal Demodulator Using Orthogonal Decomposer* IEEE 32nd Digital Avionics Systems Conference, Syracuse, NY, 2013
31. H. Andrews and C. Patterson, *Singular value decompositions and digital image processing*, in IEEE Transactions on Acoustics, Speech, and Signal Processing, vol. 24, no. 1, pp. 26-53, 1976.

32. A. D. Bailey and W. C. McClurg; *A Sum-and-Difference Interferometer System for HF Radio Direction Finding*, IEEE Transactions on Aerospace and Navigation Electronics, March 1963.
33. N. Burtnyk, C. W. McLeish and J. Wolfe; *Interferometer Direction Finder for the H.F.band*, Proc. IEE, Vol. 110, No. 7, July 1963.
34. Melvin Sandler and Robert Goodwin; *A Method of Trigonometric Interpolation for Processing Radio Direction-Finding Signals*, IEEE Transactions on Aerospace and Electronic Systems, vol. AES-7, No.5, September 1971.
35. Kaluri V Rangarao,, Satish, K *An elegant method for delay estimation in mobile applications*, TENCON 2008 - 2008, TENCON 2008. IEEE Region 10 Conference 19-21 Nov. 2008 Pages:1 - 3
36. Qin Zhi le, *Research for passive location system based on direction-finding of short baseline and time differences of long baseline*, IET International Radar Conference 2009, https://doi.org/10.1049/cp.2009.0158.
37. Hassan Elkamchouchi and Mohamed Abd Elsalam Mofeed; *Direction-Of-Arrival Methods (CIA) and Time Difference of Arrival (TDOA) Position Location Technique*, Twenty Second National Radio Science Conference (NWC 2005), March 15-17, 2005, Cairo - Egypt.
38. Gaoming Huang, Luxi Yang and Zhenya He, *Time-delay direction finding based on canonical correlation analysis [electronic warfare applications]*, 2005 IEEE International Symposium on Circuits and Systems (ISCAS), Kobe, Japan, 2005, pp. 5409-5412 Vol. 6.
39. J. Falk, P. Handel and M. Jansson, *Estimation of receiver frequency error in a TDOA-based direction-finding system*, Conference Record of the Thirty-Eighth Asilomar Conference on Signals, Systems and Computers, 2004., Pacific Grove, CA, USA, 2004, pp. 2079-2083 Vol.2.
40. G. L. Rosen, *ULA Delay-and-Sum Beamforming for Plume Source Localization*, 2007 IEEE Workshop on Signal Processing Applications for Public Security and Forensics, Washington, DC, USA, 2007, pp 1-4.
41. J. R. F. Guy and D. E. N. Davies; *Studies of the Adcock direction finder in terms of phase-mode excitations around circular arrays*, The Radio and Electronic Engineer, Vol. 53, No. 1, pp. 33-38, 1983.
42. Y. T. Chan, Q. Yuan and R. Inkol, *A frequency domain implementation of the Butler Matrix direction finder*, 1999 IEEE Pacific Rim Conference on Communications, Computers and Signal Processing (PACRIM 1999). Conference Proceedings (Cat. No.99CH36368), Victoria, BC, Canada, 1999, pp. 556-559.
43. Y. T. Chan, B. H. Lee, R. Inkol and Q. Yuon; *Direction Finding with a Four-Element Adcock-Butler Matrix Antenna Array*, IEEE Transactions on Aerospace and Electronic Systems Vol. 37, No. 4, October 2001, pp 1155-1162.
44. W. Littlefield, O. Mukhanov, D. Gupta and D. Hitt, *Ultra high speed ADCs and DSP brings direct digital RF beam forming to MILSATCOM phased array apertures*, MILCOM 2009 - 2009 IEEE Military Communications Conference, Boston, MA, USA, 2009, pp. 1-7.
45. Barry M. Leiner; *An Analysis and Comparison of Energy Direction Finding Systems*, IEEE Transactions on Aerospace and Electronic Systems, Vol. AES-15, No. 6, November 1979, pp 861-873.
46. R. Benjamin, W. Titze, P.V. Brennan and H.D. Griffiths; *Symmetric-pair antennas for beam steering, direction finding or isotropic-reception gain*, IEE Proceedings-H. Vol. 138, No. 4, August 1991 pp 368-374.
47. J. Griffiths; *A Simple Adaptive Algorithm for Real-Time Processing in Antenna Arrays*, Proceedings of the IEEE, Vol. 57, No. 10, October 1969 pp 1696-1703.
48. A. J. Berni; *Angle-of-Arrival Estimation Using An Adaptive Antenna Array*, IEEE Transactions on Aerospace and Electronic Systems, March 1975, pp 278-284.
49. Li Lei, X. Rongqing and Li Gaopeng, *Robust Adaptive Beamforming Based on Generalized Sidelobe Cancellation*, 2006 CIE International Conference on Radar, Shanghai, China, 2006, pp. 1-4.
50. Mickey S. Batson, John C. McEachen, and Murali Tummala; *A Method for Fast Radio Frequency Direction Finding using Wireless Sensor Networks*, Proceedings of the 41st Hawaii International Conference on System Sciences - 2008 pp 1-9.

51. S. M. Kay and S. L. Marple, Spectrum analysis' A modern perspective, in Proceedings of the IEEE, vol. 69, no. 11, pp. 1380-1419, 1981.
52. S. L. Marple, *A tutorial overview of modern spectral estimation*, International Conference on Acoustics, Speech, and Signal Processing,, Glasgow, UK, 1989, pp. 2152-2157 vol.4.
53. V. F. Pisarenko; *The retrieval of harmonics from a covariance function*, Geophys. J. Royal Astron. SOC., no. 33, pp. 374-366, 1973.
54. Kaluri V. Rangarao, Atul Negi, *A Novel Method of Generating Complex Sine Wave in Automotive Sensing Application*, IEEE APSCON 2025 20 - 22, 2025 IIT Hyderabad, India
55. P. A. Janakiraman and Kaluri. V. Ranga Rao, *Identification of linear modulated FM signal via a new recursive modified response error method (REM)*, in IEEE Transactions on Acoustics, Speech, and Signal Processing, vol. 36, no. 10, pp. 1675-1679, Oct. 1988.
56. Kwan Y. Wong and Elijah Polak; *Identification of Linear Discrete Time Systems Using the Instrumental Variable Method*, IEEE Transactions on Automatic Control, December 1967, pp 707-718.
57. P. Stoica, M. Cedervall and T. Soderstrom; *Adaptive instrumental variable method for robust direction of arrival estimation*, IEE Proc.-Radar, Sonar Navig., Vol. 142, No. 2, April 1995 pp 45-53.
58. H. Akaike, *A new look at the statistical model identification*, in IEEE Transactions on Automatic Control, vol. 19, no. 6, pp. 716-723, 1974
59. H. Akaikc, *Use of statistical models for time series analysis*, ICASSP '86. IEEE International Conference on Acoustics, Speech, and Signal Processing, Tokyo, Japan, 1986, pp. 3147-3155.
60. J. Capon; *High resolution frequency-wavenumber spectrum analysis*, Proc. IEEE, Vol. 57, No. 8, August 1969.
61. J. P. Burg; *Maximum entropy spectral analysis*, Proc. 37th Meet. Soc. Exploration Geophysicists, 1967; reprinted in Modern Spectrum Analysis (D. G. Childers, ed.), IEEE Press, New York, 1978, pp. 34-39.
62. Ralph O. Schmidt; *Multiple Emitter Location and Signal Parameter Estimation, IEEE Transactions on Antennas and Propagation*, Vol. AP-34, No.3, pp 276-289, March 1986.
63. Anthony J. Weiss and Benjamin Friedlander; *Direction Finding for Diversely Polarized Signals using Polynomial Rooting*, IEEE Trans. Signal Processing, Vol 41, no. 5, pp 1893-1905, 1993.
64. Bhaskar D. Rao and K. V. S. Hari, *Performance Analysis of Root-Music*, IEEE Transactions on Acoustics, Speech and Signal Processing, Vol. 37, No. 12, December 1989.
65. Q. S. Ren and A. J. Willis; *Fast root MUSIC algorithm*, Electronics Letters, 13th March 1997, Vol. 33, No.6.
66. J. Zhuang, W. Li and A. Manikas; *Fast root-MUSIC for arbitrary arrays*, Electronics Letters 21st January 2010, Vol. 46, No. 2.
67. K. V. S. Babu, *A fast algorithm for adaptive estimation of root-MUSIC polynomial coefficients*, [Proceedings] ICASSP 91: 1991 International Conference on Acoustics, Speech, and Signal Processing, Toronto, ON, Canada, 1991, pp. 2229-2232 vol.3,
68. M. Zhang, L. Ji and P. Jia, *A Fast and Robust MUSIC Algorithm for Estimating Multiple Coherent Signals*, 2024 9th International Conference on Communication, Image and Signal Processing (CCISP), Gold Coast, Australia, 2024, pp. 1-7.
69. *Algorithms for Minimization Without Derivatives*, R. Brent, Englewood Cliffs, NJ, USA: Prentice-Hall, 1983.
70. A. Paulraj., R. Roy and T. Kailath. *Estimation of signal parameters via rotational invariance techniques' ESPRIT.* In Proc. 19th Asilomar Conf. on Circuits, Systems and Comp. , pp. 83-89, Asilomar, Pacific Grove, CA, Nov. 1985.
71. B. A. Paulraj, R. Roy and T. Kailath. ESPRIT - *A subspace rotation approach to signal parameter estimation*, Proc. of the IEEE, 74(7): 1044-1045, 1986.
72. R. Roy, A. Paulraj and T. Kailath, *Estimation of Signal Parameters via Rotational Invariance Techniques - ESPRIT*, MILCOM 1986 - IEEE Military Communications Conference: Communications-Computers: Teamed for the 90's, Monterey, CA, USA, 1986, pp. 41.6.1-41.6.5.

73. Richard Roy and Thomas Kailath; *ESPRIT-Estimation of Signal Parameters via Rotational Invariance Techniques*, IEEE Transactions on Acoustics, Speech and Signal Processing, Vol. 37, No. 7, July 1989.
74. M. Haardt and J. A. Nossek; *Unitary ESPRIT: How to obtain increased estimation accuracy with a reduced computational burden*, IEEE Trans. SignalProcess., Vol. 43, No. 5, May 1995 pp 1232-1242.
75. R. L. Johnson and G. E. Miner, *Bearing discrimination methods for MUSIC, ESPRIT and moving window*, IEEE Conference on Military Communications, Monterey, CA, USA, 1990, pp. 1142-1146 vol.3.
76. H. Mewes, F. Wolf and J. Luiken ter Haseborg, *Experimental investigations on high resolution direction finding algorithms*, Proceedings of IEEE Antennas and Propagation Society International Symposium and URSI National Radio Science Meeting, Seattle, WA, USA, 1994, pp. 1540-1543 vol.3.
77. H. Mewes, F. Wolf and J. L. ter Haseborg, *High resolution direction finding algorithms-applications in the HF band*, IEEE Antennas and Propagation Society International Symposium. 1996 Digest, Baltimore, MD, USA, 1996, pp. 1344-1347 vol.2
78. W. Featherstone, H. J. Strangeways, M. Darnell and H. Mewes; *The Application of Superresolution Direction Finding to a variety of Channel Conditions in the HF Band*, Radio Systems and Techniques, 7-10 July 1997, Conference Publication No. 411, IEE, 1997, pp 306-310.
79. S. Sivanand, Jar-Fen Yang, Member, and M. Kaveh; *Focusing Filters for Wide-Band Direction Finding*, IEEE Transactions on Signal Processing, Vol. 39, No. 2, 1991 437.
80. Bjorn Ottersten and Thomas Kailath; *Direction-of-Arrival Estimation for Wide-Band Signals Using the ESPRIT Algorithm*, IEEE Transactions on Acoustics, Speech, and Signal Processing, Vol. 38, No. 2, February 1990 317.
81. H. Hung and M. Kaveh, *Coherent wide-band ESPRIT method for directions-of-arrival estimation of multiple wide-band sources*, in IEEE Transactions on Acoustics, Speech, and Signal Processing, vol. 38, no. 2, pp. 354-356, 1990.
82. M. Di Renzo, A. D'Onofrio, F. Graziosi and F. Santucci, *A Distributed Direction of Arrival Estimation Algorithm for Self-Organizing Ultra Wide-Band Wireless Sensor Networks*, 2006 3rd International Symposium on Wireless Communication Systems, Valencia, Spain, 2006, pp. 93-97.
83. M. G. Amin, *High resolution direction of arrival estimation of multiple wide-band sources in multichannel adaptive nulling systems*, 1996 IEEE International Conference on Acoustics, Speech, and Signal Processing Conference Proceedings, Atlanta, GA, USA, 1996, pp. 2888-2891 vol. 5.
84. Yeo-SunYoon, Lance M. Kaplan and JamesH. McClellan; *TOPS: New DOA Estimator for Wideband Signals*, IEEE Transactions on Signal Processing, Vol. 54, No. 6, June 2006 1977.
85. Chye Huat Peck and Philip J. Moore; *A Direction-Finding Technique for Wide-Band Impulsive Noise Source*, IEEE Transactions on Electromagnetic Compatibility, Vol. 43, No. 2, May 2001 149.
86. Xu You-gen, Liu Zhi-wen and Yao Guang-xiang; *Uni-Vector-Sensor SOS/HOS-CSS for Wideband Non-Gaussian Source Direction Finding*, 2005 IEEE International Symposium on Microwave, Antenna, Propagation and EMC Technologies for Wireless Communications Proceedings.
87. Texas Instruments User Guide *AWR1642 Evaluation Module Single-Chip mmWave Sensing Solution User's Guide* (Rev. C) May 2020.
88. Kaluri. V. Rangarao and A. Negi, *Formant Based Direction of Voice for Smart Microphone Array*, 2024 IEEE International Workshop on Technologies for Defense and Security (TechDefense), Naples, Italy, 2024, pp. 363-367

Chapter 2
Matrix Algebra and Transformations

Our aim is not to provide a comprehensive study of linear algebra, but rather to focus on the essential aspects of matrix algebra [1] used in DF algorithms. We will also address some numerical considerations. This chapter will cover topics such as matrix algebra, digital filters, the discrete Fourier Transform, and its extensions, all of which are relevant to DOA applications. Additionally, we will provide access to the C code for all the functions. We aim to minimize the need for the reader to consult additional books, except for specific details that may require further reference.

2.1 Vectors and Matrices

There are numerous definitions of these topics [2]. Authors often represent vectors as points in space. For example, a two-vector $\mathbf{x}^T = [x_1\ x_2]$ can be visualized as a point in a two-dimensional Cartesian frame. Understanding the functions of several variables is a crucial component, particularly in estimating system parameters. This section aims to establish a foundation for comprehending parameters in more than one or two dimensions.

The human mind has limitations when it comes to perceiving dimensions beyond three. Two dimensions are the easiest to understand; even a school graduate can comprehend them. In a Cartesian frame, a point is represented by an ordered pair with x_1 and x_2 axes, depicted in Fig. 2.1. Our minds are well-trained to understand concepts in two dimensions but struggle when dealing with higher dimensions.

V. R. Kaluri, *Direction Finding Algorithms for Practicing Engineers*,
https://doi.org/10.1007/978-3-032-06997-9_2

Fig. 2.1 Two dimensional representation

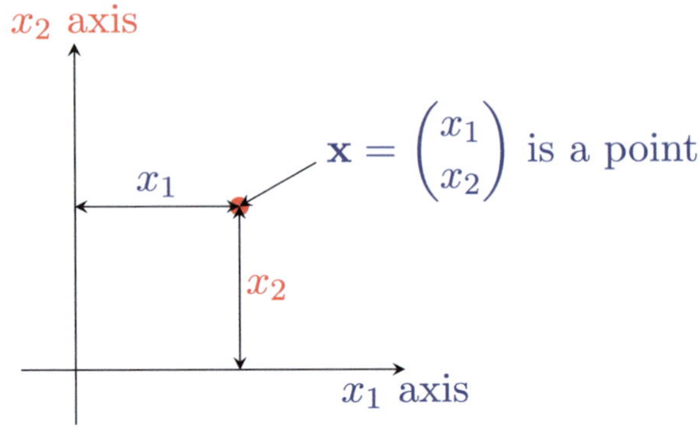

2.1.1 *Vectors of More Than Two Dimensions*

The following text presents a new way to visualize multi-dimensional variables [3]. The traditional approach involves imagining a hyper-space and viewing it as a point. However, in line with the concept of this book, we will introduce a straightforward method for examining multi-dimensional vectors without sacrificing generality. For instance, consider a 4-dimensional vector $\mathbf{x}^T = [x_1, x_2, x_3, x_4]$. It can be visualized as a polygon with four sides, as shown in Fig. 2.2. This visualization offers a deeper insight into understanding parameters across multiple dimensions. Recognizing that a multi-dimensional vector is a "figure" and not just a "point." Visualizing an n-dimensional vector as an nth order polygon is crucial for understanding multi-variate systems. This visualization method is a tool necessary for understanding and comparing multivariate systems, as well as binary operations on them. Often, we need to find the maximum or minimum values within this domain. This will help us better understand these concepts. Comparing or performing familiar binary operations like $+, -, \div, \times$, which are easily done on numbers, cannot be done so easily, since it involves a polygon. It doesn't mean that we cannot compare two polygons. There are methods available for doing so.

2.2 System of Equations

This section explores multivariate functions [12], which are explained in detail using a system of simultaneous equations [4], as illustrated in Fig. 2.3a, b. Let's focus on the following equations for simplicity. In this scenario, each row $\mathbf{x}_k^T$ (denoted as k) of the matrix represents an equation depicting a straight line as $y_k = \mathbf{x}_k^T \mathbf{p}$, which is meant to intersect at an unknown point $\mathbf{p}^T = (x_1, x_2)$, indicated by a red-filled circle in the same figure. The intersections of the straight lines are shown in Fig. 2.3a, and a closer look at Eqs. (2.6) to (2.8) is provided in Fig. 2.3b. The lines may or may not pass through the point. Our goal is to determine the best estimate

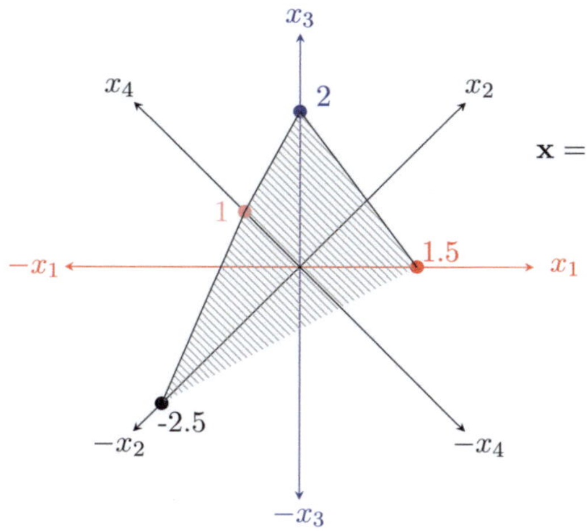

$$\mathbf{x} = \begin{pmatrix} x_1 \\ x_2 \\ x_3 \\ x_4 \end{pmatrix} = \begin{pmatrix} 1.5 \\ -2.5 \\ 2 \\ 1 \end{pmatrix} \text{ is a polygon}$$

Fig. 2.2 Multi dimensional representation

$\hat{\mathbf{p}}$ of $\mathbf{p}$. In an ideal scenario, all lines should pass through $\mathbf{p}$; this is known as being concurrent, but this may not be true for various reasons. Equations of this nature are encountered in various applications, and comprehension of this subsection will offer better insight into many solutions. Equation 2.3 represents the system of equations shown in Fig. 2.3 in a concise matrix notation. In this instance, the matrix $\mathbf{A}$ is of size $8 \times 2(n \times m)$. The inverse of a matrix is only defined when $\mathbf{A}$ is a square matrix and its determinant is not zero. Notably, Moore-Penrose [5] introduced an innovative approach to inverting a rectangular matrix, making a significant contribution to our understanding of matrix operations. By pre-multiplying Eq. 2.3 by $\mathbf{A}^T$, we obtain

$$\mathbf{A}^T\mathbf{A}\mathbf{p} = \mathbf{A}^T\mathbf{y} \tag{2.1}$$

The matrix $\mathbf{A}^T\mathbf{A}$ is square and can also be written as

$$\begin{aligned} \mathbf{A}^T\mathbf{A} &= \begin{pmatrix} 6 \\ 9 \end{pmatrix}(6\ 9) + \begin{pmatrix} 6 \\ 0 \end{pmatrix}(6\ 0) + \ldots + \begin{pmatrix} 3 \\ -6 \end{pmatrix}(3\ -6) \\ &= \sum_{k=1}^{8} \mathbf{x}_k\mathbf{x}_k^T \text{ where } \mathbf{x}_k^T \text{ is } k\text{th row vector of } \mathbf{A} \end{aligned} \tag{2.2}$$

The column vector $\mathbf{A}^T\mathbf{y}$ can be written as

$$\mathbf{A}\mathbf{p} = \mathbf{y} \text{ is of size } n \times m \tag{2.3}$$

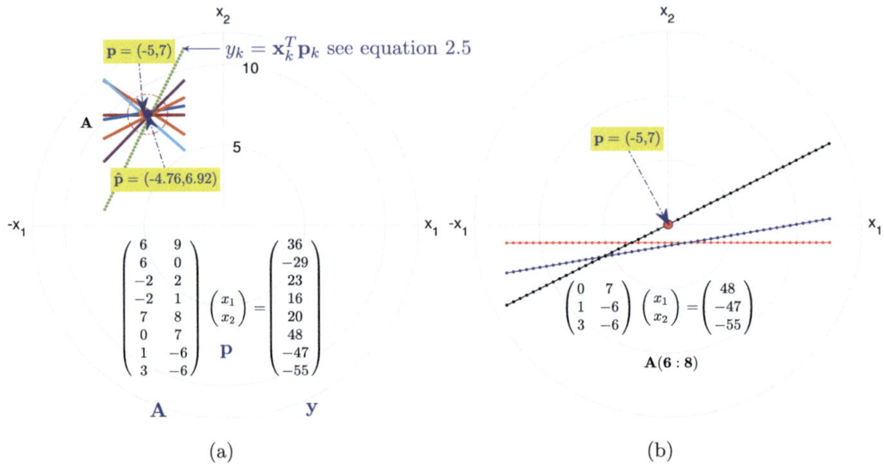

Fig. 2.3 System of linear equations

$$\mathbf{A}^T\mathbf{y} = 35\begin{pmatrix}6\\9\end{pmatrix} - 29\begin{pmatrix}6\\0\end{pmatrix} + \ldots - 57\begin{pmatrix}3\\-6\end{pmatrix}$$
$$= \sum_{k=1}^{8} \mathbf{x}_k^T y_k \tag{2.4}$$

we can also write Eq. 2.3 as row wise Modeling as any straight line shown in Fig. 2.3.

$$y_k = \mathbf{x}_k^T \mathbf{p}_k \tag{2.5}$$

Under the assumption $\mathbf{A}^T\mathbf{A}$ is non-singular, the inverse can be obtained recursively or enblock. Then the solution for Eq. 2.3 a system of equations as given in Fig. 2.3 is given as

$$\hat{\mathbf{p}} = \underbrace{\left[\mathbf{A}^T\mathbf{A}\right]^{-1}}_{\mathbf{P}} \mathbf{A}^T\mathbf{y} = \mathbf{P}\mathbf{A}^T\mathbf{y} \tag{2.6}$$

And also, we define $\mathbf{A}^+ \triangleq \left[\mathbf{A}^T\mathbf{A}\right]^{-1}\mathbf{A}^T$ is known as Moore Penrose pseudo inverse [5]. The least squares solution [6] is $\hat{\mathbf{p}} = \mathbf{A}^+\mathbf{y}$. There are two ways to interpret it. One option is that it corresponds to the best intersection of all the intersections in Fig. 2.3, in the least squares sense. The second perspective is that the rows of $\mathbf{A}^+$ represent MA processes or FIR filters. The error $\mathbf{e}$ which, in simple terms, is the deviation from the straight-line fit, and sometimes called the innovation process is defined as $\mathbf{e} = \hat{\mathbf{y}} - \mathbf{y}$, where $\hat{\mathbf{y}} = \mathbf{A}(\mathbf{P}\mathbf{A}^T\mathbf{y})$, according to Eqs. 2.6 and 2.3. When there are k equations, the solution for Eq. 2.5, combined with Eqs. 2.6 and others, applies. 2.2 and 2.4 provide a block solution as shown in Eq. 2.7. This equation can be made recursive [7], as discussed in the next section.

$$\mathbf{p}_k = \left(\sum_{i=0}^{k} \mathbf{x}_i \mathbf{x}_i^T\right)^{-1} \left(\sum_{i=0}^{k} \mathbf{x}_i y_i\right). \tag{2.7}$$

2.2.1 Recursive Solution

In Eq. 2.7, we identify the real symmetric matrix as

$$\mathbf{P}_k = \left(\sum_{i=0}^{k} \mathbf{x}_i \mathbf{x}_i^T\right)^{-1} \tag{2.8}$$

Applying the *matix inversion lemma* Sherman-Morrison formula [8] in Eq. 2.8

$$\boxed{\left(\mathbf{B} + \mathbf{x}\mathbf{x}^T\right)^{-1} = \mathbf{B}^{-1} - \left(\frac{\mathbf{B}^{-1}\mathbf{x}\mathbf{x}^T\mathbf{B}^{-1}}{1 + \mathbf{x}^T\mathbf{B}^{-1}\mathbf{x}}\right)} \tag{2.9}$$

We can write as

$$\mathbf{P}_k = \left(\mathbf{P}_{k-1} - \frac{\mathbf{P}_{k-1}\mathbf{x}_k\mathbf{x}_k^T\mathbf{P}_{k-1}}{1 + \mathbf{x}_k^T\mathbf{P}_{k-1}\mathbf{x}_k}\right) \tag{2.10}$$

We rewrite Eq. 2.7 using matrix inversion lemma as

$$\mathbf{p}_k = \left(\mathbf{P}_{k-1} - \frac{\mathbf{P}_{k-1}\mathbf{x}_k\mathbf{x}_k^T\mathbf{P}_{k-1}}{1 + \mathbf{x}_k^T\mathbf{P}_{k-1}\mathbf{x}_k}\right) \left(\sum_{i=0}^{k-1} \mathbf{x}_i y_i + \mathbf{x}_k y_k\right) \tag{2.11}$$

Now by expanding Eq. 2.11 we get

$$\mathbf{p}_k = \left\{ \mathbf{P}_{k-1}\left(\sum_{i=0}^{k-1} \mathbf{x}_i y_i\right) - \frac{\mathbf{P}_{k-1}\mathbf{x}_k\mathbf{x}_k^T\mathbf{P}_{k-1}\left(\sum_{i=0}^{k-1} \mathbf{x}_i y_i\right)}{1 + \mathbf{x}_k^T\mathbf{P}_{k-1}\mathbf{x}_k} \right\}$$
$$- \left\{ \frac{\mathbf{P}_{k-1}\mathbf{x}_k\mathbf{x}_k^T\mathbf{P}_{k-1}\mathbf{x}_k y_k}{1 + \mathbf{x}_k^T\mathbf{P}_{k-1}\mathbf{x}_k} + \mathbf{P}_{k-1}\mathbf{x}_k y_k \right\} \tag{2.12}$$

we identify the term $\mathbf{P}_{k-1}\left(\sum_{i=0}^{k-1} \mathbf{x}_i y_i\right)$ as $\mathbf{p}_{k-1}$. The expression $\mathbf{P}_{k-1}\mathbf{x}_k$ represents the predicted state vector in column form $\hat{\mathbf{x}}_k$. By performing algebraic manipulations, Eq. 2.12 can be simplified to take the structured form of Eq. 2.13. The scalar term $\mathbf{x}_k^T\hat{\mathbf{x}}_k$ in Eq. 2.13 approaches zero as the recursion progresses, as illustrated in Fig. 2.4. This enables us to observe the mean μ and standard deviation σ of the dot product, which provides a good measure of the convergence of the recursion.

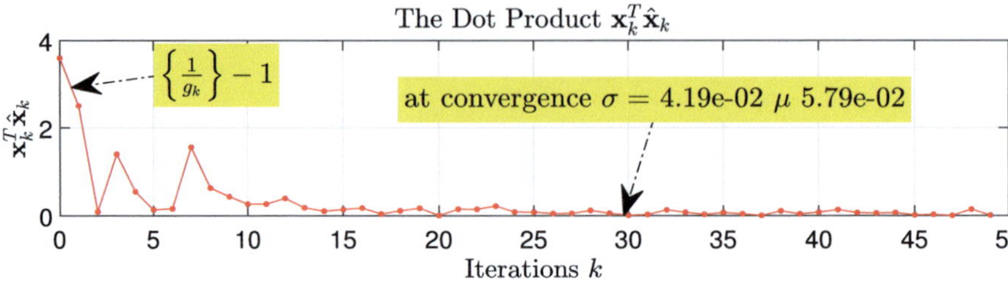

Fig. 2.4 The dot product in the recursive model

$$
\begin{aligned}
\mathbf{p}_k &= \mathbf{p}_{k-1} - \frac{\hat{\mathbf{x}}_k\mathbf{x}_k^T}{1+\mathbf{x}_k^T\hat{\mathbf{x}}_k}\mathbf{p}_{k-1} - \frac{\mathbf{x}_k\hat{\mathbf{x}}_k^T y_k}{1+\mathbf{x}_k^T\hat{\mathbf{x}}_k}\hat{\mathbf{x}}_k + \hat{\mathbf{x}}_k y_k \\
&= \mathbf{p}_{k-1} - \left[\frac{\hat{\mathbf{x}}_k}{1+\mathbf{x}_k^T\hat{\mathbf{x}}_k}\right]\mathbf{x}_k^T\mathbf{p}_{k-1} + \left[\frac{\hat{\mathbf{x}}_k}{1+\mathbf{x}_k^T\hat{\mathbf{x}}_k}\right] y_k \\
&= \mathbf{p}_{k-1} + \left(\frac{\hat{\mathbf{x}}_k}{1+\mathbf{x}_k^T\hat{\mathbf{x}}_k}\right)(y_k - \hat{y}_k) \text{ where } \hat{y}_k = \mathbf{x}_k^T\mathbf{p}_{k-1}. \qquad (2.13)
\end{aligned}
$$

2.2.1.1 Recursive Algorithm

$$
\begin{aligned}
\hat{\mathbf{x}}_k &= \mathbf{P}_{k-1}\mathbf{x}_k \text{ prediction} && (2.14)\\
\hat{y}_k &= \mathbf{x}_k^T\mathbf{p}_{k-1} \text{ predicted output} && (2.15)\\
g_k &= \left(1+\mathbf{x}_k^T\hat{\mathbf{x}}_k\right)^{-1} \; g_k \text{ is a scalar} && (2.16)\\
y_k &= \mathbf{x}_k^T\mathbf{p}_k && (2.17)\\
e_k &= (y_k - \hat{y}_k) && (2.18)\\
\mathbf{p}_k &= \mathbf{p}_{k-1} + g_k\hat{\mathbf{x}}_k e_k \text{ filter adaptation} && (2.19)\\
\mathbf{P}_k &= \mathbf{P}_{k-1} - g_k\left(\hat{\mathbf{x}}_k\hat{\mathbf{x}}_k^T\right) && (2.20)\\
&\text{since } \mathbf{P}_{k-1}^T = \mathbf{P}_{k-1} \text{ symmetric}
\end{aligned}
$$

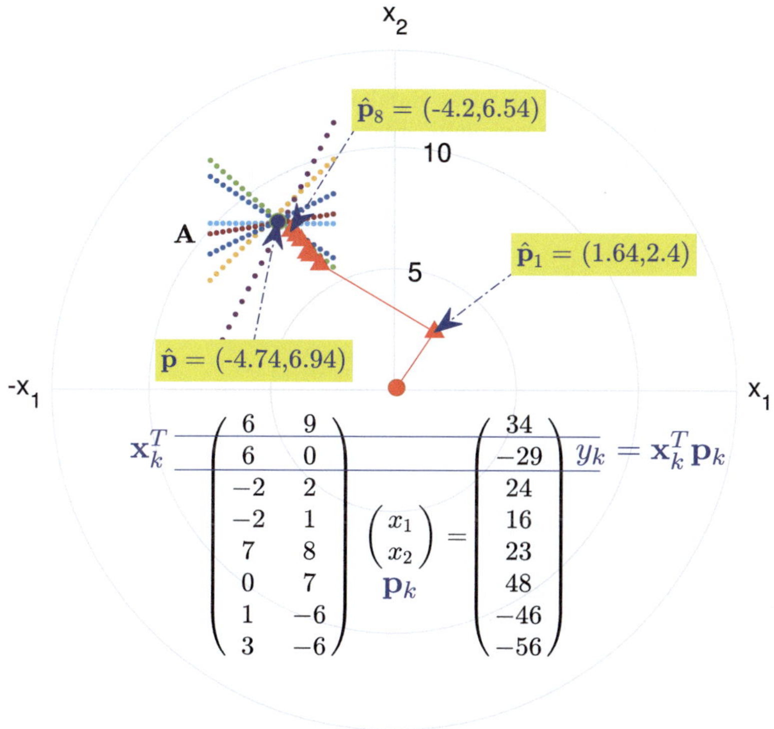

Fig. 2.5 Recursive solution for system linear equations

2.2.1.2 Illustration

Using Eq. 2.5, we define a scalar as $\hat{y}_k = \mathbf{x}_k^T \mathbf{p}_{k-1}$. Next, we will describe the recursive or adaptation procedure for estimating $\mathbf{p}_k^T = [\hat{x}_1 \ \hat{x}_2]$ with an initial condition $\mathbf{P}_0 = \sigma^2 \mathbf{I}$ and an arbitrary $\mathbf{p}_0$. A less computationally expensive recursive solution is defined by a series of Eqs. 2.14 to 2.20 in Sect. 2.2.1.1. The solution improves as it processes each row from the matrix, and the corresponding companion row vector value is displayed as $y_k = \mathbf{x}_k^T \mathbf{p}_k$. Each row equation is a straight line, passing through the solution point. The convergence of the recursive solution is shown in Fig. 2.5.

The red-filled triangle represents the trajectory of $\mathbf{p}_k$, while the blue solid circle represents the block solution. The red solid circle, representing the arbitrarily chosen initial conditions $\mathbf{p}_0$, does not play a significant role in the convergence process. With only eight equations, the solution quickly converges to the block solution within eight iterations. With more equations, the solution would be close to the block solution. The recursive solution remains the same even in multivariate situations. The authors have used a two-dimensional example to facilitate better perception and understanding.

$$y_k = \mathbf{x}_k^T \mathbf{p}_k \tag{2.21}$$

2.2.2 Optimization View

The solution to the system of linear simultaneous equations given by 2.5 can be obtained using optimization and multivariate calculus [9, 10]. In the recursive algorithm 2.2.1.1, the expression for $y_k = \mathbf{x}_k^T \mathbf{p}_k$ can be reformulated. We can define the objective function $J_k(\mathbf{p})$ as

$$J_k = e_k^2,$$

where $e_k = \hat{y}_k - y_k$ as shown in Eq. 2.18. The gradient of J_k with respect to $\mathbf{p}$ is given by

$$\nabla J_k = \frac{\partial J_k}{\partial \mathbf{p}_k} = 2e_k \frac{\partial e_k}{\partial \mathbf{p}_k} = 2e_k \frac{\partial \hat{y}_k}{\partial \mathbf{p}_k} \tag{2.22}$$

knowing $\hat{y}_k = \mathbf{x}_k^T \mathbf{p}_k$ and $\frac{\partial \hat{y}_k}{\partial \mathbf{p}_k} = \mathbf{x}_k^T$. Now Eq. 2.22 takes the form as

$$\nabla J_k = 2e_k \mathbf{x}_k^T \text{ note gradient is a vector} \tag{2.23}$$

a multivariate general incrementation procedure [11, 12] for parameter is of the form

$$\delta \mathbf{p}_k = \mu_k \mathbf{P}_{k-1} \nabla J_k \text{ where } \mathbf{P}_{k-1} \text{is the Hessian} \tag{2.24}$$

Combining Eqs. 2.14 and 2.19 we get

$$\delta \mathbf{p}_k = g_k \times \left(\mathbf{P}_{k-1} \mathbf{x}_k^T e_k\right) \text{ as in Eq.2.24}$$

can be compacted as

$$\delta \mathbf{p}_k = \frac{g_k}{2} \times \left(\nabla^2 J_{k-1} \times \nabla J_k\right) \tag{2.25}$$

The Hessian $\nabla^2 J_k = \mathbf{P}_k$ is the covariance matrix given by Eq. 2.8. In the parameter incrementation, as in Eq. 2.25, two factors, ∇J_k and g_k, play a key role. The gradient, being a vector, is depicted as $|\nabla J_k|$ in Fig. 2.6, which approaches zero at convergence, while g_k approaches unity, as depicted in Fig. 2.4. The recursive estimation of the

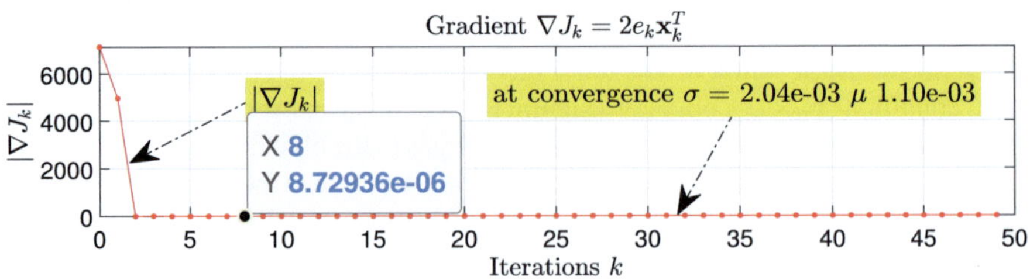

Fig. 2.6 Step size in the gradient model

Hessian is defined by Eq. 2.20. It is worth noting that the same problem was addressed by control engineers, statisticians, and optimization experts [13], who arrived at the same solution. The matrix $\mathbf{P}_k$ has received significant attention in various fields, often in the form of a Hermitian matrix. We denote it as $\mathbf{H}_k$ or simply $\mathbf{H}$ of size $n \times n$. One example in our context is

$$y_k = \mathbf{x}^T \mathbf{w} \text{ where } \mathbf{x}^T = [1\ e^{j(2\pi fk+\varphi)}\ e^{j(2\pi fk+2\varphi)}\ e^{j(2\pi fk+3\varphi)}] \tag{2.26}$$

where y_k and $\mathbf{x}^T$ are known.

2.3 Eigen Spectrum

The solution of a matrix equation

$$\mathbf{He} = \lambda \mathbf{e} \tag{2.27}$$

Has an essential role in many areas or disciplines and interpretations for the λ and $\mathbf{e}$. There are many methods available for solving Eq. 2.27. The scalar λ is known as an eigenvalue and the vector $\mathbf{e}$ is known as an eigenvector. Both of them have interesting properties. This is an important relationship between the Matrix $\mathbf{H}$ of $n \times n$ and its eigenvalues λ_i and eigenvectors $\mathbf{e}_i$ given as

$$\mathbf{H} = \sum_{i=1}^{n} \left(\lambda_i \mathbf{e}_i \mathbf{e}_i^T\right) \tag{2.28}$$

Equation 2.28 is used in many contexts, and good conceptual understanding is fundamental. Let us examine one that evaluates the eigenanalysis algorithms.

$$\mathbf{E}_{er} = \mathbf{H} - \sum_{i=1}^{n} \left(\lambda_i \mathbf{e}_i \mathbf{e}_i^T\right) \tag{2.29}$$

Understanding the numerical efficacy of the method employed we use $J_e = trace(\mathbf{E}_{er}\mathbf{E}_{er}^{*T})$ as a measure of performance. Ideally, the value of J_e must be zero. The entire code is written in C and is MATLAB callable, shown in Fig. 2.7. The values of J_e along with the eigenvalues are shown in Fig. 2.9. Notably, MATLAB outperforms the other methods. It is primarily because it utilizes double-precision and different thresholds for convergence. Jacobi Rotation Matrix method is simple but computationally heavy. We employed the Householder Method throughout the book.

```
clc; clear all; close all;
r = 512; c = 30;
x = randn([r c]); y = randn([r c]);
A = x + sqrt(-1)*y;

[Eh,Lh,Jk] = HEIGmH(A);
[Ej,Lj,JkJ]= HEIGmJ(A);                mex command

H = A'*A; big = max(max(abs(H))); H = H/big;
[Em l] = eig(H); Lm = diag(l)';
[a,erM] = Er(H,Em,Lm); [a,erH] = Er(H,Eh,Lh);
[a,erJ] = Er(H,Ej,Lj);
Er =[erM erH erJ];
lableFig(Lj,Lh,Lm,JkJ,Er,a);
```

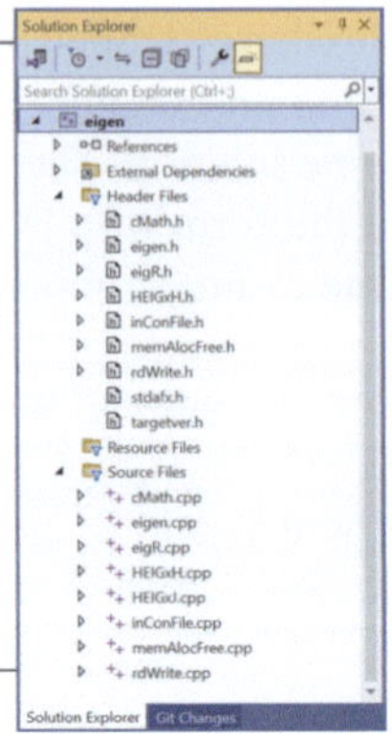

Fig. 2.7 Hermitian eigenvectors and values

2.4 Hermitian Using Real Matrices

The Hermitian matrix, say $\mathbf{H}$, is commonly encountered in direction finding. It has the important property $\mathbf{H} = \mathbf{H}^{*T}$, and its eigenvalues are always real. This property is known as conjugate symmetry. To convert the eigenanalysis of the Hermitian matrix to a real symmetric one, we can express [14–16] the $\mathbf{H}$ matrix as $\mathbf{H} = \mathbf{C} + j\mathbf{D}$, where $\mathbf{C}^T = \mathbf{C}$ and $\mathbf{D}^T = -\mathbf{D}$ are real matrices. This property ensures that the augmented matrix in Eq. 2.31 is symmetric and contains only real values. When solving for the eigenvalues and eigenvectors of the Hermitian matrix, we can formulate the eigenvalue equation.

$$(\mathbf{C} + j\mathbf{D})(\mathbf{u} + j\mathbf{v}) = \lambda(\mathbf{u} + j\mathbf{v}) \text{ where } \mathbf{u} \text{ and } \mathbf{v} \text{ are real vectors} \tag{2.30}$$

The solution for Eq. 2.30 gives desired eigenvector is $(\mathbf{u} + j\mathbf{v})$, and the eigenvalues λ. The above equation can be written as an augmented matrix form as in Eq. 2.31 with only real entries, reducing the solution to eigensolution for a real symmetric matrix $\mathbf{B}$ as in Eq. 2.32

$$\begin{pmatrix} \mathbf{C} & -\mathbf{D} \\ \mathbf{D} & \mathbf{C} \end{pmatrix} \begin{pmatrix} \mathbf{u} \\ \mathbf{v} \end{pmatrix} = \lambda \begin{pmatrix} \mathbf{u} \\ \mathbf{v} \end{pmatrix} \tag{2.31}$$

$$\mathbf{B} \quad \mathbf{x} = \lambda \quad \mathbf{x} \tag{2.32}$$

For illustration, the numerical solution is depicted in Fig. 2.8. The complex look matrix $\mathbf{A}$ is of the size 512 by 4.

The Hermitian is $\mathbf{H} = \mathbf{A}^{*T}\mathbf{A}$, the augumented matrix shown in Eq. 2.31 has 8 real eigenvectors and eigenvalues. For better understanding, these eight eigenvectors are shown as four blocks of 4 by 4. Thus if $\{\lambda_1, \lambda_2 \ldots \lambda_n\}$ are the eigenvalues of $\mathbf{H}$, then the 2n eigenvalues of the augmented problem (2.31) are $\{\lambda_1, \lambda_1, \lambda_2, \lambda_2 \ldots \lambda_n, \lambda_n\}$

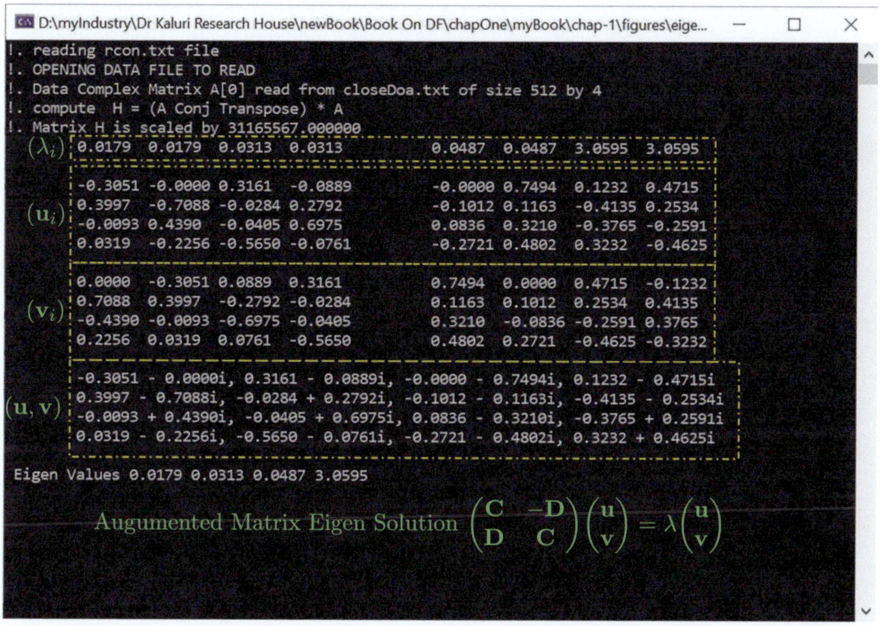

Fig. 2.8 Computing eigenvalues and vector for augumented matrix Eq. 2.31

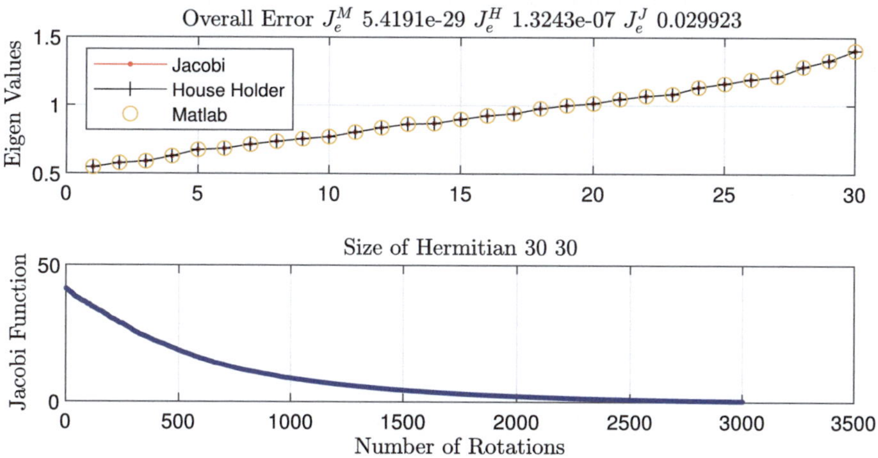

Fig. 2.9 Relative performance of computing eigenvalues and vector

each, in other words, is repeated twice. The eigenvectors are pairs of the form $\mathbf{u} + j\mathbf{v}$ and $j(\mathbf{u} + j\mathbf{v})$; that is, they are the same up to an inessential phase. Thus we solve the augmented problem (2.31), and choose one eigenvalue and eigenvector from each pair. These give the eigenvalues and eigenvectors of the original matrix $\mathbf{H}$. Working with the augmented matrix requires a factor of 2 more storage.

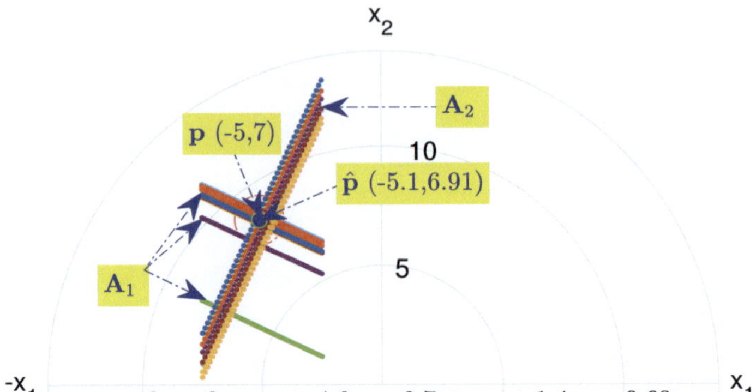

$$\underbrace{\begin{pmatrix} 6 & 9 \\ 6 & 0 \\ -2 & 2 \\ -2 & 1 \\ 7 & 8 \\ 0 & 7 \\ 1 & -6 \\ 3 & -6 \end{pmatrix}}_{\mathbf{A}} = \underbrace{\begin{pmatrix} 4.6 & 9.7 \\ 1.1 & 2.3 \\ 0.41 & 0.87 \\ 0.022 & 0.047 \\ 4.4 & 9.2 \\ 2.7 & 5.7 \\ -2.1 & -4.5 \\ -1.8 & -3.8 \end{pmatrix}}_{\mathbf{A}_1} + \underbrace{\begin{pmatrix} 1.4 & -0.68 \\ 4.9 & -2.3 \\ -2.4 & 1.1 \\ -2 & 0.95 \\ 2.6 & -1.2 \\ -2.7 & 1.3 \\ 3.1 & -1.5 \\ 4.8 & -2.2 \end{pmatrix}}_{\mathbf{A}_2}$$

Fig. 2.10 Decomposition system linear equations

2.5 Partitioning of Simultaneous Equations

We have seen the partitioning of a square matrix using Eq. 2.28 with eigenvalues and eigenvectors. Similarly, a rectangular matrix $\mathbf{A}$ of size $n \times m$ can be decomposed using a method known as Singular Value Decomposition. We describe as

$$\mathbf{A} = \sum_{i=1}^{m} \underbrace{\left(\lambda_i \mathbf{u}_i \mathbf{v}_i^T\right)}_{\mathbf{A}_i} = \sum_{i=1}^{m} \mathbf{A}_i \text{ assuming } m < n \tag{2.33}$$

where $\mathbf{u}_i$ is an $n \times 1$ vector and $\mathbf{v}_i^T$ is an $1 \times m$ vector and λ_i is a real positive number.

$$y_k = \mathbf{x}_k^T \mathbf{p}_k \tag{2.34}$$

$$\sum_{i=1}^{m} \mathbf{A}_i \mathbf{p} = \mathbf{y} \text{ is of size } n \times m \tag{2.35}$$

In Fig. 2.5, the displayed set of lines represents each equation passing statistically through a point $\mathbf{p}$, with its estimate denoted as $\hat{\mathbf{p}}$ and shown as a blue-filled circle. Equation 2.34 is graphically represented in Fig. 2.10 for better understanding. There are two sets of lines, denoted as $\mathbf{A}_1$ and $\mathbf{A}_2$, which are orthogonal. Furthermore, each set of lines, represented by each partition matrix, parallels the others. In three-dimensional space, these lines become planes, and in a multi-dimensional case, it is a hyperplane. We define two orthogonal matrices as

$\mathbf{U} = [\mathbf{u}_1 \ldots \mathbf{u}_m]$ is an $n \times m$ matrix and $\mathbf{V} = [\mathbf{v}_1 \ldots \mathbf{v}_m]$ is an $m \times m$ square matrix

2.5.1 *Singular Value Decomposition (SVD)*

In order to solve the Eqs. 2.33 and 2.35 we formulate matrix equation as [17, 18]

$$\mathbf{A} = \mathbf{U}\Sigma\mathbf{V}^T \text{ and } \mathbf{A}^T = \mathbf{V}\Sigma\mathbf{U}^T \tag{2.36}$$

where Σ is a diagonal matrix of $m \times m$ and the matrices $\mathbf{U}(n \times m)$ and $\mathbf{V}(m \times m)$ are unitary matrices. Now we can see that

$$\mathbf{A}\mathbf{A}^T = \mathbf{U}\Sigma\mathbf{V}^T\mathbf{V}\Sigma^T\mathbf{U}^T$$

we realize that $\mathbf{V}$ is an orthogonal matrix and implies $\mathbf{V}\mathbf{V}^T$ is an identity matrix. Now we get

$$\boxed{\mathbf{A}\mathbf{A}^T = \mathbf{U}\Sigma^2\mathbf{U}^T = \mathbf{U}\mathbf{D}\mathbf{U}^T} \tag{2.37}$$

Since the matrix $\mathbf{A}\mathbf{A}^T$ is symmetric, the diagonal eigenvalues of $\mathbf{D}$ are real and positive, and the corresponding eigenvectors are in $\mathbf{U}$. We also have the matrix

$$\mathbf{A}^T\mathbf{A} = \mathbf{V}\Sigma\mathbf{U}^T\mathbf{U}\Sigma\mathbf{V}^T$$

which leads to

$$\boxed{\mathbf{A}^T\mathbf{A} = \mathbf{V}\Sigma^2\mathbf{V}^T = \mathbf{V}\mathbf{D}\mathbf{V}^T} \tag{2.38}$$

We get eigenvectors of $\mathbf{A}^T\mathbf{A}$ as $\mathbf{V}$. We obtain $\Sigma = \mathbf{D}^{\frac{1}{2}}$ denoted as $\sqrt{\mathbf{D}}$.

2.5.1.1 Steps for SVD

When computing the Singular Value Decomposition (SVD) for a matrix where the number of rows m is less than the number of columns n, it is essential to consider the non-uniqueness of eigenvectors.

1. $\mathbf{A}^T\mathbf{A} = \mathbf{C}$ is an $m \times m$ matrix

2. $\mathbf{C} = \mathbf{V}\mathbf{D}\mathbf{V}^T$ Perform eigenanalysis to get $\mathbf{V}$ is an $m \times m$ matrix and diagonal matrix $\mathbf{D}$.
3. Obtain Σ as $\sqrt{\mathbf{D}}$ is an $m \times m$ matrix
4. $\mathbf{U} = \mathbf{A}\mathbf{V}\Sigma^{-1}$ as $(n \times m)(m \times m)(m \times m) \longrightarrow$ giving an $(n \times m)$ matrix using Eq. 2.36

For a more in-depth understanding of the practical aspects of SVD computation, the reader is advised to consult Chap. 45 in the Handbook of Linear Algebra [19]. This resource offers valuable insights into the computational challenges and considerations associated with SVD when working with matrices of varying dimensions.

2.6 Transformations

In this section, we will explore two frequently used signal transformations. For a more comprehensive understanding, you can explore specialized books that provide detailed discussions. Signal manipulation involves the application of diverse mathematical operations to enhance comprehension, presentation, and visibility.

2.6.1 Laplace and Fourier Transforms

The Laplace Transform is a powerful mathematical tool used to analyze time-varying signals. When a time-varying signal is denoted as $h(t)$, its Laplace Transform is represented by $H(s)$,[1] where s is a complex variable. The Laplace Transform of a function $h(t)$ is given as

$$H(s) \triangleq \int_{-\infty}^{\infty} h(t)e^{-st}dt \, . \tag{2.39}$$

The complex variable s is often represented as $\sigma + \jmath\omega$, where $\jmath$ is the square root of negative one, σ is the fundamental part of s representing the rate of decay or rise of the signal, and ω is the imaginary part of s representing the periodic variation or *frequency* of the signal. The variable s is also sometimes referred to as the complex frequency. When we are only interested in the frequency content of the signal $h(t)$, we use the Fourier Transform, denoted as $H(\omega)$, and is given by

$$H(\omega) \triangleq \int_{-\infty}^{\infty} h(t)e^{-\jmath\omega t}dt \, . \tag{2.40}$$

When we combine the given Eq. 2.40 with the Euler equation,[2] we can derive that the Fourier Series is a fundamental transformation for periodic functions. These

[1] This is a two-sided Laplace Transform.

[2] Euler equation $e^{j\omega t} - cos\omega t + jsin\omega t$.

transformations are linear, meaning that the Laplace or Fourier transform of the sum of two signals is the sum of their transforms, and the Laplace or Fourier transform of a scaled version of a signal by some time-independent scale factor is the scaled version of its transform by the same factor.

2.6.2 Z-Transform

When we transition from the continuous-time domain to the discrete-time domain, integrands are mapped to summations. Replacing e^s with z and $h(t)$ with h_k in (2.39), we get a new transform in the discrete-time domain known as the z-transform, one of the powerful tools representing discrete-time systems. The z-transform of a discrete-time signal h_k is denoted as $H(z)$ and is given by

$$H(z) \triangleq \sum_{k=-\infty}^{\infty} h_k z^{-k} . \tag{2.41}$$

As a simple illustration, consider a sequence of numbers.

$$h_k = \begin{cases} 0.5^k \,, & k \geq 0, \\ 0 \,, & k < 0. \end{cases} \tag{2.42}$$

Using Eq. (2.42) for the sequence h_k we get

$$\begin{aligned} H(z) &= \sum_{k=0}^{\infty} 0.5^k z^{-k} \\ &= \sum_{k=0}^{\infty} (0.5z^{-1})^k \\ &= 1 + 0.5z^{-1} + 0.25z^{-2} + 0.125z^{-3} + \cdots \end{aligned} \tag{2.43}$$

Using the simple *geometric progression* relation

$$\sum_{k=0}^{\infty} a^k = \frac{1}{1-a}, \quad |a| < 1,$$

we get

$$H(z) = \frac{1}{(1-0.5z^{-1})}, \tag{2.44}$$

under the condition $|0.5z^{-1}| < 1$, that is, $|z| > 0.5$. Note that this condition represents the region of the complex z-plane in which the series (2.43) converges and (2.44) holds, and is called the *region of convergence* (ROC). We can also write h_k in the form.

$$h_k = 0.5h_{k-1} + \delta_k \,, \tag{2.45}$$

where δ_k is the *unit sample function*, given by

$$\delta_k = \begin{cases} 1\,, & k = 0, \\ 0\,, & k \neq 0. \end{cases} \tag{2.46}$$

If, instead of the variable z, we use the variable $e^{\jmath\omega}$, where ω is the frequency, then we get the Discrete Fourier Transform (DFT), which is defined as

$$H(e^{\jmath\omega}) \triangleq \sum_{k=-\infty}^{\infty} h_k e^{-\jmath\omega k} \,. \tag{2.47}$$

The z-transform is thus a discrete-time version of the Laplace transform and the DFT a discrete-time version of the Fourier transform.

2.6.3 *Transfer Function $H(z)$*

We are working with an infinite sequence h_k (2.43), which is also expressed as $H(z)$, referred to as the transfer function (TF) in Eq. (2.44), and a recursive form in Eq. (2.45). These multiple representations of the same signal are essential and fundamental to the use of Digital Signal Processing in DOA applications. This transfer function has widespread and standard representation as

$$H(z) = \frac{b(z)}{a(z)} \tag{2.48}$$

In Eq. 2.48, $b(z)$ represents the numerator polynomial, and $a(z)$ represents the denominator polynomial.

2.6.3.1 Digital Filter

Let's consider a simple example in recursive form as shown in Eq. 2.45.

$$\boxed{x_k = rpx_{k-1} - r^2 x_{k-2} + g(u_k - u_{k-2})} \text{ where } r < 1 \text{ and } |p| < 2 \text{ with } g = \frac{1-r^2}{2} \tag{2.49}$$

can be written as using the relation[3] $x_{k-1} = x_k z^{-1}$

[3] The symbol z^{-1} is treated as a delay operator.

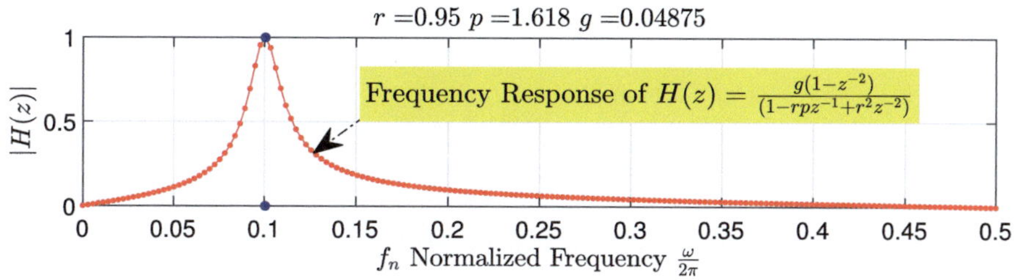

Fig. 2.11 Frequency response of $H(z)$ as in Eq. 2.50

$$x_k = rpz^{-1}x_k - r^2z^{-2}x_k + g(u_k - z^{-2}u_k)$$

now separating the variables x_k and u_k we get

$$x_k(1 - rpz^{-1} + r^2z^{-2}) = gu_k(1 - z^{-2})$$

This can be written as Eq. 2.50 in the form given by Eq. 2.48, representing a narrow band filter as well.

$$x_k = u_k \left[\frac{g(1 - z^{-2})}{(1 - rpz^{-1} + r^2z^{-2})} \right] = u_k H(z) \tag{2.50}$$

In this case, $H(z)$ stands for the transfer function of the digital filter. We can plot $|H(z)|$, known as the frequency response of the filter, by substituting $z = e^{j\omega}$, as shown in Fig. 2.11. For a more in-depth understanding, please refer to specialized books on DSP.

2.7 Discrete Fourier Transform (DFT)

The DFT relation is obtained from the continuous Fourier Transform (FT) as shown in Eq. 2.40 of a signal by replacing ω with $2\pi f$. Consider a signal $x(t)$ and its FT.

$$s(f) \triangleq \int_{-\infty}^{\infty} x(t)e^{-j2\pi ft}dt\,. \tag{2.51}$$

If the signal is such that $x(t) = 0$ for $t < 0$ then the FT takes the form

$$s(f) = \int_{0}^{\infty} x(t)e^{-j2\pi ft}dt\,. \tag{2.52}$$

We replace the integral in Eq. 2.52 by a summation ($\int \rightarrow \sum$), replace continuous variable t with k ($t \rightarrow k$), and f with n ($f \rightarrow n$). This results in the DFT relation for a discrete sequence x_k of length N.

$$s_n = \sum_{n=0}^{N-1} x_k e^{-jn\delta\omega k} \text{where } \delta\omega = \frac{2\pi}{N} \tag{2.53}$$

It is very convenient and mathematically tractable to use the notation $W_N = e^{j\frac{2\pi}{N}}$ and rewrite Eq. 2.53 as

$$s_n(\omega) = \sum_{n=0}^{N-1} x_k W_N^{nk} \tag{2.54}$$

The complex quantity W_N is a constant for a given value of N. A helpful way to visualize this quantity is as $W_N^{nk} = \cos(n\delta\omega k) + \jmath \sin(n\delta\omega k)$, which will aid in understanding. Another important transformation is $W_N^2 = \left(e^{j\frac{2\pi}{N}}\right)^2$, which can be expressed as $W_N^2 = e^{j\frac{2\pi}{\left[\frac{N}{2}\right]}}$, equivalent to $W_{\frac{N}{2}}$. It is beneficial to consider a specific example, such as $W_{16}^2 = W_8$, for clarity.

2.7.1 Matrix Formulation of DFT

The DFT Eq. 2.54 can also be written in the matrix form for N points as

$$\mathbf{s} = (\mathbf{W}_N)\,\mathbf{x} \tag{2.55}$$

In Eq. 2.55, $\mathbf{s}$ is a vector with components s_1 to s_{N-1}, and $\mathbf{x}$ is a time-sampled complex or real data vector with a size of $M \times 1$. The vector $\mathbf{s}$ is known as spectrum of $\mathbf{x}$. To gain a thorough understanding, the reader must refer to Fig. 2.12 while reading the content. The coefficient matrix $\mathbf{W}_N$ has a size of $N \times M$, and in most applications, the value of M is equal to N. Each row of the matrix represents an FIR filter with complex coefficients sampled as complex cosines and sine waves. Additionally, each row can be seen as a complex oscillator $\mathbf{w}_n^T$. The equation for each row can be expressed as $s_n = \mathbf{w}_n^T \mathbf{x}$. Notably, the frequency of the sine wave in each row increases linearly as we move from the top to the bottom of the matrix. This concept is fundamental in evaluating accuracy using the Gold-Fourier-Kaluri Method [20], which overcomes the limitation posed by the number of time samples.

2.7.2 Sliding DFT

The transfer function of the nth row filter as shown in Fig. 2.12 can also be written as an IIR filter.

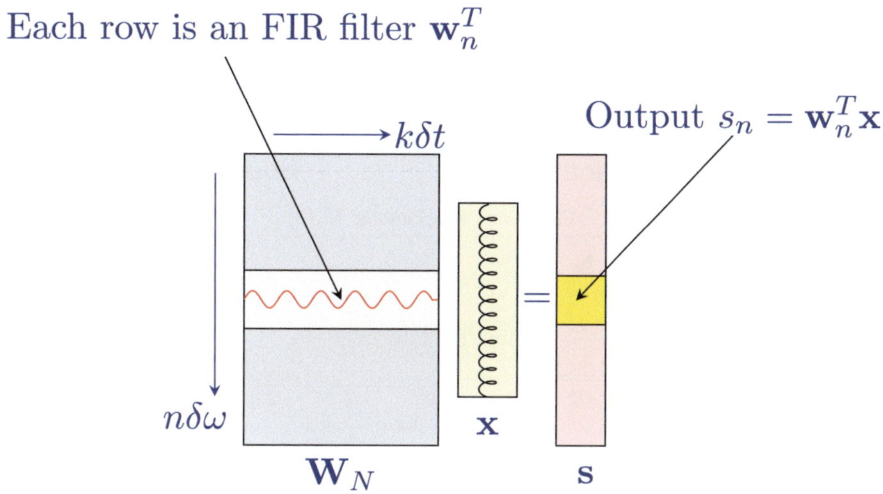

Fig. 2.12 Discrete fourier transform Eq. 2.55

$$H_n(z) = \frac{1 - z^{-N}}{1 - W_N^{-n} z^{-1}} \text{ for } n = 0, 1, \ldots, N-1 \tag{2.56}$$

The numerator polynomial $1 - z^{-N}$ has N roots. The pole at $z = W_N^{-n}$ of $H_n(z)$ is canceled by one of its zeros, resulting in an FIR filter. For $N = 8$ we get

$$\frac{(1 - W_8^4 z^{-1})(1 - W_8^3 z^{-1})(1 - W_8^{-3} z^{-1})(1 - W_8^2 z^{-1})(1 - W_8^{-2} z^{-1})(1 - W_8^0 z^{-1})(1 - W_8^1 z^{-1})(1 - W_8^{-1} z^{-1})}{1 - W_8^{-k} z^{-1}} \tag{2.57}$$

where $W_8 = e^{-j\frac{\pi}{4}}$. The above numerical example shows the pole-zero cancellation. Each nth row can also be written in the form of a difference equation.

$$s_k = W_N^{-n} s_{k-1} + \frac{e_k}{N} \tag{2.58}$$

$$\text{where } e_k = (x_k - x_{k-N}) \tag{2.59}$$

The transfer function of the filter $H_n(z)$, as shown in Eq. 2.56, can be observed in Fig. 2.13, alongside the frequency response. This visually represents each row of the DFT matrix, as seen in Fig. 2.12. It's important to note that the complete DFT can be understood as a set of narrow-band filters, as mentioned in Eq. 2.55.

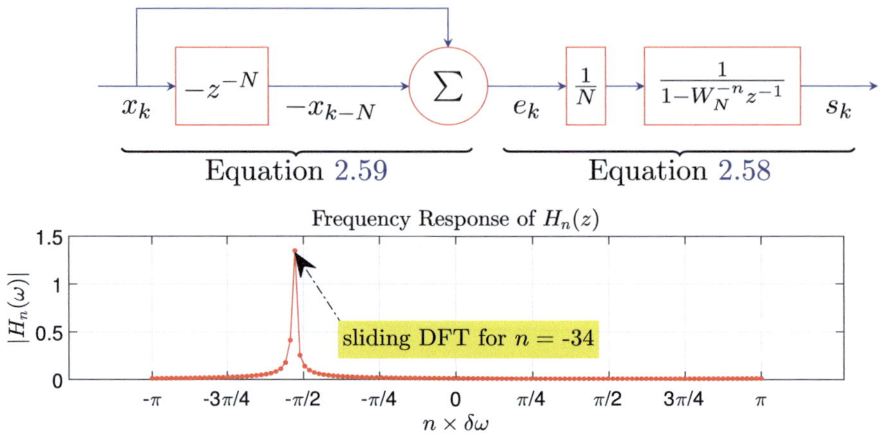

Fig. 2.13 Each row is a narrow band filter $s_n = \mathbf{w}_n^T \mathbf{x}$ in Eq. 2.55

2.8 Windowing Effect

The calculated spectrum may contain errors due to physical constraints when there is a limited observation period. For example, let's consider the sequence $x_k = \cos(2\pi f k)$. According to the mathematical formulation, the Discrete Fourier Transform (DFT) of this sequence should yield a unit sample at $\pm f$. However, the following illustration will demonstrate the limitations imposed by finite observations. We'll choose $f = \frac{1}{10}$ numerically, meaning that we are sampling the sequence ten times per cycle, as shown in Fig. 2.14a. Our observation is limited to 32 samples. The transition from Fig. 2.14a to b can be described using Eq. 2.55 and visually with Eq. 2.60. It's important to note that Fig. 2.14b corresponds to the magnitude of the vector $\mathbf{s}$; this vector is conjugate symmetric since the input is a real sequence.

2.8.1 Observations

In an ideal situation, it was expected that bin 3 or 29 would have a value of $\frac{32}{2} = 16$, while all other bins would have a zero value. However, the actual values obtained differed from this expectation, as illustrated in Fig. 2.14b. This difference is attributed to the Fourier transform of a rectangular window, which takes the form $\frac{\sin x}{x}$ and leads to leakage in the side lobes. To address the issue of limited observations, we will multiply the observations element-wise with another sequence $\mathbf{w}$ known as a windowing function, as shown in Fig. 2.15a. The window function used is the Hamming Function, and the process is expressed as

$$\underbrace{\text{Fig.2.14a} \rightarrow \text{Fig.2.15a}}_{\mathbf{w}(.\times)\mathbf{x} \rightarrow \mathbf{z}}$$

$$\underbrace{\text{Fig.2.14a} \rightarrow \text{Fig.2.14b}}_{(\mathbf{W}_{32})\mathbf{x} \rightarrow \mathbf{s}} \tag{2.60}$$

The operation $(.\times)$ represents the element-wise multiplication of two sequences. In Fig. 2.15b, a non-rectangular windowed spectrum is observed, meeting the condition of having values close to zero except around $\pm f$ for the sequence x_k. Windowing is an excellent tool in many applications where spectral integrity plays a crucial role, specifically for lower values of N.

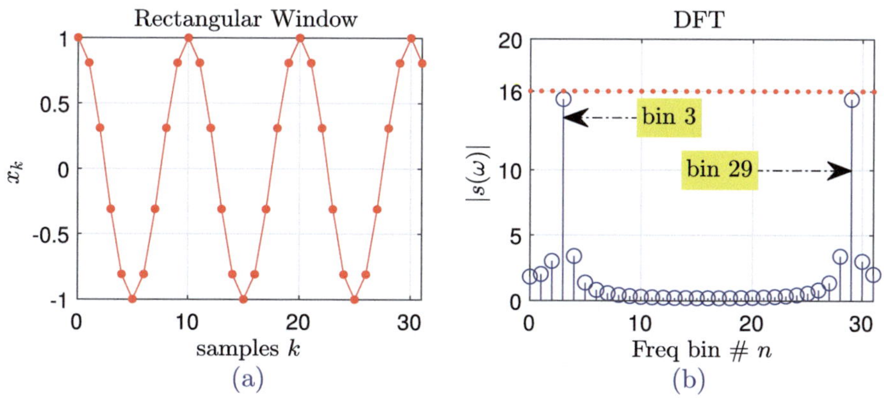

Fig. 2.14 Windowing effect

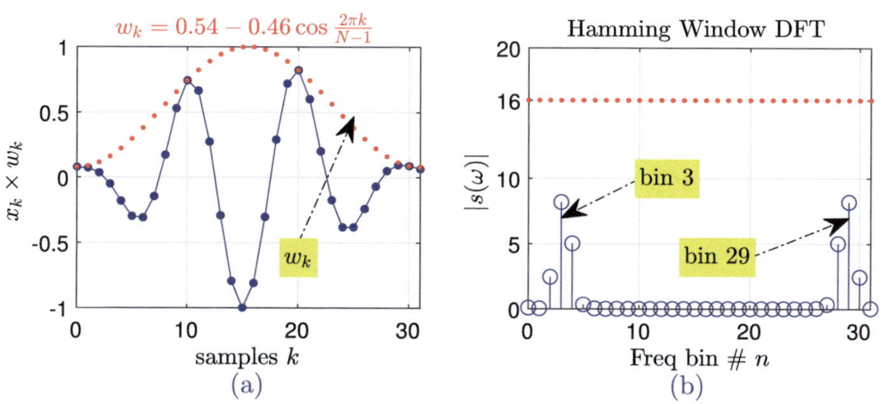

Fig. 2.15 Non rectangular windowing effect

2.8.2 Frequency Resolution and Range

The specified frequency range spans from −0.5 to 0.5 and is divided into 32 divisions, resulting in a resolution of $\delta f = \frac{1}{N}$. When the observation time is longer, the spectrum's resolution improves. The Discrete Fourier Transform (DFT) is a bank of narrow-band filters as in Fig. 2.13 separated by δf. Due to conjugate symmetry, the valid range is from 0 to 15 bins. However, by selecting the appropriate complex sequence as the input $x_k = 0.5\cos(2\pi f k) + j0.5\sin(2\pi f k)$ for the DFT, the range can be adjusted from 0 to 1, or all 32 bins represent unique frequencies with the exact resolution $\delta f = \frac{1}{N}$. This can be seen in Fig. 2.16b. By carefully selecting the appropriate complex input x_k, the range can be extended to all the bins. As seen here, bin 29 has been eliminated, as illustrated in Fig. 2.16b. The reader may see Fig. 2.14b for comparison. This concept is employed in FMCW radars to achieve an extended range while maintaining the same sampling rate.

2.9 Numerical Method Fast Fourier Transform (FFT)

Matrix multiplication in Eq. 2.55 can be done very efficiently [21]. Since coefficients in the matrix $\mathbf{W}_N$ being periodic allows us to arrive at a much more efficient method of computation. The given sequence can be transformed to the frequency domain by multiplying with an $N \times N$ Matrix. Direct computing involves sizeable. computations and is[4] OO(N^2) Consider a 16 point Sequence of numbers for which the DFT equation is

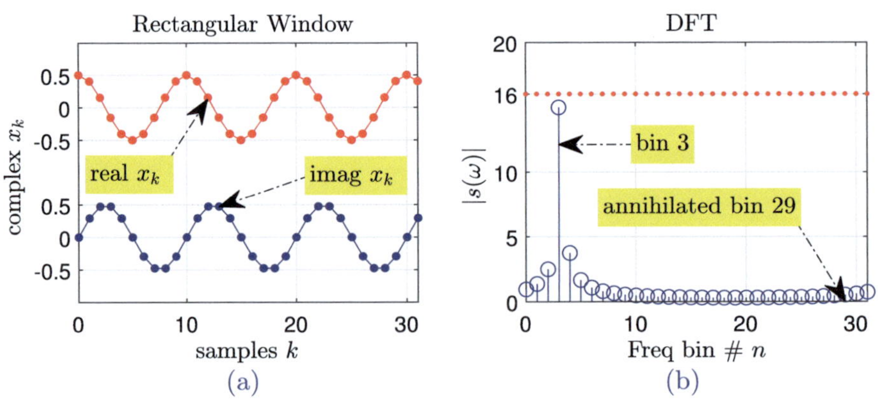

Fig. 2.16 Complex balanced input

[4] OO to be read as of the *order of*.

$$s_n(\omega) = \sum_{n=0}^{N-1} x_k W_N^{nk} \tag{2.61}$$

We illustrate the two methods *viz* decimation in time and frequency with a numerical example. Example. We need to note that the value of N is such that $N = 2^p$ where p is an integer.

2.9.1 Decimation in Time

We could also split the input sequence as an odd and even sequence and compute the DFT. We can write the Eq. 2.61 in a different way as

$$s_n = \sum_{k=even}^{14} x_k W_{16}^{nk} + \sum_{k=odd}^{15} x_k W_{16}^{nk} \tag{2.62}$$

For an even case, k takes the form of $2m$, and for an odd case, it takes the form of $2m + 1$. With this in mind, we write Eq. 2.62 as

$$\begin{aligned} s_n &= \sum_{m=0}^{7} x_{even} W_{16}^{2mn} + \sum_{m=0}^{7} x_{odd} W_{16}^{(2m+1)n} \\ &= \left(\sum_{m=0}^{7} x_{even} W_8^{mn}\right) + W_{16}^{n} \left(\sum_{m=0}^{7} x_{odd} W_8^{mn}\right) \end{aligned} \tag{2.63}$$

The following steps involve obtaining a 16-point discrete Fourier transform (DFT) using an 8-point DFT. Split the time sequence into two sets: the odd-indexed samples $\mathbf{x}_o$ and the even-indexed samples $\mathbf{x}_e$. Compute the 8-point DFT of both sets, denoted

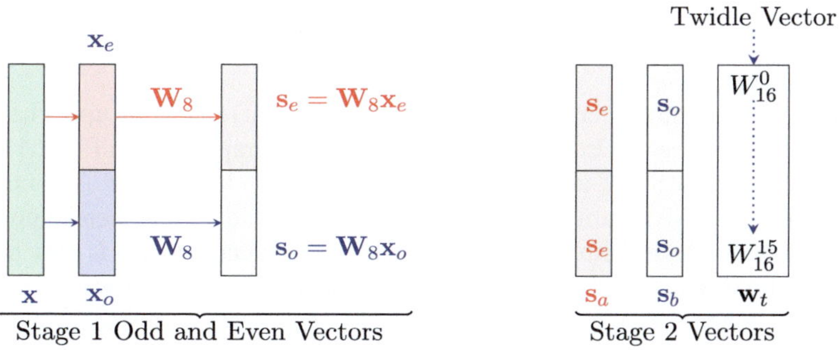

Fig. 2.17 Decimation in Time 16 DFT using 8 DFT

as $\mathbf{s}_o$ and $\mathbf{s}_e$, respectively shown as stage 1 in Fig. 2.17. Replicate the DFT of the odd sequence to create a 16-point sequence $\mathbf{s}_b$. Multiply this sequence point by point with a twiddle vector $\mathbf{w}_t$, where W_{16}^{k} is the designated twiddle factor. Replicate the DFT of the even sequence to create another 16-point sequence $\mathbf{s}_a$ shown as stage 2 in Fig. 2.17. Add both 16-point sequences together to obtain the desired 16-point DFT. This process can be recursively used and leads to an efficient computation of the DFT. Figure 2.17 illustrates these stages, and Eq. 2.64 describes the process.

$$\mathbf{s} = \mathbf{s}_a + \mathbf{s}_b(.\times)\mathbf{w}_t \text{ where the notation } (.\times) \text{is element by element multiplication} \tag{2.64}$$

2.9.2 *Decimation in Frequency*

In this process, we divide the sequence x_k into *two* halves and pre-multiply with weights known as *twiddle* factors and compute DFT. To understand the process, we rewrite the DFT Eq. 2.61 as

$$s_n = \sum_{n=0}^{7} x_k W_{16}^{nk} + \sum_{n=8}^{15} x_k W_{16}^{nk} \tag{2.65}$$

In Eq. 2.65 when n is even we can write as $n = 2m$ for $m = 0$ to 7 and the even spectrum is

$$\begin{aligned} s_n^e &= \sum_{n=0}^{7} x_k W_{16}^{k2m} + \sum_{n=8}^{15} x_k W_{16}^{k2m} \\ &= \sum_{n=0}^{7} x_k W_{8}^{km} + \sum_{n=8}^{15} x_k W_{8}^{km} \\ &= \left(\sum_{m=0}^{7} x_m W_8^{nm}\right) + \left(\sum_{m=0}^{7} x_{8+m} W_8^{nm}\right) \end{aligned} \tag{2.66}$$

After splitting the sequence x_k into two halves, we can refer to the upper half as $\mathbf{x}_t$ and the lower half as $\mathbf{x}_b$. Equation 2.66 is represented graphically in Fig. 2.18 as an even-indexed spectrum $\mathbf{s}_e$ and is mathematically defined by Eq. 2.67. To obtain the even values of the spectrum, we add the two halves, $\mathbf{x}_t$ and $\mathbf{x}_b$, and then compute the Discrete Fourier Transform (DFT) of the resulting sequence, which is only half the length of the original sequence. Earlier, we handled cases where n was even. Now, in Eq. 2.65, when n is odd, we can express n as $2m + 1$ for $m = 0$ to 7 to generate odd indexed spectrum as

$$\begin{aligned}
\mathbf{s}_e &= \mathbf{W}_8(\mathbf{x}_t + \mathbf{x}_b) && (2.67)\\
\mathbf{x}_t^{new} &= \mathbf{x}_t(.\times)\mathbf{w}_a \quad (.\times) \text{ is element by element multiplication}\\
\mathbf{x}_b^{new} &= \mathbf{x}_b(.\times)\mathbf{w}_b\\
\mathbf{s}_o &= \mathbf{W}_8\left[\mathbf{x}_t^{new} + \mathbf{x}_b^{new}\right] && (2.68)
\end{aligned}$$

$$\begin{aligned}
s_n^o &= \sum_{k=0}^{7} x_k W_{16}^{k(2m+1)} + \sum_{k=8}^{15} x_k W_{16}^{k(2m+1)} \text{ using } W_{16}^{2km} = W_8^{km}\\
&= \sum_{k=0}^{7}\left[x_k W_8^{km}\right] W_{16}^{k} + \sum_{k=8}^{15}\left[x_k W_8^{km}\right] W_{16}^{k}\\
&= \left(\sum_{k=0}^{7} \boxed{\left\{x_k W_{16}^{k}\right\}} W_8^{km}\right) + \left(\sum_{k=0}^{7} \boxed{\left\{x_{k+8} W_{16}^{k+8}\right\}} W_8^{km}\right) && (2.69)
\end{aligned}$$

Let's closely examine it to gain a deeper understanding of Eq. 2.69. The terms within the boxes in Eq. 2.69 can be considered two new sequences. These sequences are created by carrying out a point-by-point multiplication with constant sequences $\mathbf{w}_a$ and $\mathbf{w}_b$, as shown in the equations in Fig. 2.18. For clarity, we write them as

$$\begin{aligned}
\mathbf{x}_t^{new} &= [\dots x_i W_{16}^{i} \dots] = \mathbf{x}_t(.\times)\mathbf{w}_a\\
\mathbf{x}_b^{new} &= [\dots x_{8+i} W_{16}^{8+i} \dots] \text{ for } i = 0 \text{ to } 7 && (2.70)
\end{aligned}$$

To obtain the odd indexed spectrum $\mathbf{s}_o$, we can add the new sequences $\mathbf{x}_t^{new}$ and $\mathbf{x}_b^{new}$ and then compute the DFT of the resulting sequence. The odd part of the spectrum is illustrated in Fig. 2.18, and its mathematical representation is given by Eq. 2.68. To summarize the process, we start by splitting the input sequence into two

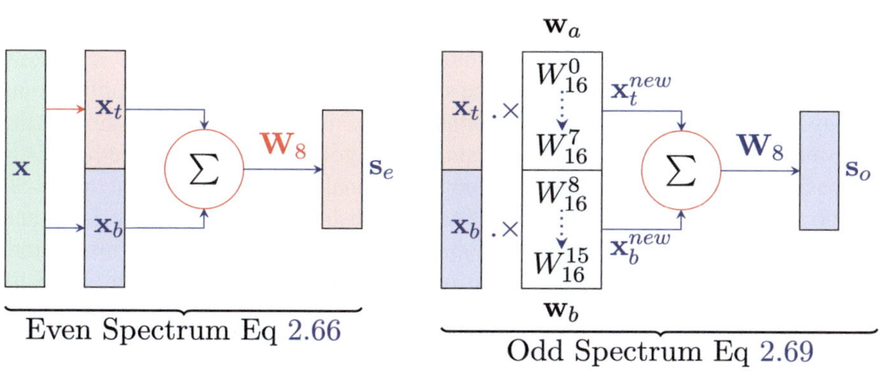

Fig. 2.18 Decimation in frequency 16 DFT using 8 DFT

halves, labeled as $\mathbf{x}_t$ and $\mathbf{x}_b$. Then, we add the two sequences and apply the Discrete Fourier Transform (DFT) to obtain an even-indexed spectrum. Following this, we multiply the sequences $\mathbf{x}_t$ and $\mathbf{x}_b$ by corresponding twiddle factors $\mathbf{w}_a$ and $\mathbf{w}_b$ to produce new sequences, $\mathbf{x}_t^{new}$ and $\mathbf{x}_b^{new}$. After adding these new sequences, we take the DFT of the resulting sequence to get the odd-indexed spectrum. The even and odd spectra need to be merged with proper index to get the final spectrum $\mathbf{s}$.

2.9.3 Computing Effort Estimate

Consider a real sequence of length N. Computing the Discrete Fourier Transform (DFT) is equivalent to multiplying an $N \times N$ complex matrix with an N-length vector. Each row-by-column multiplication requires $2N$ multiplications and $2N$ additions, assuming little difference between the cost of multiplication and addition (valid in the case of floating-point arithmetic). This results in a total of $4N$ operations per row. For the entire matrix, we need $4N^2$ operations. Generally, this complexity is denoted as $O(N^2)$ in engineering contexts without delving into specific computational details.

By performing either decimation in time or frequency once, as illustrated above, we have reduced computations from $O(N^2)$ to $O(2(\frac{N}{2})^2)$. The computing effort has been reduced by 50%. By repeating this process until we get a 2-point DFT, generating a DFT becomes a *fast* Fourier Transform (FFT), and the effort will be $O(Nlog_2N)$.

2.10 gold Fourier-Kaluri (gFK) Method

The Discrete Fourier Transform (DFT) is a mathematical tool used to analyze the frequency content of a signal. The DFT is like passing the signal through a bank of narrow-band filters $H_n(z)$ defined by Eq. 2.56 and the frequency response as shown in Fig. 2.13. However, the accuracy of the DFT is limited by the number of samples used in the calculation. It is essential to address this limitation to accurately determine the frequency and phase at the spectrum's peak in real-world applications, such as direction-of-arrival (DOA) estimation. One method that aims to improve the precision of frequency and phase estimation is the gold-Fourier-Kaluri method. This approach, which introduces additional computational load and focuses on optimization principles, is not just a theoretical concept. It has real-world applications and is a key tool in overcoming the limitations of the DFT. In our upcoming discussion, we will provide a detailed explanation of the gold-Fourier-Kaluri method and its practical application.

2.10.1 High Accuracy Spectral Peak

In the equation for Discrete Fourier Transform (DFT) shown in 2.55, we utilize Fast Fourier Transform (FFT) to calculate the spectrum at integral multiples of $\delta\omega$, which are represented as complex numbers s_n. In applications related to Direction of Arrival (DOA) [22, 23], it's often essential to determine the precise phase and amplitude at the actual peak. Since we only have a limited number of samples (e.g., 512, 256, or 128), the actual peak falls between the samples. Accurately estimating the peak frequency is crucial as it directly influences the phase value, requiring the identification of the same peak frequency across the data. The peak frequency and phase information can be reliably estimated in the approach outlined in Ref. [20]. This process is analogous to identifying the Fourier Spectrum at fractional bins. To accomplish this, minimization techniques are employed to pinpoint the peak.

2.10.2 gold-Fourier-Kaluri (gFK) Illustration

In FMCW radar applications, a trade-off often exists between computational efficiency and accuracy. In Direction of Arrival (DOA) applications, the typical input is a complex data matrix denoted as $\mathbf{A}$ with dimensions of 128×4. Each column of data in $\mathbf{A}$ represents spatially sampled data, as shown in Fig. 2.19. The main objective is to determine the precise spectral peak and corresponding phase information for each column. This method addresses the issue by using a 128-point FFT on the vector $\mathbf{x}$, which represents the first column of $\mathbf{A}$ in Eq. 2.71, to locate peaks roughly. It then applies gold-section univariate (GSU) minimization [24, 25] to pinpoint precise peaks, resulting in highly accurate outcomes. This approach, illustrated in Fig. 2.20a, involves calculating the objective function and identifying peaks and phase at fractional bins. The phase value for each column of $\mathbf{A}$ is estimated using the

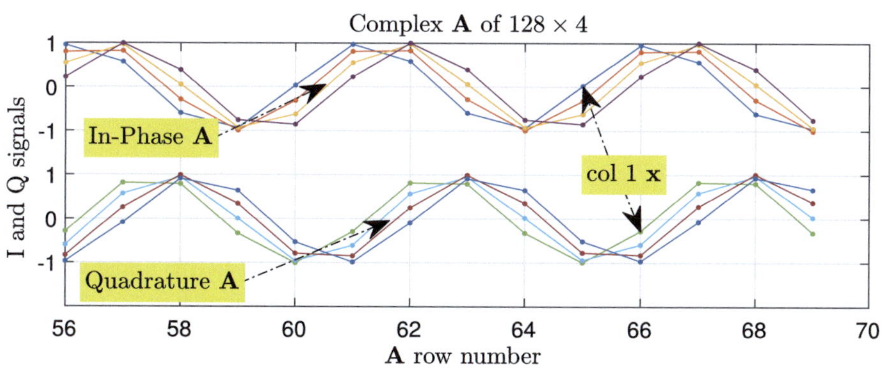

Fig. 2.19 Complex data matrix $\mathbf{A}$

gFK algorithm 2.10.5. The phase of the time series in each column shown in 2.20b is separated by 20°.

2.10.3 Coarse Objective Function

In Eq. 2.54, we can substitute ω with $n\delta\omega = n\frac{2\pi}{N}$ to express the Discrete Fourier Transform (DFT) in a matrix form by reformulating Eq. 2.55 with an optimization approach.

$$\mathbf{J}(n\delta\omega) = \mathbf{W}_N\mathbf{x}.\text{or } J_n^C \text{ as in Fig.2.20a.} \tag{2.71}$$

The FFT can compute $J(n\delta\omega)$ as given in Eq. 2.71 for integral multiples of $\delta\omega$. The objective function J_n^C is sampled at a *coarse* resolution of δf within the interval [0, 1]. Using the notation $f = \frac{\omega}{2\pi}$ is simpler.

$$X_n^C = \sum_{k=0}^{N-1} x_k \times W^{nk} \text{ where } W = e^{j\frac{2\pi}{N}} \tag{2.72}$$

The function X_n^C is asymmetric because the vector $\mathbf{x}$ is complex and the output of the I and Q channels of a Uniform Linear Array.

$$J_n^C = \sqrt{X_n^C \times \text{conj}\,(X_n^C)} \text{ for } n = 0 \text{ to } N - 1 \tag{2.73}$$

For $N = 128$, we obtain 128 samples of the coarse objective function, since the input vector is complex. Using the 128 FFT algorithm, we get J_n^C as shown in Fig. 2.20a.

2.10.4 Fourier Objective Function

The function $J(\omega)$ is called an objective function as

$$J(\omega) = \sum_{k=0}^{N-1} x_k e^{-j\omega k} \text{ where } 0 < \omega < 2\pi \tag{2.74}$$

To scale the peaks of $J(\omega)$, we transform Eq. 2.53 into a continuous form concerning the variable ω in the objective function $J(\omega)$ as in Eq. 2.74. This transformation is applicable for any arbitrary $\omega = 2\pi f$. It's important to note that ω is continuous and is limited by machine precision. We define Fourier Objective Function $J^F(f_a)$ evaluated at f_a as

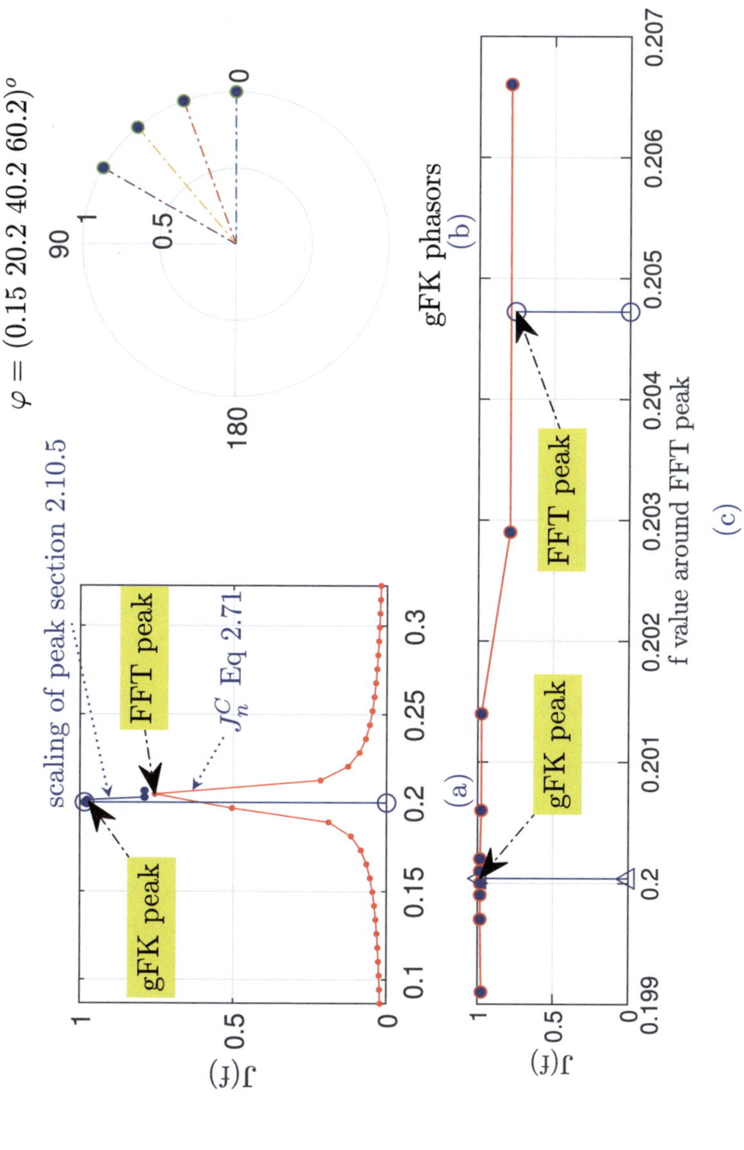

Fig. 2.20 Illustration of gold-Fourier-Kaluri

$$A_{f_a} = \sum_{k=0}^{N-1} (x_k \times \cos(2\pi f_a k)) \tag{2.75}$$

$$B_{f_a} = \sum_{k=0}^{N-1} (x_k \times \sin(2\pi f_a k)) \tag{2.76}$$

in which f_a is in the interval [0, 1]. The objective function takes the form

$$\boxed{J^F(f_a) = \frac{\sqrt{(A_{f_a})^2 + (B_{f_a})^2}}{N} \text{ and } \varphi_{f_a} = \tan^{-1}\frac{B_{f_a}}{A_{f_a}}} \tag{2.77}$$

is abbreviated as J_a^F, and the corresponding phase as φ_a, where N is the number of samples in the complex time series $\{x_k\}$. The computational burden and repeated use of Eq. 2.77 is mitigated by using special methods. It is to be noted that $f_a \in \mathcal{R}$ in the interval [0, 1].

2.10.5 *Scaling of Peaks Via Gold Minimization*

This minimization method [26, 27] accurately finds the extreme values of a univariate function. The algorithm works by successively narrowing the range of values within which the extremum is known to exist. Figure 2.21 illustrates the algorithm 2.10.5, which is presented below as a sequence of steps. We evaluate the unimodal function $-J_a^F$ as mentioned in Eq. 2.77 to find the peak and phase. Let $[f_a, f_b]$ denotes the coarse interval, where $f_a < f_b$, for a potential peak. This interval is obtained for all potential peaks by performing a coarse sweep in the interval [0, 1], using J_n^C from Eq. 2.73, as shown in step 1 of the algorithm. We choose intermediate points f_c and f_d as defined by the algorithm in steps 3 and 4, and iterate the algorithm steps 3 to 11 fixed number of times say 20, leading to a rapid and accurate determination of the negative minimum value, which is the peak value of the spectrum. The results are displayed in Algorithm 2.10.5 at Step 13, which shows two diagrams. The first Fig. 2.21 A diagram illustrates the gFK iteration and convergence. The second diagram Fig. 2.21b portrays the trajectory of φ in the $J - \varphi$ plane as the iteration progresses. It can be observed that convergence occurs at 40.2° at the gFK peak. It's important to highlight that the values stabilized by the 8th iteration, with phase values in the four columns of **A** being (0, 20, 40, 60)°.

2.10.5.1 Phase at gFK Peak

For each value of J_a, we also obtain φ_a, as per Eq. 2.77. The scaling of the gFK peak given by algorithm 2.10.5 is illustrated in Fig. 2.20a. In the $J - f$ plane, the

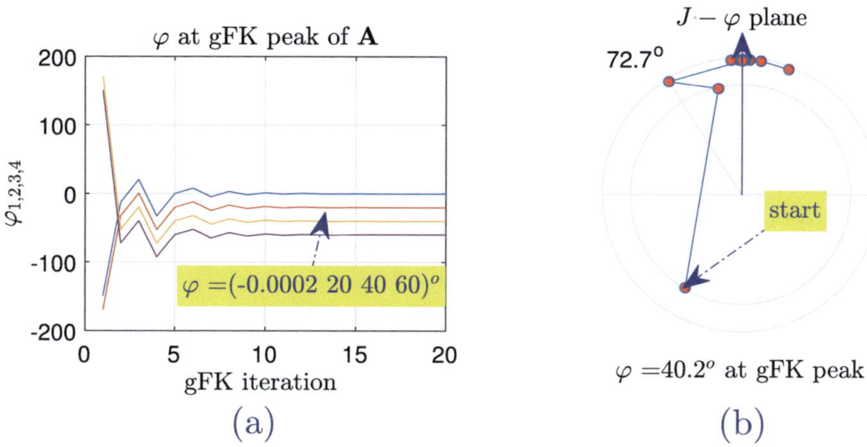

Fig. 2.21 Algorithm for scaling of peaks

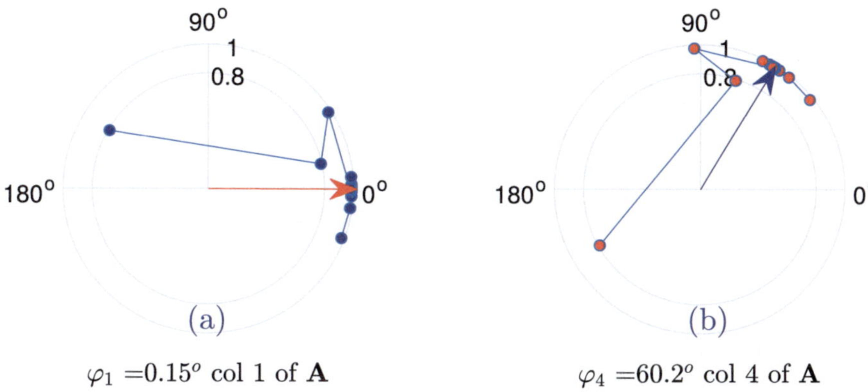

Fig. 2.22 Illustration of gold-Fourier-Kaluri

trajectory of J is shown in Fig. 2.20c as the algorithm is iterated. The value of J is almost the same for all the columns of $\mathbf{A}$. The phase value is sensitive around the peak, and as we accurately identify the spectral peak and phase for each column of the matrix $\mathbf{A}$ through the iteration process. The value of φ_a also converges toward the phase at the spectral peak. Figure 2.22a, b depict the convergence to $0.15°$ and $60.2°$ for columns 1 and 4 in the $J - \varphi$ plane.

2.11 Summary

This chapter offers an overview of matrix algebra and its uses in solving systems of equations and signal processing. It explains basic ideas of vectors and matrices, along with solution methods for linear equations, including recursive and optimization techniques. It examines the importance of the eigen spectrum in the behavior of linear systems. Furthermore, it examines partitioning methods for simultaneous equations, with an emphasis on Singular Value Decomposition (SVD) and its applications in system analysis and dimension reduction.

The chapter covers essential transformation methods in signal processing, including Laplace, Fourier, and Z-transforms, along with transfer functions and digital filters. It explains the Discrete Fourier Transform (DFT) using matrix form and the sliding DFT version, while analyzing how windowing affects frequency resolution. The Fast Fourier Transform (FFT) is discussed extensively, with a focus on decimation in time and frequency, as well as computational efficiency. Lastly, it introduces the advanced gold Fourier-Kaluri (gFK) technique for improved peak detection accuracy and concludes with a summary of the main concepts and the program structure.

2.11.1 MEX File Generation

The C source files and MATLAB scripts used to generate MEX files in Chap. 1 are Organized into two directories: `chap2\figures\eigen\eigen` and `chap2\figures\gFK\gFK`. Each MATLAB `.m` file contains a `mex` compile directive that links the Appropriate C code to produce the corresponding platform-specific MEX file. A total of three MEX files are generated in this chapter. The following table presents the generated `.mex` files in the first column, the location of the C source files in the second column, and the MATLAB `.m` Files containing the `mex` commands in the third column.

Chapter 2 C Files for MEX

MEX File	Location of C Files	Command
HEIGmH.mexw64	chap2\figures\eigen\eigen	mexHEIGmH.m
HEIGmJ.mexw64	chap2\figures\eigen\eigen	mexHEIGmJ.m
gFKtst.mexw64	chap2\figures\gFK\gFK	myMexGFK.m

2.11.2 File Organization

This subsection provides a complete list of program files related to the chapter titled *Matrix Algebra and Transformations*. The files are carefully organized into eight separate directories: `figGFK`, `figHerm`, `figLinEqMat`, `figRecurMatA`, `figRecurMatAdot`, `figNBF`, `figFFTnbf`, and `figSvdMat`. Each directory includes files specifically associated with different aspects of matrix algebra and its transformations. To improve clarity and navigation, the directory names are highlighted in yellow at the top of their columns in a well-organized table. This feature enables users to quickly identify and access relevant files for specific topics.

Chapter 2 Program Files

figGFK	figHerm	figLinEqMat	figRecurMatA	figRecurMatAdot
ds2nfu.m	Er.m	A2ThetaR.m	A2ThetaR.m	A2ThetaR.m
figGFKalgo.eps	figHerm.eps	adata.mat	adata.mat	ds2nfu.m
figGFKinA.eps	HEIGmH.mexw64	figLinEqMat.eps	figRecurMatA.eps	figRecurMatAdot.eps
figGFKphi.eps	HEIGmJ.mexw64	figLinEqMat.m	figRecurMatA.m	figRecurMatAdot.m
figGFKphiA.eps	lableFig.m	figLinEqMatZ.eps	polarDS2nfu.m	figRecurMatAdotG.eps
gFKalgo.m	tstEig.m	linRegA.m	recurA.m	label311grad.m
gFKeval.m		polarDS2nfu.m	recurEq.m	label311xDot.m
gFKinA.m		recurA.asv	strMat.m	recurEq.m
gFKobj.csv		strMat.m		
gFKphi.m				figSvdMat
gFKphiA.m				A2ThetaR.m
gFKtst.mexw64				adata.mat
labelgFKA.m				figSvdMat.eps
labelgFKalgo.m	figNBF		figFFTnbf	figSvdMat.m
labelgFKfn.m	ds2nfu.m		ds2nfu.m	polarDS2nfu.m
labelgFKPhi.m	figNbf.eps		figFFTnbf.eps	strMat.m
polarDS2nfu.m	figNbf.m		figFFTnbf.m	svdA.m

Additionally, it is essential to note that the source code for these files is maintained separately in the associated repository and is not included in this document. This approach enables more precise documentation while ensuring that users can easily access and utilize the underlying code for their applications and experiments.

Disclaimer

These demo programs are intended solely for academic and illustrative purposes in connection with the book *Direction Finding Algorithms for Practicing Engineers*, published by Springer Nature. Authored by Dr. Venkata Ranga Rao Kaluri (kaluri@ieee.org) this material is protected under copyright © 2025. All rights are reserved. Unauthorized reproduction, distribution, or use of the code in any form is strictly prohibited without prior written permission. The author assumes no responsibility or liability for any outcomes resulting from the use of this code.

References

1. Bellman, Introduction to Matrix Analysis. New York: McGraw-Hill, 1960.
2. P. Lancaster, *Theory of matrices*, Academic Press. Chapter: Perturbations in Linear Equations.
3. D. C. Montgomery *et al., Introduction to Linear Regression Analysis*, New York: Wiley, 1982, ch. 8, pp. 287–342

4. H. A. Schulke, *Matrix factorization*, in IRE Transactions on Circuit Theory, vol. 2, no. 2, pp. 128–132, 1955
5. A. Albert, *Regression and the Moore-Penrose Pseudoinverse*. New York: Academic Press, 1972.
6. G. H. Golub, *Numerical methods for solving linear least squares problems*, Numer. Math., vol. 7, pp. 206–216, 1965.
7. Peter C. Young *Recursive Estimation and Time-Series Analysis - An Introduction for the Student and Practitioner* Second Edition 2011, Springer Heidelberg Dordrecht London New York
8. Press William H, Teukolsky Saul A, Vetterling William T, Flannery Brian P(2007), *Section 2.7.1 Sherman – Morrison Formula*, Numerical Recipes: The Art of Scientific Computing (3rd ed.), New York: Cambridge University Press.
9. H. J. Kelley, *Method of gradients in Optimization Techniques*, G. Leitmann, Ed. New York: Academic, 1962.
10. Barnett, S. *The calculus of variations and optimal control: An introduction*. Acta Appl Math 1, 97–98 (1983).
11. P. A. Janakiraman and K. V. Ranga Rao, *Identification of linear modulated FM signal via a new recursive modified response error method (REM)*, in IEEE Transactions on Acoustics, Speech, and Signal Processing, vol. 36, no. 10, pp. 1675–1679, Oct. 1988.
12. Himmelblau David M *Applied Nonlinear Programming*, p 75, 1972 McGraw-Hill Inc., US.
13. A. S. Willsky, *Relationships between digital signal processing and control and estimation theory*, in Proceedings of the IEEE, vol. 66, no. 9, pp. 996–1017, 1978.
14. William H. Press, Saul A. Teukolsky, William T. Vetterling, Brian P. Flannery, *Numerical Recipes in C The Art of Scientific Computing*, Cambridge University Press, Second Edition pp 482–482.
15. Wilkinson, J.H., and Reinsch, C. 1971, *Linear Algebra, vol. II of Handbook for Automatic Computation* (New York: Springer-Verlag).
16. Smith, B.T., et al. 1976, *Matrix Eigensystem Routines' EISPACK Guide*, 2nd ed., vol. 6 of Lecture Notes in Computer Science (New York: Springer-Verlag).
17. H. Andrews and C. Patterson, *Singular value decompositions and digital image processing*, in IEEE Transactions on Acoustics, Speech, and Signal Processing, vol. 24, no. 1, pp. 26–53, 1976. 1976. 1976.
18. G. H. Golub and C. Reinsch, *Singular value decomposition and least squares solutions*, Numer. Math., vol. 14, pp. 403–420, 1970.
19. *Handbook of Linear Algebra* Edited By Leslie Hogben, Chapter 45, *Computation of the Singular Value Decomposition*, Alan Kaylor Cline, Inderjit S. Dhillon The University of Texas at Austin, November 2006, New York, Chapman and Hall/CRC.
20. Kaluri. V. Rangarao and V. Arumuru, *gold-Fourier Kaluri method for estimating vortex shedding frequency,* 2016 IEEE Region 10 Symposium (TENSYMP), Bali, Indonesia, 2016, pp. 379–383.
21. E. Oran Brigham, *Fast Fourier Transform and Its Applications*, Pearson, ISBN-10: 0133075052, April 8, 1988.
22. Kaluri V. Rangarao, Atul Negi, *A Perception Engine in Automotive FMCW Radar*, 2023 IEEE International Workshop on Technologies for Defense and Security (TechDefense), Rome, Italy, 2023, pp. 234–239.
23. Kaluri V. Rangarao, and Balaji Kanigicherla, *DOA Estimation via kMUSIC in FMCW Radar Application*, in Proc IEEE Aug ICSP2018, pp 903–908, Beijing, China
24. Richard P Brent, *Algorithms for Minimization without Derivatives.* Prentice - Hall, Inc. (1973).
25. Kaluri V. Rangarao, *et al., Estimating the Directions of Arrival of Narrow Band Signals using Spatial Tuned Filter* in Proc of RADAR-2011 at Chengudu, pp 319–22
26. Richard P Brent, *Algorithms for Minimization without Derivatives.* Prentice - Hall, Inc. (1973).
27. Kaluri V. Rangarao and Shridhar V, *An Accurate Numerical Method for Estimating the Delay Between Two Omni-Directional Receiving Elements* 30th Digital Avionics Systems Conference Oct-2011, Seattle, Washington, pp 8C3-4-8C3-7.

Chapter 3
Time Difference of Arrival

Estimating the time delay between received signals is fundamental to determining the direction of arrival (DOA) [1]. The performance of direction-finding systems critically depends on both the characteristics of the signal and the geometry of the sensor array in the TDOA approach. In particular, sensor spacing plays a pivotal role, with conventional designs typically assuming half-wavelength separation.

Over the decades, numerous algorithms have been developed to meet the challenges of accurate delay estimation. One of the earliest and most historically significant contributions came from Friis at Bell Labs in New York City in 1934 [2], laying the groundwork for modern time delay techniques. These early advancements continue to influence contemporary approaches to direction finding.

3.1 Parametric Delay Estimation

In this chapter, we present a new approach to parametric delay estimation [3–5] using an all-pass filter [6] pole position. This method remains effective even when multiple sensors use different wavelengths. This method addresses a common practical challenge in wide-aperture systems and large-scale sensor arrays. We propose different estimation strategies for short and long baselines and combine them into a hybrid method. This enhances accuracy and computational efficiency by utilizing a digital filter for phase shifting [7, 8], compared to traditional correlation-based estimators [9, 10]. Although delay estimation is a broad [11–16], we focus on key principles

V. R. Kaluri, *Direction Finding Algorithms for Practicing Engineers*,
https://doi.org/10.1007/978-3-032-06997-9_3

relevant to direction finding and provide an accessible, application-oriented solution. For a more comprehensive overview of existing techniques, readers are directed to the survey in [17].

3.2 Signal Characterization

It is well known that when two spatially separated sensors, especially acoustic ones, are used to capture a distant signal, they will inevitably experience a time delay τ in their recordings. This applies to signals with finite energy, such as the resonant peal of a bell or the sharp crack of a gunshot echoing through the air. The physical distance between these sensors can be as little as a few wavelengths or less than half a wavelength, particularly when working with a narrow-band signal with center frequency f_c. This highlights the complex relationship between sensor spacing and sound propagation in the detection and analysis of auditory events. To clarify, we cite an audio signal, but the phenomenon and the equations remain the same for RF signals as well.

1. When sensors separated more than a few wavelengths $\tau >> \frac{1}{f_c}$ Accurate Detection and Minimization
2. When the sensors are placed at half a wavelength $\tau < \frac{0.5}{f_c}$ Only Minimization.

A parametric delay estimation was well-attained in earlier works [3] using an FIR filter. The phase shifters in this illustration use an all-pass filter [5] that *good to have* the center frequency of the received signal and its characteristics, which we must estimate in real-time. Often, when calculating the time difference between two signals, we need to establish a reference between them. Signals can be pulsed narrowband or pulsed chirp signals.

3.2.1 Nature of the Signal

In real life, various opportunistic signals are received from different sources, including radio frequency (RF), acoustic, and both above and below-water environments. Standard RF signals can include communication signals from push-to-talk devices [18] or signals originating from radar reflections or direct sources [19, 20]. To understand the time difference of arrival between two received signals, let's consider the example of a brass bell that is periodically struck, as illustrated in Fig. 3.1a. We would analyze the nature of the signal to determine whether it is narrowband or not. The response from the bell is shown in Fig. 3.1b as a time series $y(t)$ and in discrete form as $y(k\delta t)$, or simply y_k, where we omit the constant term δt. It is crucial to extract h_k from y_k, as indicated within the red bounding box in Fig. 3.1b, through a process known as detection [21]. While our primary focus will be on Direction of Arrival (DOA), we will also discuss some foundational methods.

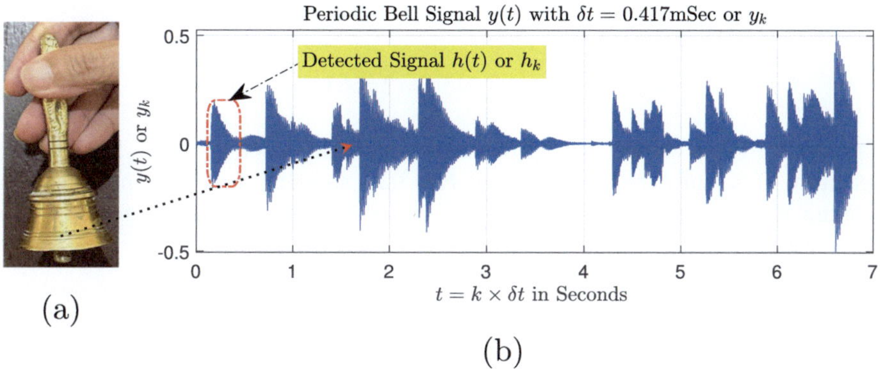

Fig. 3.1 Typical opportune signal

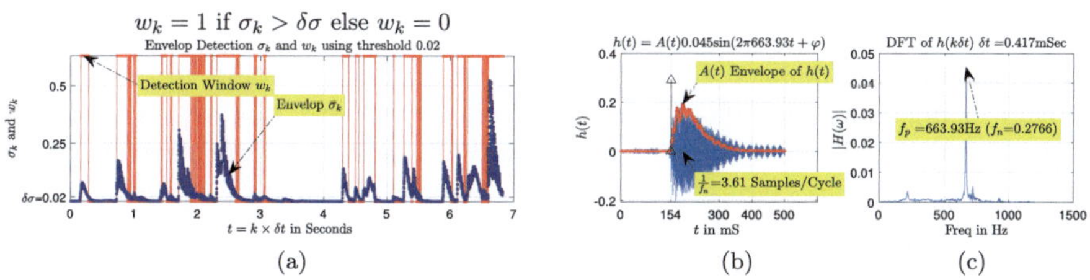

Fig. 3.2 Estimating the center frequency f_c

3.2.2 Estimating Unknown Signal

We pass the signal y_k^2 through a mean filter, as described in Eq. 3.1, to obtain the energy envelope σ_k. The energy envelope σ_k is shown in Fig. 3.2a.

$$\sigma_k = a\sigma_{k-1} + (1-a)y_k^2 \tag{3.1}$$

The typical value of a is chosen as 0.9.

The threshold $\delta\sigma_k$ is applied to the envelope σ_k, represents a hard limiter to produce the detection window w_k. The detection window w_k is shown in Fig. 3.2a. A small hysteresis is applied to reduce jitter in the detection window w_k. The discrete signal within this initial window is h_k or $h(k\delta t)$ of the continuous signal $h(t)$. In this book, we consistently use the discrete version of the signal.

3.2.3 Estimating f_n for Phase Shifter

In our TDOA, we use an all-pass filter for phase shifting, and its operating point is a function of f_n, which we quickly estimate. We can see that the signal in the detection window can be modeled as

$$h(t) = A(t) \times 0.045 \sin(2\pi 663.65t + \varphi) \tag{3.2}$$

The signal $h(t)$ is shown in Fig. 3.2b along with the envelope $A(t)$. The Fourier Spectrum $H(\omega)$ of $h(t)$ is depicted in Fig. 3.2c, showing a narrow spectral band peaking at the natural frequency f_p of the bell at 664 Hz. The discrete form of $h(t)$ is given as

$$\begin{aligned} h_k &= A(k\delta t) \times 0.045 \sin(2\pi \overbrace{\underbrace{}_{664}}^{f_p} k\delta t + \varphi) = A_k \times 0.045 \sin(2\pi f_p k\delta t + \varphi) \\ &= A_k \times 0.045 \sin(2\pi f_n k + \varphi) \text{ where } A_k \text{ is envelope and } \boxed{f_n = f_p\delta t = 0.2766} \end{aligned} \tag{3.3}$$

where f_n is the normalized frequency given in Eq. 3.3, as shown in the spectral domain in Fig. 3.2c, additionally, $\frac{1}{f_n}$ represents the number of samples per cycle of the narrow-band signal, which is equal to 3.62. In Direction of Arrival (DOA) applications, it is necessary to determine or estimate the time delay between two receiving elements of the same signal.

3.3 Orthogonal Detection

Detection and delay estimation are well presented in detail by Chan in his paper [22]. Cabot reports the earliest work on the Hilbert transformation for detection [23]. Recent methods focus on phase transitions based on detection concepts [24–26]. For Binary Frequency Shift Keying (BFSK) and Amplitude Shift Keying (ASK), the issue is approached by detecting *phase transitions*. In this award-winning detection technique [27, 29], we do not rely on energy; instead, we utilize the phase transitions that can occur in any signal, whether it is On-Off Keying (OOK), ASK, Frequency Shift Keying (FSK), or Binary Phase Shift Keying (BPSK).

This method demonstrates tolerance to varying Signal-to-Noise Ratio (SNR) conditions. The discrete Hilbert Transform [24] $\mathcal{H}(.)$ given as

$$\mathcal{H}[x_k] = x_k^{\frac{\pi}{2}} = \begin{cases} \frac{2}{\pi} \sum_{n\ odd} \left(\frac{x_n}{k-n}\right) & \text{if k even} \\ \frac{2}{\pi} \sum_{n\ even} \left(\frac{x_n}{k-n}\right) & \text{if k odd} \end{cases} \tag{3.4}$$

Several techniques have been developed to compute $\hat{\mathcal{H}}(.)$ in order to generate a signal $x_k^{\frac{\pi}{2}}$ that is orthogonal to x_k. A common approach is to utilize the Discrete Fourier Transform (DFT). Our focus is on the concept of orthogonal functions, which enhance the edges of the signal x_k. Figure 3.3 illustrates the Hilbert Transform of x_k, as described in Eq. 3.4. We have found that this technique is highly effective for

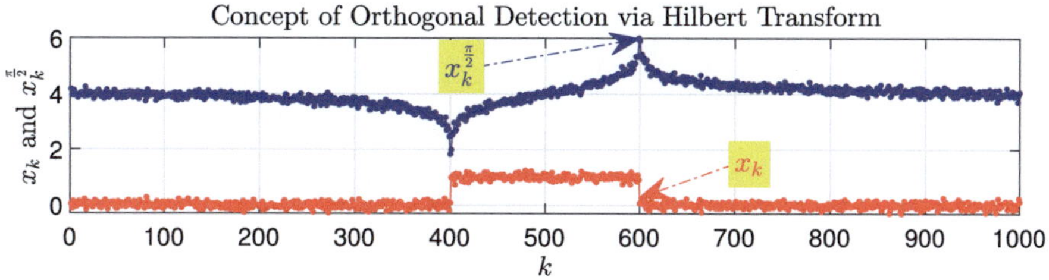

Fig. 3.3 Hilbert transform $\mathcal{H}(x_k)= x_k + jx_k^{\frac{\pi}{2}}$

envelope detection, producing sharp peaks at both the positive and negative edges, as shown in the blue graph of Fig. 3.3.

3.3.1 Delay by Orthogonal Detection

This method introduces a new technique for detecting the phase rate of signals using an Orthogonal Decomposer [27], as illustrated in Fig. 3.4 as a block diagram. In this figure, the block relating z_k and e_k delays the signal by i_w samples and subtracts it from the original signal before delaying, thereby generating the error signal e_k. The error signal is then normalized by the window width i_w. This error e_k is integrated to generate p_k for detection, as shown in Fig. 3.4b. Orthogonal Decomposer estimates and tracks the instantaneous phase of the incoming signal. These phase transitions are directly proportional to changes in frequency. An essential part of this method is the All-Pass Filter (APF), which is explained in detail in Sect. 3.4. Focusing on phase transitions, we introduce a new detection trend. This method detects the phase transition rate at phase change boundaries using x_k, without prior knowledge of the carrier frequency. The signal passes through an Orthogonal Decomposer that estimates and adjusts the phase of the incoming signal, producing a new signal $x_k^{\frac{\pi}{2}}$ that is phase-shifted by $\frac{\pi}{2}$. Phase transitions are detected using signal p_k, as shown in Fig. 3.4b. This novel detection approach focuses on phase transitions and does not require prior knowledge of the modulation type.

3.3.2 Implementation

The delay [8] observed between two signals, x_k^A and x_k^B, commonly seen in scenarios like those shown in Fig. 3.8, consists of two components. The first component, referred to as the coarse delay, is represented by an integer number of samples. The second component, known as the fine delay, is less than one complete cycle of the narrowband signal. The coarse delay between the signals x_k^A and x_k^B can be deter-

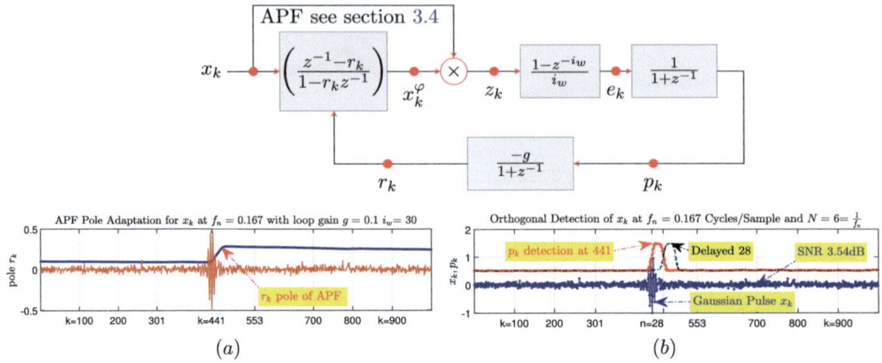

Fig. 3.4 Orthogonal detection for narrow band signals

mined with precision equal to the sampling time or an integral multiple of it. This level of precision can be achieved through orthogonal detection, as described, or by utilizing the more time-consuming method of cross-correlation [9].

In Fig. 3.4b, we see a coarse delay of 28 samples at an SNR of 3.5 dB. However, the acceptable delay requires specialized algorithms that we will discuss in this chapter. One crucial component often used for fine delay estimation is the all-pass filter.

3.4 Non Integer Phase Shifter

Fractional delay is essential in communication and audio systems and has been extensively studied by Valimaki [30] and many others [31]. This concept is crucial for accurately estimating the exact delay through minimization. We have developed a simple parametric method that uses the pole position of an all-pass filter. Consider the difference equation representing a first-order all-pass filter (APF):

$$x_k^B = r x_{k-1}^B - r x_k^A + x_{k-1}^A \tag{3.5}$$

The equation in 3.5 is presented in the block diagram shown in Fig. 3.5a, while Fig. 3.5b illustrates the input and output sequences. In this context, the input signal x_k^A is defined as $\cos\left(\frac{2\pi}{N}k\right)$, and the output sequence is denoted as x_k^B, where k represents the integer index of the sample in the sequence. To motivate the readers, we specify that $\delta\varphi = \frac{360}{30} = 12°$. This means that each sample shift corresponds to a phase shift of 12°, as depicted in Fig. 3.5b. To maintain numerical stability, it is essential to select the radial pole position r such that $0.1 < |r| < 0.98$. When the difference equation (3.5) is executed, the variable x_k^A experiences a phase shift of φ in relation to x_k^B. This phase shift is determined by the pole position r. We define the phase shift as $\varphi = \frac{2\pi}{N}\tau$, where τ represents a real number, expressed as $x_k^B = x_{k-\tau}^A$. We assume that φ indicates a delay ranging from 0 to 2π, which implies

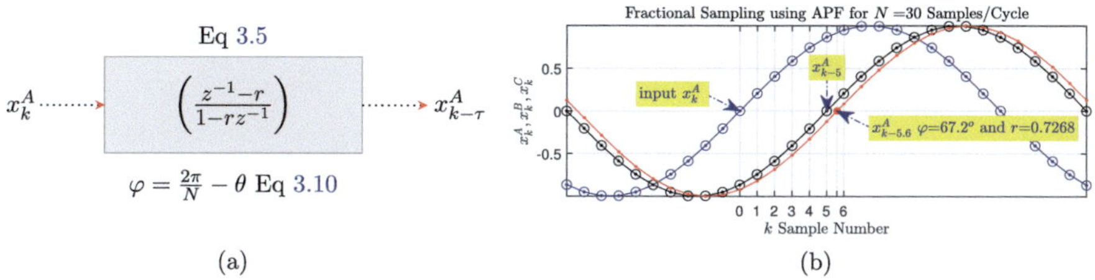

Fig. 3.5 All pass filter interpolator

$0 < \tau < N$. In Fig. 3.5b, we observe three wave-forms: one being the input and the other two shifted by integer samples, along with a shift of 67.2° for a pole position of $r = 0.727$. In this section, we will develop the relationship between r and φ, as well as methods for accurately estimating the fine delay.

3.4.1 *Phase Shift of APF*

In this section, we explicitly derive the relationship between r and φ. Equation (3.5) represents an operator relationship between x_k^A and x_{k-1}^A. We explore the phase shift within a cycle (360°) and which constitutes *fine delay.*

$$x_{k-1}^A = z^{-1} x_k^A \tag{3.6}$$

Same relationship also exists between x_k^B and x_{k-1}^B. Using these relationships, Eq. (3.5) can be re-written as

$$\begin{aligned}
x_k^B &= rz^{-1}x_k^B - rx_k^A + z^{-1}x_k^A \quad = \left(\frac{z^{-1}-r}{1-rz^{-1}}\right) x_k^A \\
&= \left(\frac{(z^{-1}-r)(1-rz)}{(1-rz^{-1})(1-rz)}\right) x_k^A \quad = \left(\frac{(z^{-1}-r)(1-rz)}{(1-r[z^{-1}+z]+r^2)}\right) x_k^A \\
&= z^{-1}\left(\frac{(1-rz)(1-rz)}{(1-r[z^{-1}+z]+r^2)}\right) x_k^A
\end{aligned} \tag{3.7}$$

we can easily see that by using the substitution $z = e^{j\omega}$ and $z = \cos\omega + j\sin\omega$

$$\begin{aligned}
1 - rz &= (1 - r\cos\omega) - j \times (r\sin\omega) \\
\text{mag } (1 - rz) &= \sqrt{1 + r^2\cos^2\omega - 2r\cos\omega + r^2\sin^2\omega} \quad = \sqrt{1 + r^2 - 2r\cos\omega} \\
\text{arg } (1 - rz) &= \tan^{-1}\frac{-r\sin\omega}{1 - r\cos\omega} = \frac{\theta}{2}
\end{aligned} \tag{3.8}$$

Using Eq. 3.8 we obtain simplified form as $(1 - rz)^2 = (1 + r^2 - 2r\cos\omega)e^{j\theta}$ substituting the above in equation (3.7), we get

$$x_k^B = e^{-j\omega}\left(\frac{(1 + r^2 - 2r\cos\omega)e^{j\theta}}{(1 + r^2 - 2r\cos\omega)}\right)x_k^A$$
$$= \left[e^{-j\omega}e^{j\theta}\right]x_k^A = \left[e^{j(\theta-\omega)}\right]x_k^A \tag{3.9}$$

where the intermediate value θ given as

$$\theta = 2\tan^{-1}\frac{-r\sin\omega}{1 - r\cos\omega} \text{ and } \omega = \frac{2\pi}{N} \tag{3.10}$$

As shown in Eq. (3.9), the desired phase-shift delay angle is given by $\varphi = \omega - \theta$. The intermediate parameter θ can be calculated for a desired phase shift as $\theta = \omega - \varphi$. Equation (3.10) can potentially be used to select the value of r for a desired phase shift φ. It is imperative to notice that the phase shift $\varphi = \theta - \omega$ is a function of r and the sampling rate of the signal.

$$r = \frac{\tan(\frac{\theta}{2})}{\tan(\frac{\theta}{2})\cos\omega - \sin\omega}$$

$$r(\omega, \varphi) = \boxed{\frac{\tan(\frac{\omega-\varphi}{2})}{\tan(\frac{\omega-\varphi}{2})\cos\omega - \sin\omega} \text{ where } \omega = 2\pi f_n} \tag{3.11}$$

Figure 3.5b shows the plot of x_k^A and x_k^B. We chose a phase shift of 67.2°, which corresponds to 5.6 samples—a non-integer number of samples. The number of samples per cycle was set to $N = 30$, so the normalized frequency is $f_n = \frac{1}{30}$. Using Eq. (3.11), we found r to be 0.7268.

The phase shift is illustrated in Fig. 3.5b, where the blue circles with dots represent the input signal, while the connected red dot signifies the output signal. The black circles with dots depict the sequence x_{k-5}^A, indicating an integral shift by five samples. As evident from Fig. 3.5b, the new sequence $x_k^B = x_{k-5.6}^A$ is generated by applying the difference equation (3.5) to x_k^A. From the above explanation and the information presented in Fig. 3.5b, we can conclude that any arbitrary real phase shift can be chosen. However, before using the value of r, it is essential to ensure that $0 < |r| < 1$.

3.4.1.1 Phase Shift by Pole Position

This is a crucial derivation using Eq. 3.10 and standard trigonometric identity.

$$(\omega - \varphi) = 2\tan^{-1}\frac{-r\sin\omega}{1 - r\cos\omega} = \tan^{-1}\left[\frac{2\left(\frac{-r\sin\omega}{1-r\cos\omega}\right)}{1-\left(\frac{-r\sin\omega}{1-r\cos\omega}\right)^2}\right]$$
$$\frac{\sin\omega\cos\varphi - \cos\omega\sin\varphi}{\cos\omega\cos\varphi + \sin\omega\sin\varphi} = \frac{-2r\sin\omega + r^2\sin 2\omega}{1 - 2r\cos\omega + r^2\cos 2\omega}$$

By cross multiplying and separating the variables, we get

$$\sin\omega - \boxed{r\sin 2\omega} + r^2\cos 2\omega\sin\omega + \underbrace{\tan\varphi\left(\boxed{2r\cos^2\omega} - \cos\omega - r^2\cos 2\omega\cos\omega\right)}$$
$$+\boxed{r\sin 2\omega} - r^2\sin 2\omega\cos\omega + \underbrace{\tan\varphi\left(\boxed{2r\sin^2\omega} - r^2\sin 2\omega\sin\omega\right)} = 0$$

We notice that boxed terms vanish or merge, and take $\tan\varphi$ as a common factor, bringing it to one side of the equation.

$$\tan\varphi\left(-2r + \cos\omega + r^2\frac{\overbrace{[\sin 2\omega\sin\omega + \cos 2\omega\cos\omega]}}{\cos\omega}\right) = \sin\omega + r^2\frac{\overbrace{[\sin\omega\cos 2\omega - \cos\omega\sin 2\omega]}}{-\sin\omega}$$

The closed-form solution for the phase shift is given as

$$\varphi = \tan^{-1}\frac{(1-r^2)\sin\omega}{(1+r^2)\cos\omega - 2r} \quad \text{where } \omega = 2\pi f_n. \tag{3.12}$$

3.4.1.2 Limitations of Simple APF

For *stability* reasons, the r values are generally considered within some thresholds such as $0.1 < |r| < 0.95$, rather than using values close to 0 and 1. Figure 3.6 shows a plot of f_n and φ depicting unsuitable r values (filled space) for APF for a range of 0° to 360°, whereas the unfilled space is suitable, representing valid r space, which is only 41.2%. It is clear that, given a normalized frequency f_n, it may not always be possible to find a suitable r for creating delay using APF, for some ranges of phase-shift angles φ.

It is well known that first-order APFs have limitations when used with varying sampling rates during the optimization process. This chapter presents innovative logic and methodology to address these issues. The algorithm is applied to a three-element Direction Finding (DF) system that covers the entire azimuth plane. DOA results are provided for various signal-to-noise ratio (SNR) conditions, along with an explanation of the algorithm's complexities.

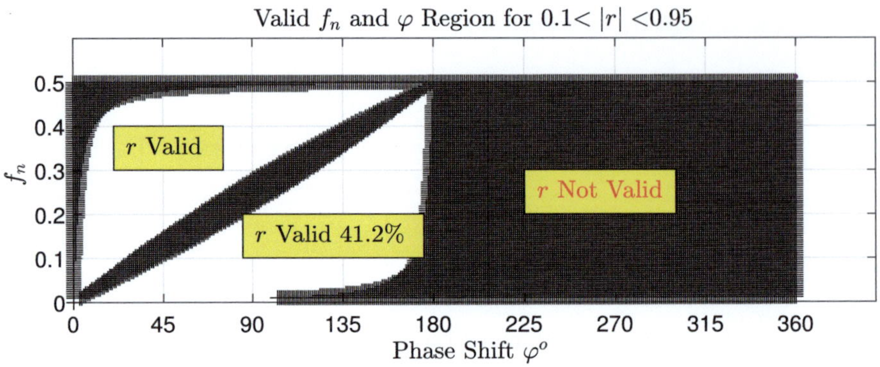

Fig. 3.6 First order all pass filter coverage using Eq. 3.11

3.4.2 *Modified all Pass Filter*

To address the issue of reduced (φ, f_n) space for certain values of f_n and φ, when the value of r is outside the range for a single filter as shown in Fig. 3.6, it is suggested to use two filters in cascade as in step 7 algorithm Sect. 3.4.2 shown in Fig. 3.7. Each filter would provide a shift of $\frac{\varphi}{2}$, significantly expanding the usable $\{f_n, \varphi\}$ space. For example, let $f_n = \frac{1}{30}$ and the desired phase delay be 225°. The r value obtained using Eq. (3.11) is 1.0910, which is unstable. Hence, we use the angle $\frac{225}{2}^{\circ}$, i.e., 112.5°, for which r turns out to be 0.8688. Even after splitting the phase-shift angle into two parts for a given normalized frequency, f_n, we may not find a suitable value for r for specific ranges of phase-shift angles φ. To further narrow down the set of values of f_n and φ for which r goes out of bounds we use the phase as $\varphi - \pi$ and use the APF with input x_k^A as $-x_k^A$ as in step 11 in the algorithm Sect. 3.4.2, the last step when it fails here we half the phase angle $\varphi - \pi$ and use the cascade of two filter with input as $-x_k^A$ as in step 15 in the same algorithm and the rest of the conditions the process comes to a hard stop 17. In Fig. 3.7, we present the results of the modified algorithm Sect. 3.4.2 as a diagram alongside the algorithm. Illustrates how most of the $\{f_n, \varphi\}$ space 94.2% is usable with this approach and is presented as an algorithm in Sect. 3.4.2. In the rare case where r is still unsuitable even with this model, we may opt for a cascade of $\frac{\varphi}{3}$ filters.

3.5 Time Delay

One of the earliest and most efficient methods for finding direction is to estimate the Time Difference of Arrival (TDOA). In any two elements of a sensor array with omnidirectional receiving elements, the effect of a narrow-band (NB) signal incident on them is the same, except for a phase lag or lead between them. This section explains

Algorithm Modified All Pass Filter 3.4.2

```
Start Choose (f_n, φ) and compute r Eqn 3.11
if (0.1 ¡—r—¡ 0.95) then
    x_k^B = r x_{k-1}^B − r x_k^A + x_{k-1}^A
else
    Set φ = φ/2 and compute r using Eqn 3.11
    if (0.1 ¡—r—¡ 0.95) then
        y_k = r y_{k-1} − r x_k^A + x_{k-1}^A and x_k^B = r x_{k-1}^B −
        r y_k + y_{k-1}
    else
        Set φ = φ − π and compute r using Eqn 3.11
        if (0.1 ¡—r—¡ 0.95) then
            x_k^B = r x_{k-1}^B + r x_k^A − x_{k-1}^A
        else
            Set φ = φ/2 and compute r using Eqn 3.11
            if (0.1 ¡—r—¡ 0.95) then
                y_k = r y_{k-1} + r x_k^A − x_{k-1}^A and x_k^B = r x_{k-1}^B +
                r y_k − y_{k-1}
            else
                Report Failure
            end if
        end if
    end if
end if
```

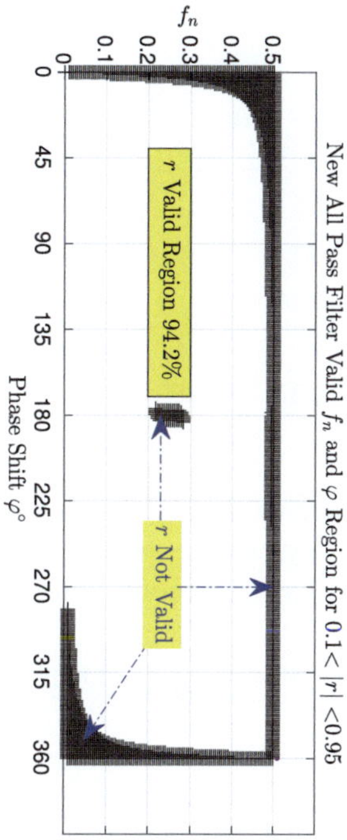

(a)

Fig. 3.7 Algorithm for modified all pass filter and outcome valid r

a numerical algorithm for estimating the delay between the time series acquired by these two spatially separated elements.

As described earlier, this method utilizes a first-order modified all-pass filter (APF), as detailed in Sect. 3.4.2, to introduce a delay relative to one of two elements, which is then compared to the second element. An objective function that varies with the delay is established and minimized using the gold-section univariate minimization algorithm, which does not rely on gradients. This approach yields an accurate estimate of the acceptable delay while the coarse delay is estimated using a robust detection technique.

3.5.1 *Sensor Topology*

In Fig. 3.8a, you can see the arrangement of the sensors and the emitter's orientation required to create the delay τ. A and B sensors are spaced apart to generate a delay. There are several ways to measure the delay τ between two received signals, as discussed in [4, 5]. By determining this delay, we can estimate the signal's Direction of Arrival (DOA). The delay depends on the angle of arrival θ, the inter-element

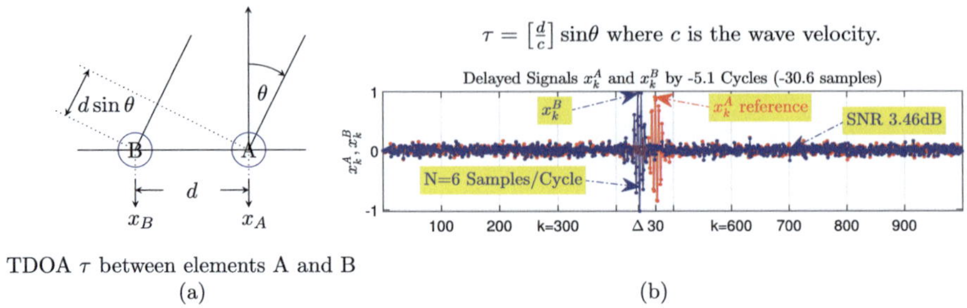

Fig. 3.8 Signals received at two elements A and B

spacing d, and the wave's propagation velocity c. To compute the DOA from the delay, we use the following formula where: τ units of time in seconds, c units of meters per second, and d has the units of meters.

$$\sin\theta = \left[\frac{c\tau}{d}\right] \text{ this implies } c\tau < d \text{ since } |\sin\theta| \leq 1 \text{ the solution range is } -\frac{\pi}{2} < \theta < \frac{\pi}{2} \tag{3.13}$$

To understand how sensors are positioned and the constraints used in Direction Finding, we need to examine some specifics with the help of Fig. 3.8 and Eq. 3.13. The DOA estimate with a two-element topology can only be obtained between $-\frac{\pi}{2}$ and $-\frac{\pi}{2}$. Therefore, when designing a direction-finding system, the choice of d, the number of sensor elements, and their geometry are crucial to overcome these limitations. One example is a 3 element configuration [5] with $d = \frac{\lambda}{2}$.

3.5.2 *Estimating Total Delay*

In this method [5], an algorithm is described for estimating the time delay τ between two time series x_A and x_B collected by the sensor elements A and B, which are spatially separated as shown in Fig. 3.8b. The waveform that is received first in time is said to lead the other. In case θ is positive, x_A leads x_B, and the delay is positive by convention. In this setup, the signal received at B, x_B, will be delayed compared to the signal received at A, x_A. The delay is depicted in the diagram of Fig. 3.8b, where the signal x_k^B is shown in blue and leads the signal x_k^A, shown in red, by negative τ, since x_k^B is leading. We use normalized units in cycles, where one cycle has $\tilde{N}$ samples and $f_n = \frac{1}{\tilde{N}}$ is the normalized frequency, expressed as samples per cycle. The signals x_A and x_B are sampled at $\tilde{N}$ samples per cycle, and we define phase shift due to one sample $\delta\varphi = \frac{2\pi}{\tilde{N}}$ radians. This method establishes the delay τ as the sum of two components, as

$$\tau = \tau_c + \tau_f \text{ where } \tau_c = n\delta\varphi \text{ and } \tau_f = \epsilon\delta\varphi \text{ where } n \text{ is an integer and } \epsilon \text{ is a real number.} \tag{3.14}$$

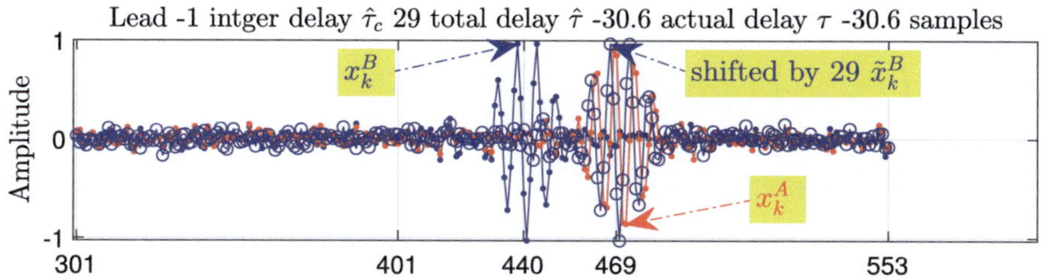

Fig. 3.9 Integer and fraction delay between x_A and x_B

There are three distinct steps. The first step is to find the detection window. The other two steps are finding coarse τ_c and acceptable τ_f delay. The reader may note that a single sample shift introduces a phase shift of $\delta\varphi$.

3.5.3 Integer Delay

Figure 3.9 shows detection window (301, 553) Detection performed using orthogonal detection. The signals x_k^B and x_k^A were detected at $k = 440$ and 469, respectively. This detection is described in the earlier section, and Fig. 3.4 shows the detection process. The integer delay is obtained by taking the difference of the detection points, which is a 29-sample value of $n = 469 - 440$. The leading wave shifted by n samples as $x_B \longrightarrow \tilde{x}_k^B$ is depicted as blue circles.

We notice that $\tilde{x}_k^B$ is very close to the delayed reference x_k^A. The integer delay $\hat{\tau}_c = 29 \times \delta\varphi$. The original delay created, $\tau = -30.6$, is depicted in Figs. 3.9 and 3.8. This is because when $\frac{d}{\lambda}$ is much larger than 0.5, say 20. These applications are not uncommon in the field of engineering. It's essential to note that the distance between the two sensors, A and B, must comply with the constraint specified in Eq. 3.13. The last step would be to determine the fractional delay, which would be less than half of $\tilde{N}$. The Signal-to-Noise Ratio (SNR) is a crucial parameter that significantly impacts detection ability and introduces errors in estimating integer delays. Specialized algorithms, such as orthogonal detection, are reasonably tolerant to noise in obtaining the detection time envelope that contains the signals x_A and x_B.

3.5.4 Fractional Delay

We have shifted the leading signal x_k^B by $\hat{\tau}_c = 29$ samples, denoted as $\tilde{x}_k^B$, which is only a few samples away from x_k^A, as shown in Fig. 3.9. Now we move x_k^A in fractional samples as close as to $\tilde{x}_k^B$ in the least squares sense with the help of an objective function, using an APF. Having realized the limitations of APF, we would use a cascade of two identical all-pass filters to phase shift the signal x_k^A to obtain

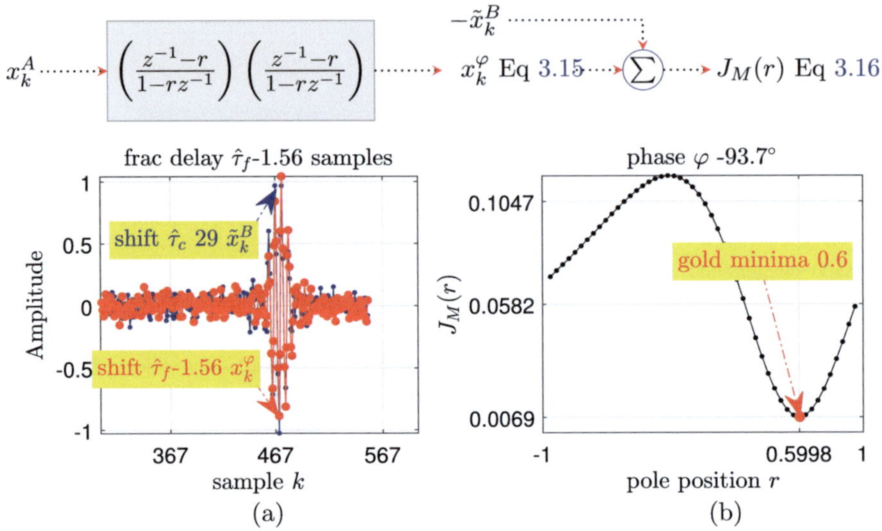

Fig. 3.10 Fraction delay between x_k^A and $\tilde{x}_k^B$

x_k^φ as

$$x_k^\varphi = 2rx_{k-1}^\varphi - r^2 x_{k-2}^\varphi + r^2 x_k^A - 2rx_{k-1}^A - x_{k-2}^A \tag{3.15}$$

would create a phase shift of $\varphi = 2\tan^{-1}\frac{(1-r^2)\sin\omega}{(1+r^2)\cos\omega - 2r}$ using Eq. 3.12 which is twice the phase shift of single APF. We define an objective function over M samples as

$$J_M(r) = \frac{\sum_{k=1}^{M}(x_k^\varphi - \tilde{x}_k^B)^2}{M} \tag{3.16}$$

where x_k^φ is the output of the second-order all-pass filter with input x_k^A as given by Eq. 3.15, the objective function $J_M(r)$ is a function of r and values are obtained by performing a coarse sweep over the interval $-0.95 < r < 0.95$. This is illustrated in Fig. 3.10b, where the coarse function is used to determine two values, r_a and r_b, before and after the minima.

3.5.4.1 Locating the Minima

The minimization algorithm is *gold section univariate* method without derivatives [32] Is employed to locate the exact minima shown as red dot on the curve $J_M(r)$ (Eq. 3.16) in the Fig. 3.10b. In this method, two end-points r_a and r_b are used as initial values. The intermediate points r_c and r_d are chosen such that $r_c = r_a + g(r_b - r_a)$ and $r_d = r_c + g(r_b - r_c)$ where $g = \frac{3-\sqrt{5}}{2}$. The objective function, say J_M, is evaluated at r_a, r_b, r_c and r_d. If $J_M(r_c) \le J_M(r_d)$, r_b takes the value of r_a and

r_a takes the value of r_d in the next iteration. Otherwise, r_a takes the value of r_c and r_c takes the value of r_d in the next iteration.

Typically, a fixed number of iterations is used, and the minimum value is quickly obtained quite accurately. Converges rapidly in about 20 iterations. The gold minima $r = 0.596$ is depicted in Fig. 3.10b. Using this value r we compute the phase shift $\varphi = -93.7°$ which corresponds to $\hat{\tau}_f = -1.56 = -\frac{\tilde{N}}{360°} \times 93.7°$ samples with $\tilde{N} = 6$ in this illustration. Now the total delay $\hat{\tau} = 29(\hat{\tau}_c) - (-1.56)(\hat{\tau}_f)$ is -30.56 samples shown in Fig. 3.9. This is at SNR 3.46 dB. The phase shifted signal x_k^{φ} for $r = 0.6$ along with x_k^A is shown in Fig. 3.10a, with dot in the circle, for $J_M(r = 0.6) = 0.0069$.

3.5.5 Performance

A detailed performance analysis in the context of TDOA was provided by Chan [33]. Estimating the delay between two received signals is crucial to the direction-finding (DF) problem. In this time delay method, we measure the delay in units of cycles (either 2π or 360°), as the received signal is narrowband. A typical sensor configuration is illustrated in Fig. 3.8a, with the corresponding waveforms delayed by τ, as shown in Fig. 3.8b. The value of the delay, denoted as τ, is varied from -8 cycles to +8 cycles. The algorithm described earlier estimates this delay as $\hat{\tau}$, and the relationship between these two variables is illustrated in the top diagram of Fig. 3.11. A linear fit has been applied to the data, and the resulting equation is provided as follows:

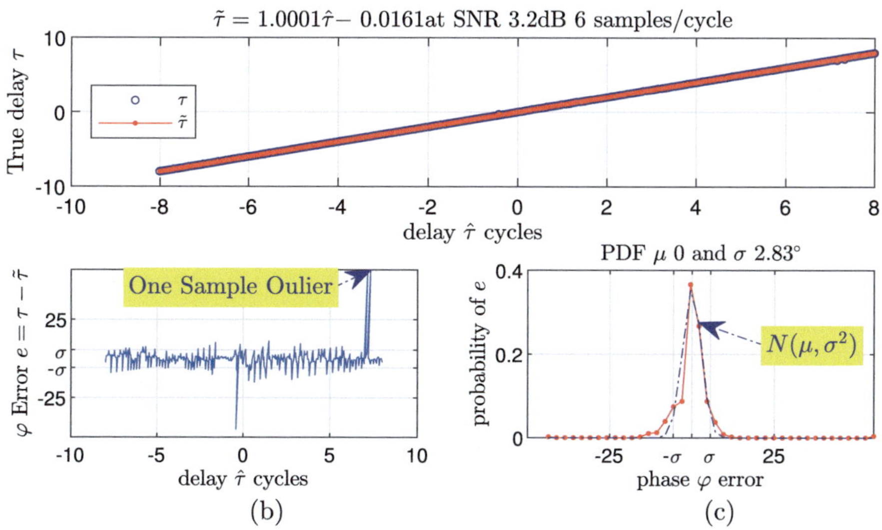

Fig. 3.11 Performance of delay estimator

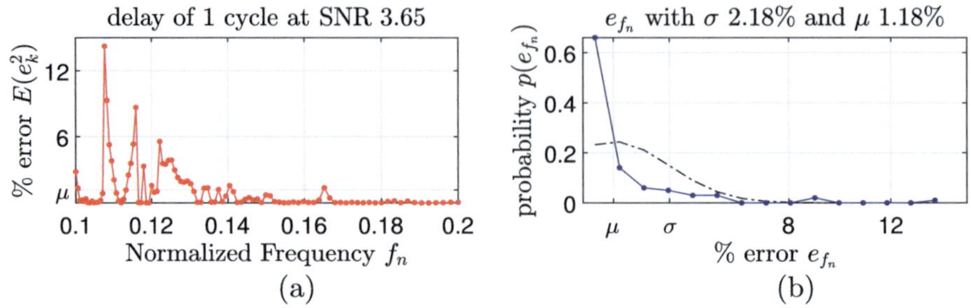

Fig. 3.12 Sensitivity to sampling rate

$$\tilde{\tau} = 1.0001\hat{\tau} - 0.0161 \tag{3.17}$$

In ideal conditions, the slope coefficient of $\hat{\tau}$ in Eq. 3.17 must be unity, and we obtained 1.0001. The intercept should be zero in the ideal case; however, we obtained 0.0161, indicating a need for offset correction. The residue error $e = \tau - \tilde{\tau}$ is shown in Fig. 3.11b. We notice a couple of outliers may be due to a program bug. The statistical property of e is shown in Fig. 3.11c, with zero mean(μ) and minimal variance(σ^2). The exact figure shows the Gaussian curve.

3.5.5.1 Sensitivity to Sampling Rate

Another factor that affects delay estimation is the sampling rate. The same algorithm was applied, similar to a Monte Carlo simulation, with a delay of $\tau = 1$ at SNR = 3.55, and repeated for each normalized frequency f_n 100 times to obtain the mean value of the square of error as $e_{f_n} = E(e_k^2)$. The error e_{f_n} is shown for various values of f_n in Fig. 3.12a. The normalized frequency, which is the reciprocal of the number of samples per cycle, is varied from 5 to 10, corresponding to $f_n = 0.2$ to 0.1.

3.6 DOA Performance

We can recall Eq. 3.13 for determining the Direction of Arrival (DOA) based on the configuration shown in Fig. 3.8. The path difference, given by $d \sin\theta$, is estimated as τc and can be expressed as $\frac{d}{\lambda}\sin\theta = f_c \times \tau$ [28]. Here, f_c represents the frequency of the narrowband signal and $T = \frac{1}{f_c}$. Additionally, we can write it in a normalized form, eliminating the speed of the wave c, as shown in Eq. 3.18.

$$\frac{d}{\lambda}\sin\theta = \frac{\tau_r}{T} \text{ we notice } (d, \lambda) \text{ has units of meters and } (\tau_r, T) \text{ has units of seconds} \tag{3.18}$$

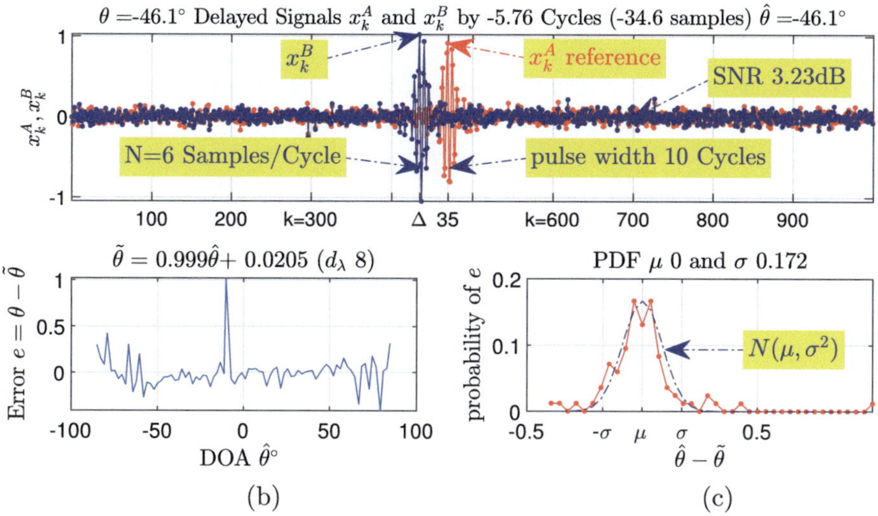

Fig. 3.13 Performance of DOA estimation

Making the quantities $\frac{d}{\lambda}$ and $\frac{T_r}{T}$ non-dimensional, one is a spatial parameter and the other is a time parameter. Typical signal pair x_k^A and x_k^B received by sensors spaced at distance d depicted in Fig. 3.13, corresponding to an angle θ of $-46.1°$. This signal pair undergoes processing as outlined in Sect. 3.5 to extract the normalized time delay τ. We write Eq. 3.18 in normalized units using the notation as $d_\lambda = \frac{d}{\lambda}$ and $\tau = \frac{T_r}{T}$

$$d_\lambda \sin\theta = \tau \text{ we see that } d_\lambda \geq \tau \text{ and } \boxed{\theta = \sin^{-1}\frac{\tau}{d_\lambda}} \tag{3.19}$$

Understanding the normalized Direction of Arrival (DOA) Eq. 3.19 is crucial. The variable τ is measured in time cycles, while d_λ, expressed in spatial cycles, serves as a topology constant. The DF algorithm demonstrates an accuracy, measured as standard deviation (σ), of 1° or better for SNR values below 4 dB. This method is highly accurate for pulsed or coded waveforms since detecting signals is very efficient.

3.6.1 Evaluation

The direction of arrival (DOA), denoted as θ, is swept from $-85°$ to $85°$ based on the configuration parameters illustrated in Fig. 3.13. We set the geometry constant d_λ to 8 cycles in this example. The signal is a Gaussian pulse with a width of 10 cycles and a sampling rate of six samples per cycle. Figure 3.13 presents a typical signal pair, x_k^A and x_k^B, which are delayed by τ and received by sensors spaced at a distance d, corresponding to an angle of $\theta°$.

We estimate the delay $\hat{\tau}$ using the value of d_λ in Eq. 3.19, which allows us to then estimate the DOA $\hat{\theta}$. This process is repeated for all values of θ in the range of $-90°$ to $90°$ to obtain $\hat{\theta}$. A linear regression analysis is performed, resulting in the equation $\tilde{\theta} = 0.9999\hat{\theta} + 0.008257$. The error, defined as $e = \theta - \hat{\theta}$, is depicted in Fig. 3.13b. The error e is a zero-mean normally distributed random variable shown in Fig. 3.13c gives us an idea about the error, and the accuracy of DOA is represented by σ, which is less than $1°$ as reported [5].

3.6.2 Some Real Life Application

Let's analyze how sound waves propagate and the delay experienced by two microphones. To explain the concept in practical terms, consider a narrow-band signal with a frequency of $f_c = 1000$ Hz. This corresponds to a period of $T = 1$ ms. The delay for a direction of arrival (DOA) of $\theta = 47.1°$ is $\tau_r = 5.76$ ms. Using a propagation velocity of $c = 330$ m/s, we can calculate the wavelength λ as follows: $\lambda = \frac{c}{f_c} = 0.33$ m. This suggests a spacing of $d = 2.64$ m.

Consider an example of a millimeter wave with a carrier frequency of $f_c = 77$ GHz and a propagation speed of $c = 3 \times 10^8$ m/s. The wavelength λ is approximately 3.8961 mm. We choose the geometry constant d_λ to be 0.5. For a direction of arrival (DOA) angle of $\theta = -46.1°$, we calculate a normalized delay of $\tau = -0.3603$. This corresponds to a phase angle of $\varphi = 360 \times \tau = 129.7°$ between x_k^B and x_k^A. Additionally, this phase angle corresponds to a delay of approximately 2.1617 samples, given a sampling rate of 6 samples per cycle.

3.7 Quadrant Ambiguity

R. L. Haupt and D. H. Werner, in their book [34], discuss in Chap. 5 the limitation of angular coverage in linear arrays. Specifically, conventional uniform linear arrays (ULAs) suffer from front-back ambiguity and typically provide only 180° coverage. We propose an alternate approach while still using a ULA configuration. Direction of Arrival (DOA) estimation using a pair of sensors is inherently limited to an azimuth range of only two quadrants, specifically: $-\frac{\pi}{2} < \theta < \frac{\pi}{2}$. This limitation arises from the symmetric response of the array, making it impossible to distinguish between sources arriving from front and back using phase difference alone.

We must use more than two elements arranged in different configurations to address this limitation. In this case, we adopt a triangular configuration. An algorithm for achieving the full azimuth range of 360° is described here. The triangular array of sensors, labeled A, B, and C, as shown in Fig. 3.14, enables DOA estimation for

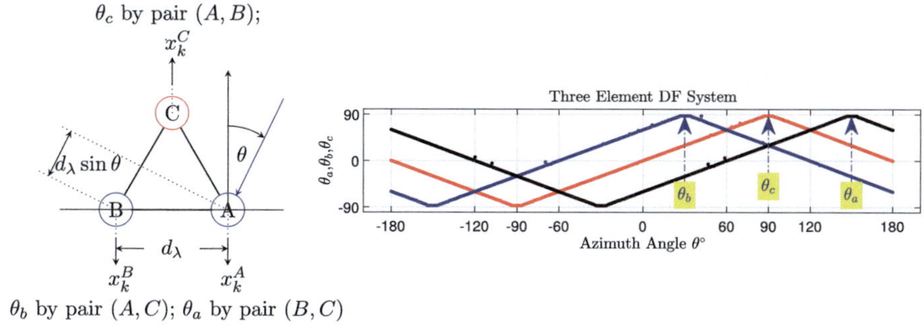

Fig. 3.14 Three elements configuration for 360° Azimuth coverage

complete coverage. The configuration is an equilateral triangle, providing an angular shift of $\frac{\pi}{3}$ for each pair of measurements. Using Time Difference of Arrival (TDOA), we estimate the delays between sensors: $\hat{\tau}_{AB}$ for the delay between B and A, $\hat{\tau}_{AC}$, and $\hat{\tau}_{BC}$ as described in Sect. 3.5.

3.7.1 360° Coverage

Using the delay, we determine the Direction of Arrival (DOA) for each pair of elements as described in Sect. 3.6, following the geometry illustrated in Fig. 3.14. The delay for each pair is estimated, resulting in a triplet $\Theta = \{\theta_c, \theta_b, \theta_a\}$. Additionally, we utilize the geometric constraints $\theta_b = \theta_c - \frac{\pi}{3}$ and $\theta_a = \theta_c + \frac{\pi}{3}$, where θ_c represents the two-quadrant angle observed by pair AB. The vector Θ is then used to compute the four-quadrant estimates $\hat{\theta}$, which cover the entire azimuth plane. This algorithm, referred to as Algorithm 3.7.1, is shown in Fig. 3.15. It is generic and demonstrates how adding augmented elements can enhance the limited coverage of a two-element DOA system.

3.7.2 Understanding Algorithm

The explanation is divided into two parts, as detailed in Algorithm 3.7.1, with diagrams shown in Fig. 3.15. The first part covers lines 2 to 8. The target location relative to the bore axis, whether on the port or starboard side, is represented by a 1-bit binary number called $b_{1,2,3}$ for all element pairs. This binary notation, $b = (b_1\, b_2\, b_3)$, indicates which segment of the azimuth is referenced. The 3-bit binary number b represents segments of 60° each, collectively covering a full azimuth plane of 360°. Each segment corresponding to the value of b is shown as a pie chart in Fig. 3.15a. By logically combining the outputs from each pair's Direction of Arrival (DOA), we

Algorithm Full Azimuth Coverage 3.7.1

Start Choose $\Theta = (\theta_a, \theta_b, \theta_c)$
for `i=1 to 3` and $\theta_{a,b,c}$ **do**
  if (θ_a ¿ 0) **then**
    $b_i = 1$
  else
    $b_i = 0$
  end if
end for
$b = b_1 \times 4 + b_2 \times 2 + b_3$
switch (b)
case 4(-180 to -120):
  $\theta_{ab} = -\theta_a - 120.0; \theta_{ac} = -\theta_c - 180.0; \theta = \frac{a+b}{2}$
  case 0(-120 to -60):
  $\theta_{ab} = \theta_b - 60.0; \theta_{ac} = -\theta_a - 120.0; \theta = \frac{a+b}{2}$
  case 2(-60 to 0):
  $\theta_{ab} = \theta_b - 60.0; \theta_{ac} = \theta_c; \theta = \frac{a+b}{2}$
  case 3(0 to 60):
  $\theta_{ab} = \theta_a + 60.0; \theta_{ac} = \theta_c; \theta = \frac{a+b}{2}$
  case 7(60 to 120):
  $\theta_{ab} = -\theta_b + 120.0; \theta_{ac} = \theta_a + 60.0; \theta = \frac{a+b}{2}$
  case 5(120 to 180):
  $\theta_{ab} = -\theta_b + 120.0; \theta_{ac} = -\theta_c + 180.0; \theta = \frac{a+b}{2}$
default:
  $\theta = 0$
end switch

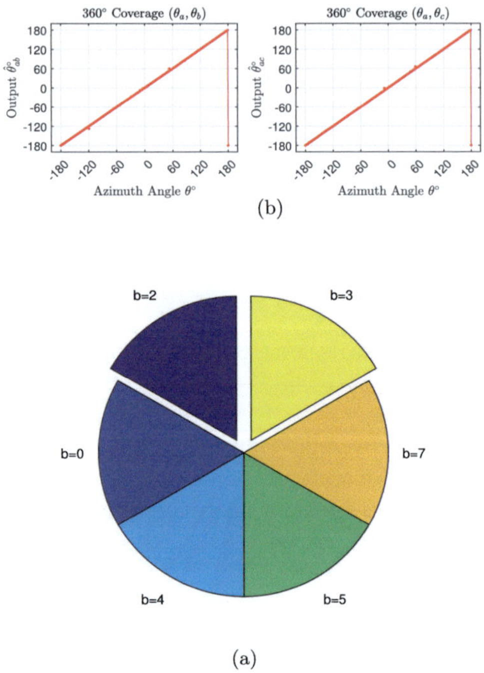

Fig. 3.15 Three elements covering full azimuth plane Fig. 3.14

can achieve full azimuth DOA coverage of 360°. This process produces two outputs: $\theta_{ab} = f(\theta_a, \theta_b)$ and $\theta_{ac} = f(\theta_a, \theta_c)$, as shown in Fig. 3.15b. This redundancy enhances the system's reliability. Several methods exist to combine these two outputs effectively. For demonstration, we have chosen to average the results, although we could alternatively calculate the distance between the two outputs and select the more optimal one.

3.7.3 Hexagonal and Other Topologies

Different topologies can be derived from the triangle topology. We have demonstrated the triangle topology, and using the same algorithm, a hexagon can be visualized as the superposition of two triangles rotated 180°. By rotating and superimposing the triangle topology, we can create additional topologies. The accuracy of direction finding improves as the number of elements increases.

3.8 Limitations of TDOA

Delay estimation involves two main components: identifying the detection window and estimating the delay itself. One major limitation of this method is its detection capability, which tends to deteriorate under higher Signal-to-Noise Ratio (SNR) conditions. Another significant drawback is its inability to process multiple signals simultaneously. Despite these limitations, this methodology is effective due to its simplicity and lower computational complexity.

3.9 Summary

This chapter explains the time difference arrival algorithm, providing an example and sample code in C and MATLAB. This algorithm represents one of the foundational techniques from the early days of direction finding. We discuss a sample signal, which could be the ringing of a bell, a push-to-talk burst, or a radar or sonar signal. We also cover energy detection and the orthogonal detection method, illustrating these concepts with a numerical example. One of the most essential delay elements in digital systems is the all-pass filter, which acts as a phase shifter. We employed a phase shifter with gold univariate minimization to estimate the direction of arrival of the accurate DF.

3.9.1 MEX File Generation

The C source files and MATLAB scripts used to generate MEX files in Chap. 3 are Primarily located in two directories: `chap3\timeDelay\timeDelay` and `chap3\figures\quadrant`. Each MATLAB `.m` file includes a `mex` compile directive that links The corresponding C or C++ source file to generate a platform-specific MEX file Usable in MATLAB.

Chapter 3 C Files for MEX

MEX File	Location of C Files	Command File
apf.mexw64	chap3\figures\timeDelay\timeDelay	mexApf.m
newAPF.mexw64	chap3\figures\timeDelay\timeDelay	mexNewAPF.m
delayT.mexw64	chap3\figures\timeDelay\timeDelay	mexDelayT.m
synthData.mexw64	chap3\figures\timeDelay\timeDelay	mexSynthData.m
DetectSigWin.mexw64	chap3\figures\timeDelay\timeDelay	mexDetectSigWin.m
doaVector2doa.mexw64	chap3\figures\quadrant	mex doaVector2doa.cpp

A total of six MEX files are generated in this chapter. The table presents the generated `.mex` files in the first column, the location of the C source files in the second column, and the MATLAB `.m` files (or direct `.cpp` reference `mex doaVectordoa.cpp`) containing the `mex` commands in the third column.

3.9.2 File Organization

This subsection provides a detailed list of program files related to the chapter titled *Time Difference of Arrival*. The files are organized into eight specific directories: `DOA`, `BellSpek`, `DelayError`, `delaySig`, `DetectWin`, `IntDelay`, `quadrant`, and `AllPassFilter`. Each directory is prominently marked in yellow at the top of its respective column, making it easy for readers to identify and navigate.

It's important to note that the actual code associated with these directories is stored in a separate repository and is not included within this document. This separation keeps the documentation focused and streamlined while allowing users to access the complete codebase when needed. The organization of the files into these directories is designed to improve usability, making it easier for users to find and use the specific components they need for their work with Time Difference of Arrival techniques.

Chapter 3 Program Files

DOA	BellSpek	DelayError	delaySig	DetectWin
delayT.mexw64	bell.wav	DelayError.eps	DelaySig.eps	DetectSigWin.mexw64
ds2nfu.m	BellDetkt.eps	delayT.mexw64	ds2nfu.m	ds2nfu.m
figtDoa.m	BellS.m4a	dlyEr.mat	figDelaySig.m	figHilb.m
labelDelaySigDoa.m	BellSig.eps	dlyErData.m	labelDelaySig.m	figOrthoDet.m
labelDoa.m	BellSig.m	ds2nfu.m	synthData.mexw64	Hilb.eps
pdf_y.m	BellSpek.eps	erData.m		labelOrthoDet.m
tDoa.eps	ds2nfu.m	figDelayError.m	IntDelay	OrthoDet.eps
	figBellDetkt.m	figFnError.m	DelaySig.eps	OrthoDetRk.eps
quadrant	figBellSpek.m	FnError.eps	delayT.mexw64	synthData.mexw64
azimuth2doa.m	labelBell.m	labelDelaySig.m	ds2nfu.m	
cover2pi.eps	labelDetkt.m	pdf_y.m	figIntDelay.m	
delayT.mexw64	labelSig.m	snrfn.mat	FineDelay.eps	AllPassFilter
doaVector2doa.mexw64	Spk.m	snrfn01.mat	IntDelay.eps	Apf.eps
ds2nfu.m			labelDelaySig.m	apf.mexw64
evalDoaData.m			labelIntFineDelay.m	ds2nfu.m
figQuadrantDoa.m			myFigEps.m	figApf.m
figQuadSeg.m				figNewPhiFnApf.m
labelAzimDoa.m				figPhiFnApf.m
QuadrantDoa.eps				labelApf.m
QuadSeg.eps				labelNewPhiFn.m
thetadata.mat				labelPhiFn.m

Disclaimer
These demo programs are intended solely for academic and illustrative purposes in connection with the book *Direction Finding Algorithms for Practicing Engineers*, published by Springer Nature. Authored by Dr. Venkata Ranga Rao Kaluri (kaluri@ieee.org) this material is protected under copyright © 2025. All rights are reserved. Unauthorized reproduction, distribution, or use of the code in any form is strictly prohibited without prior written permission. The author assumes no responsibility or liability for any outcomes resulting from the use of this code.

References

1. G. Carter, *Time delay estimation for passive sonar signal processing*, in IEEE Transactions on Acoustics, Speech, and Signal Processing, vol. 29, no. 3, pp. 463–470, 1981
2. H. T. Friis, C. B. Feldman and W. M. Sharpless, *The Determination of the Direction of Arrival of Short Radio Waves*, in Proceedings of the Institute of Radio Engineers, vol. 22, no. 1, pp. 47–78, 1934
3. Y. Chan, J. Riley and J. Plant, *A parameter estimation approach to time-delay estimation and signal detection*, in IEEE Transactions on Acoustics, Speech, and Signal Processing, vol. 28, no. 1, pp. 8–16, 1980.
4. Kaluri V Rangarao, Satish, K *An elegant method for delay estimation in mobile applications*, TENCON 2008 - 2008, TENCON 2008. IEEE Region 10 Conference 19–21 2008 Pages:1–3, http://ieeexplore.ieee.org/document/4766530/
5. Kaluri V. Rangarao and Shridhar V. *An Accurate Numerical Method for Estimating the Delay Between Two Omni-Directional Receiving Elements*, IEEE 30th Digital Avionics Systems Conference 2011, Seattle, Washington, U.S.A., 2011, pp 8C3-4-8C3-7, http://ieeexplore.ieee.org/document/6096146/
6. P. A. Regalia, S. K. Mitra and P. P. Vaidyanathan, *The digital all-pass filter: a versatile signal processing building block*, in Proceedings of the IEEE, vol. 76, no. 1, pp. 19–37, 1988.
7. P. C. Ching and Y. T. Chan, *Adaptive time delay estimation with constraints*, in IEEE Transactions on Acoustics, Speech, and Signal Processing, vol. 36, no. 4, pp. 599–602, 1988
8. B. Friedlander and B. Porat, *A Parametric Technique for Time Delay Estimation*, in IEEE Transactions on Aerospace and Electronic Systems, vol. AES-20, no. 6, pp. 729–735, 1984
9. M. Azaria and D. Hertz, *Time delay estimation by generalized cross correlation methods*, in IEEE Transactions on Acoustics, Speech, and Signal Processing, vol. 32, no. 2, pp. 280–285, 1984.
10. C. Knapp and G. Carter, *The generalized correlation method for estimation of time delay*, in IEEE Transactions on Acoustics, Speech, and Signal Processing, vol. 24, no. 4, pp. 320–327, 1976.
11. M. A. E. Mofeed and H. A. Elsalam Mofeed, *Direction-of-arrival methods (DOA) and time difference of arrival (TDOA) position location technique*, Proceedings of the Twenty-Second National Radio Science Conference, 2005. NRSC 2005., Cairo, Egypt, 2005, pp. 173–182.
12. T. Y. Min, M. Chitre and V. Pallayil, *Detecting the direction of arrival and time of arrival of impulsive transient signals*, OCEANS 2016 MTS/IEEE Monterey, Monterey, CA, USA, 2016, pp. 1–8.

13. X. Cui, K. Yu and S. Lu, *Direction Finding for Transient Acoustic Source Based on Biased TDOA Measurement*, in IEEE Transactions on Instrumentation and Measurement, vol. 65, no. 11, pp. 2442–2453, 2016.
14. D. -G. Kim, G. -H. Park, H. -N. Kim, J. -O. Park, Y. -M. Park and W. -H. Shin, *Computationally Efficient TDOA/FDOA Estimation for Unknown Communication Signals in Electronic Warfare Systems*, in IEEE Transactions on Aerospace and Electronic Systems, vol. 54, no. 1, pp. 77–89, 2018.
15. A. Weiss and E. Weinstein, *Fundamental limitations in passive time delay estimation–Part I: Narrow-band systems*, in IEEE Transactions on Acoustics, Speech, and Signal Processing, vol. 31, no. 2, pp. 472–486, 1983.
16. E. Weinstein and A. Weiss, *Fundamental limitations in passive time-delay estimation–Part II: Wide-band systems*, in IEEE Transactions on Acoustics, Speech, and Signal Processing, vol. 32, no. 5, pp. 1064-1078, 1984.
17. SPECIAL ISSUE ON TIME DELAY ESTIMATION, IEEE Transactions on Acoustics, Speech, and Signal Processing, vol. 29, no. 3, 1981
18. M. A. Soderstrand, T. G. Johnson, R. H. Strandberg, H. H. Loomis and K. V. Rangarao, *Suppression of multiple narrow-band interference using real-time adaptive notch filters*, in IEEE Transactions on Circuits and Systems II: Analog and Digital Signal Processing, vol. 44, no. 3, pp. 217–225, 1997.
19. Schlesinger, R.J., *Principles of Electronic Warfare*, Prentice-Hall, 1961.
20. G. Schrick and R. G. Wiley, *Interception of LPI radar signals*, IEEE International Conference on Radar, Arlington, VA, USA, 1990, pp. 108–111.
21. Harry L. Van Trees (Author), Kristine L. Bell and Zhi Tian, *Detection, Estimation, and Modulation Theory* Part I, Wiley 2nd Edition, April 15, 2013.
22. Y. Chan, R. Hattin and J. Plant, *The least squares estimation of time delay and its use in signal detection*, in IEEE Transactions on Acoustics, Speech, and Signal Processing, vol. 26, no. 3, pp. 217–222, 1978
23. R. Cabot, *A note on the application of the Hilbert transform to time delay estimation*, in IEEE Transactions on Acoustics, Speech, and Signal Processing, vol. 29, no. 3, pp. 607–609, 1981.
24. S. Kak, *The discrete Hilbert transform.* Proc. IEEE, vol. 58, pp. 585–586, 1970
25. Rangarao,K.V *etal An elegant method for delay-estimation in mobile applications*, TENCON2008-2008, TENCON 2008. IEEE Region10 Conference19-21, 2008 Page(s):1–3.
26. Kaluri V. Rangarao and Ranjan K. Mallik, *Digital Signal Processing: A Practitioner's Approach*, Wiley.
27. Kaluri V. Rangarao, *etal, A Robust BFSK Signal Demodulator Using Orthogonal Decomposer* IEEE 32 DASC Conference at Syracuse Oct 6-10 2013 pp 2D4-1 to 2D4-5).
28. David Halliday, Robert Resnick, and Jearl Walker, *Chapter 16 Wave Motion Fundamentals of Physics*, 12th Edition, October 2021, Wiley.
29. Kaluri V. Rangarao *Unified demodulation of any shift keying by phase matching technique* 2015 International Conference on Electronic Design, Computer Networks & Automated Verification (EDCAV), Shillong, India, 2015, pp. 130–134, http://ieeexplore.ieee.org/document/7060553/
30. V. Valimaki and T. I. Laakso, *Principles of fractional delay filters*, 2000 IEEE International Conference on Acoustics, Speech, and Signal Processing. Proceedings (Cat. No.00CH37100), Istanbul, Turkey, 2000, pp. 3870–3873 vol.6.
31. G. . -S. Liu and C. . -H. Wei, *A new variable fractional sample delay filter with nonlinear interpolation*, 1991 IEEE International Symposium on Circuits and Systems (ISCAS), Singapore, 1991, pp. 2451–2454 vol.5.
32. Richard Brent, *Algorithms for Minimization without Derivatives.* Prentice - Hall, Inc. (1973).
33. K. C. Ho and Y. T. Chan, *Solution and performance analysis of geolocation by TDOA*, IEEE Transactions on Aerospace and Electronic Systems, vol. 29, no. 4, pp. 1311–1322, 1993.

34. R. L. Haupt and D. H. Werner, *Genetic Algorithms in Electromagnetics*, Wiley-IEEE Press, 2007, pp. 167–173.
35. Zeng, X., Yu, X., Zhang, H., Lu, Y., & Zhao, Y. (2025). *Novel APD Array Configurations for Improved Detection Area and Frequency Response*. Sensors, 25(6), 1671.

Chapter 4
Subspace Methods

Subspace methods [1, 2, 5–9] are a widely used technique for overcoming the limitations of TDOA methods. Historically, Kumaresan [3], Barabell [4], Kailath [5], and Cadzow have provided crucial insights [10–12] into the role of subspace techniques in direction-of-arrival (DOA) estimation. Bhaskar Rao [13] offers an excellent description of these methods, as does Paulraj in his review article [5, 14]. Prony (1795) [1] and Pisarenko [2] were among the first to use the data model structure to estimate the parameters of cisoids (complex sinusoids) [15, 16] in additive noise using a covariance approach. Following this, Schmidt [6] and Bienvenu and Kopp [17] independently extended this method to sensor arrays of various shapes. Notably, Schmidt developed a complete geometric solution for the problem without noise and skillfully adapted these concepts to create an approximate solution that accounted for noise. This adaptation led to the development of the `MUSIC` (`MU`ltiple `SI`gnal `C`lassification) algorithm [6] and its variations [26], which has been extensively studied since its introduction.

4.1 Subspaces

The space spanned by the data matrix (often referred to as the *look matrix*) is partitioned into two orthogonal components: the **signal subspace** and the **noise subspace**, based on the eigenvalues of the matrix. Each row in the look matrix is designated as a *snapshot*, representing a measurement vector collected at a specific time or instance. In this section, although we do not explicitly categorize methods as either *noise-subspace* or *signal-subspace* based, the distinction becomes evident in the way eigenvectors are utilized. For noise-subspace-based methods, eigenvectors corresponding to the **smallest eigenvalues** we have used in ascending ($\lambda_{min} \ldots \lambda_{max}$ as in Eq. 4.18) order are used, as they represent directions dominated by noise. Conversely, signal-subspace-based methods use eigenvectors associated with the **largest**

V. R. Kaluri, *Direction Finding Algorithms for Practicing Engineers*,
https://doi.org/10.1007/978-3-032-06997-9_4

eigenvalues typically in descending ($\lambda_{max} \ldots \lambda_{min}$ see table in Fig. 4.31) order, where the leading vectors capture the dominant signal components. These selected vectors form the basis for subsequent signal processing operations.

4.1.1 Data Model

It is essential to understand the data model in the subspace methods. Figure 4.1 shows the data model for D targets radiating narrow band signals $e^{j(2\pi f_n k)}$ of signal strength A_k^i and phase shifted by φ^i due to each target i at an angle θ_i concerning true north.

The signal strength A_k^i from each target is assumed to be uncorrelated and independent. In creating this property, the value of A_k^i is chosen as a random bipolar number ± 1 given as

$$A_k^i = \begin{cases} +1, & \text{if } \gamma_{k,i} \geq 0 \text{ where } \gamma \text{ is zero mean normally distributed random variable} \\ -1, & \text{otherwise} \end{cases}$$

$$\varphi_m^i = m \times \varphi^i \text{ where } \varphi^i = 2\pi \frac{d}{\lambda} \sin\theta_i \tag{4.1}$$

$$s_k^{m\varphi^i} = A_k^i \left[\underbrace{\cos(2\pi f_n k + \varphi_m^i)}_{\tilde{s}_k^{m\varphi^i}} + j\sin(2\pi f_n k + \varphi_m^i) \right] \tag{4.2}$$

$$= A_k^i e^{j(2\pi f_n k + \varphi_m^i)} = A_k^i e^{j(2\pi f_n k)} [e^{j\varphi^i}]^m \tag{4.3}$$

$$s_k^{m\varphi} = \sum_i^D s_k^{m\varphi^i} = e^{j(2\pi f_n k)} \underbrace{\left(\sum_i^D A_k^i [e^{j\varphi^i}]^m \right)}_{\boxed{a_k [e^{j\varphi}]^m = a_k z^{-m}}} \tag{4.4}$$

$$\text{where } e^{j\varphi} = z^{-1} \text{ spatial delay operator}$$

$$\mathbf{s}_k = [s_k \; s_k^{\varphi} \; s_k^{2\varphi} \; s_k^{3\varphi} \; s_k^{4\varphi}] \tag{4.5}$$

$$= s_k [1 \; z^{-1} \; z^{-2} \; z^{-3} \; z^{-4}] = s_k \mathbf{a}^T(z) \tag{4.6}$$

4.1.2 Decomposition of Look Matrix

The snapshots $\mathbf{s}_k^T$ are captured by the sensing array and assembled into a noise free look matrix designated as $\hat{\mathbf{S}}$. The noisy look matrix $\mathbf{S} = \hat{\mathbf{S}} + N(0, \sigma^2)$ as shown in Fig. 4.2 which has a size of $N \times m$. By applying singular value decomposition,

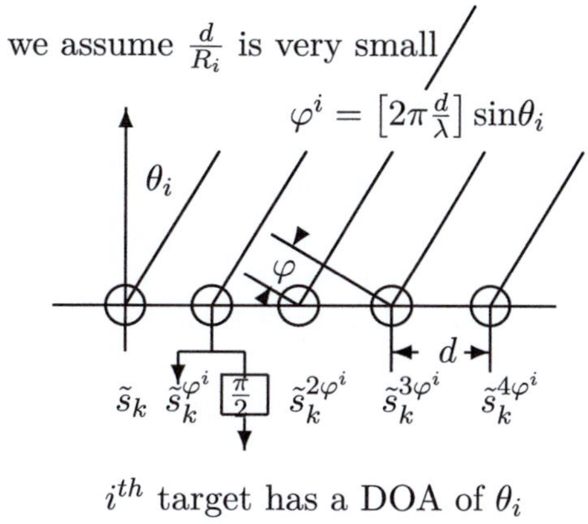

Fig. 4.1 Uniform linear array

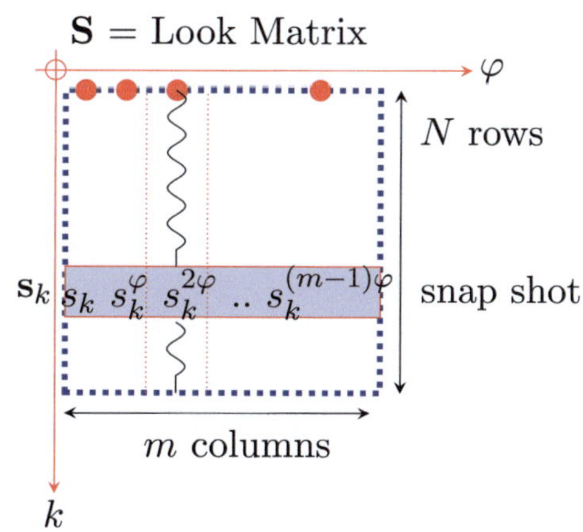

Fig. 4.2 Anatomy of look matrix

as described in Chap. 2, the look matrix can be expressed as the product of three matrices: $\mathbf{U}$, Σ, and $\mathbf{V}$.

$$\mathbf{S} = \begin{pmatrix} \mathbf{U} \\ N \times m \end{pmatrix} \begin{pmatrix} \Sigma \\ m \times m \end{pmatrix} \begin{pmatrix} \mathbf{V} \\ m \times m \end{pmatrix}$$

where $\mathbf{U} = [\mathbf{u}_1 \ldots \mathbf{u}_m]$ and $\mathbf{V} = [\mathbf{v}_1 \ldots \mathbf{v}_m]$ are orthonormal. The matrix Σ is diagonal matrix with real values $[\lambda_1 \ldots \lambda_m]$. We define $\begin{pmatrix} \mathbf{S}_i \\ N\times m \end{pmatrix} = \lambda_i \begin{pmatrix} \mathbf{u}_i \\ N\times 1 \end{pmatrix} \begin{pmatrix} \mathbf{v}_i^T \\ 1\times m \end{pmatrix}$. The look matrix is decomposed as

$$\mathbf{S} = \sum_{i=1}^{m} \mathbf{S}_i = \sum_{i=1}^{m} \lambda_i \mathbf{u}_i \mathbf{v}_i^T \tag{4.7}$$

4.1.3 *Signal to Noise Ratio*

Calculating the signal-to-noise ratio (SNR) can be challenging because it requires knowledge of the power of a clean signal. In our synthetic data model, we add zero-mean normally distributed noise, represented as $N(0, \sigma_N^2)$, to each element of the noise-free look matrix $\hat{\mathbf{S}}$. This process generates a realistic look matrix $\mathbf{S}$, which allows us to compute both the noise power and the signal power. With these values, we can then calculate the SNR using the formula:

$$\mathrm{SNR} = 10\log_{10}\left(\frac{\text{Signal Power}}{\text{Noise Power}}\right)$$

The signal power can be computed using each column vector $\hat{\mathbf{x}}_i$ of $\hat{\mathbf{S}}$.

$$\sigma_{\hat{S}}^2 = \sum_{i=1}^{m} \frac{\|\hat{\mathbf{x}}_i\|}{m} \quad \text{thus SNR} = 10\log_{10}\frac{\sigma_{\hat{S}}^2}{\sigma_N^2} \text{ in dB} \tag{4.8}$$

In reality, $\sigma_{\hat{S}}^2$ represents the mean of the trace of the covariance matrix of $\hat{\mathbf{S}}$. The mean of the trace of the covariance matrix of $\mathbf{S}$ is given by $\sigma_{\hat{S}}^2 + \sigma_N^2$, which denotes the total power.

4.2 Choice of Optimal Steering Vector

Further we can write using $D < m$ dominant eigenvalues $[\lambda_{m-D+1} \ldots \lambda_m]$ and insignificant or singular eigenvalues as $[\lambda_1 \ldots \lambda_{m-D}]$ and given $\lambda_i < \lambda_{i+1}$ for all $i = 1$ to m.

$$\mathbf{S} = \underbrace{\sum_{i=1}^{m-D} \lambda_i \mathbf{u}_i \mathbf{v}_i^T}_{\text{noise}} + \underbrace{\sum_{i=m-D+1}^{m} \lambda_i \mathbf{u}_i \mathbf{v}_i^T}_{\text{signal}} \tag{4.9}$$

Consider a steering vector $\mathbf{w}$ and the corresponding complex polynomial $h(z)$ which represents the energy at phase angles φ in the interval $\{-\pi, \pi\}$

$$h(z) = \mathbf{w}^{\mathbf{T}} \mathbf{S}^{*\mathbf{T}} \mathbf{S} \mathbf{a}(z)$$

and this can be rewritten using the covariance matrix $\mathbf{H} = \mathbf{S}^{*T}\mathbf{S}$ and the energy polynomial takes the form $h(z) = \mathbf{w}^{\mathbf{T}}\mathbf{H}\mathbf{a}(z)$

$$\mathbf{H} = \underbrace{\sum_{i=1}^{m-D} \lambda_i \mathbf{v}_i \mathbf{v}_i^T}_{\mathbf{H}_n \,=\, \text{noise}} + \underbrace{\sum_{i=m-D+1}^{m} \lambda_i \mathbf{v}_i \mathbf{v}_i^T}_{\text{signal}} \tag{4.10}$$

And the polynomial takes the form

$$H(z,\mathbf{w}) = \underbrace{\sum_{i=1}^{m-D} \mathbf{w}^T \lambda_i \mathbf{v}_i \mathbf{v}_i^T \mathbf{a}(z)}_{\text{noise}} + \underbrace{\sum_{i=m-D+1}^{m} \mathbf{w}^T \lambda_i \mathbf{v}_i \mathbf{v}_i^T \mathbf{a}(z)}_{\text{signal}} \tag{4.11}$$

We minimize $H(z, \mathbf{w})$ by selecting $\mathbf{w} = \mathbf{v}_p$ from the noise space, where $1 \leq p \leq m - D$. This selection corresponds to the noise part of the eigenvectors in Eq. 4.11. We observe that

$$\forall i \;\; \mathbf{v}_p^T \mathbf{v}_i = \begin{cases} 1, & \text{if } p = i \text{ due to ortho normal property} \\ 0, & \text{otherwise} \end{cases} \tag{4.12}$$

By applying the property stated in Eqs. 4.12 to 4.11, the phase spectrum energy polynomial $H(z)$ simplifies to the following form:

$$H(z) = \boxed{\sum^{p} \lambda_p \mathbf{v}_p^T \mathbf{a}(z)} = \sum^{p} \lambda_p h_p(z) = \sum^{p} \lambda_p \prod_{i=1}^{m} (1 - r_i^p e^{j\varphi_i^p} z^{-1}) \text{ where } 1 \leq p \leq m - D \tag{4.13}$$

The key to locating emitters lies in identifying all the minima[1] of $H(z)$ within the noise subspace over the angular domain φ. These minima correspond to the roots of a specific polynomial associated with the noise eigenvectors. The expression $r_i^p e^{j\varphi_i^p}$ in Eq. 4.13 represents the roots of the following polynomial of order $(m - 1)$:

$$h_p(z) = \mathbf{v}_p^T \mathbf{a}(z) \tag{4.14}$$

where $\mathbf{v}_p$ is the p-th noise eigenvector and $\mathbf{a}(z)$ is the array manifold vector expressed as a function of the complex variable z. The locations of these roots [4] relative to the unit circle provide critical insights into the direction or frequency of arrival of the underlying sources. This complex polynomial $h_p(z)$ is evaluated for any value of φ as $\|h_p(z)\|_\varphi$ as achieves its minimum at zeros. It is important to note that the roots of $h_p(z)$ are independent of λ_p. The value $\|h_p(z)\|_{\varphi=\{-\pi,\pi\}} = h_p(\varphi)$ reaches its minimum at the zeros, or roots, of the polynomial $h_p(z)$, as indicated in Eq. 4.13. For the set of polynomials $h_p(z)$ within the noise space, there will be $(m - D) \times (m - 1)$ zeros. We recast $H(z)$ droping λ_p as

[1] Minima are evaluated by computing the norm $\|.\|$ of the complex function, as in Eq. 4.16, and visualized in Fig. 4.3.

$$H(z) = \|\mathbf{E}_n \mathbf{a}(z)\| \text{ where } \mathbf{E}_n^T = [\mathbf{v}_1 \ldots \mathbf{v}_{m-D}] \text{ noise space eigen vectors} \tag{4.15}$$

We evaluate $H(z)$ (see Eq. 4.37) was derived very well by Wang [33] using $\mathbf{H}_n = \mathbf{E}_n \mathbf{E}_n^T$ over the unit circle as

$$H(\varphi) = \|\mathbf{E}_n \mathbf{a}(z)\|_{\varphi=\{-\pi,\pi\}} \tag{4.16}$$

However, it is crucial to understand that not all zeros $r_i^p e^{j\varphi_i^p}$ as in Eq. 4.13 contribute to a minimum of

$$H(\varphi) = \{h_p(\varphi)\} \;\forall\; p. \tag{4.17}$$

4.2.1 Numerical Example

To enhance understanding, we have selected $m = 5$ sensing elements, along with a complex look matrix **S**. We are utilizing two emitters ($D = 2$) at a signal-to-noise ratio (SNR) of approximately 0 dB. The number of snapshots N was chosen to be 128, resulting in a matrix size of 128×5. The Hermitian matrix **H** serves as the covariance matrix, with its eigenvalues categorized into singular and nonsingular values, denoted as

$$\mathbf{L}^T = \Bigg[\underbrace{0.3993\ 0.4733\ 0.5249}_{(m-D)}\ \underbrace{1.37\ 1.843}_{D}\Bigg] = [\lambda_1 \ldots \lambda_m] \tag{4.18}$$

The less dominant eigenvectors defined by the corresponding eigenvalues, often called singular values, are defined as noisy eigenvectors and are labeled as

$$\mathbf{E}_n = \boxed{\begin{array}{lcl} \mathbf{v}_1 &=& [0.38e^{j0.0391}\ 0.36e^{j43.3}\ 0.3e^{-j177}\ 0.54e^{-j24.9}\ 0.59e^{-j106}] \\ \mathbf{v}_2 &=& [0.15e^{j91.9}\ 0.63e^{-j67.3}\ 0.25e^{-j135}\ 0.44e^{-j101}\ 0.57e^{-j159}] \\ \mathbf{v}_3 &=& [0.66e^{j90}\ 0.13e^{-j53.8}\ 0.71e^{j51.8}\ 0.16e^{-j37.4}\ 0.12e^{-j78.8}] \end{array}}$$

The polynomial $h(z)$, as described in Eq. 4.13, is evaluated along the unit circle over the interval from $-\pi$ to π. Figure 4.3 depicts this as $h(\varphi)$ for the $m - D$ row vectors in the matrix $\mathbf{E}_n$.

In Fig. 4.3, all the values of $h(\varphi)$ corresponding to the minima of noisy vectors are indicated by red solid circles. There are $m - D = 3$ graphs of $h(\varphi)$. The roots of the polynomial $h_p(z) = 0 \;\forall\; p$ near the unit circle are represented as solid blue squares in the same figure.

$$\boxed{\begin{array}{l} h_1(z) = (1 - 1.7e^{-j178}z^{-1})(1 - 1e^{j60.6}z^{-1})(1 - 0.87e^{-j31.9}z^{-1})(1 - 1e^{-j105}z^{-1}) \\ h_2(z) = (1 - 4.3e^{j13.5}z^{-1})(1 - 0.99e^{-j102}z^{-1})(1 - 1.1e^{j58.2}z^{-1})(1 - 0.84e^{j139}z^{-1}) \\ h_3(z) = (1 - 1e^{-j108}z^{-1})(1 - 1e^{j59.4}z^{-1})(1 - 0.51e^{j108}z^{-1})(1 - 0.32e^{j70.8}z^{-1}) \end{array}}$$

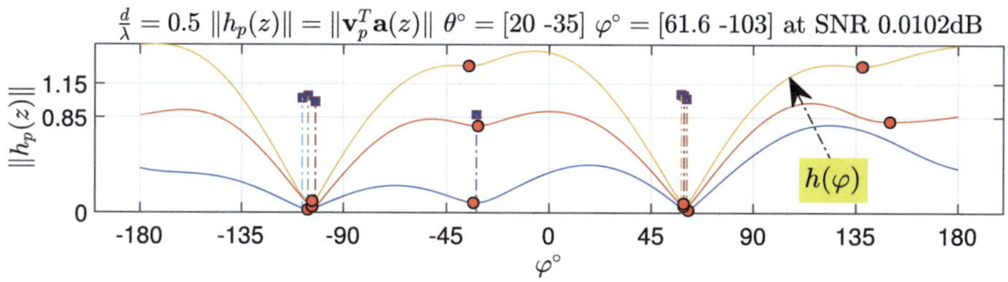

Fig. 4.3 Phase spectrum $h(\varphi)$ for eigenvectors in $\mathbf{E}_n$

The roots of each noisy polynomial $h(z)$ are shown in polar form above. This numerical example clarifies the forthcoming sections on MUSIC and root-MUSIC.

4.2.2 *Validation*

All the results presented here reflect the outcomes of the code written in C, while the graphics are generated using MATLAB (Fig. 4.4). The same look matrix **S** is used as input for both computations to validate the C code. MATLAB independently performs the same calculations, and the results are displayed graphically in Fig. 4.5. The dot is precisely located at the center of the circle in this figure. The entire Sect. 4.2 should be read thoroughly, as it establishes the foundation for the whole chapter in detailing all the subspace methods.

```
%Copy Right Protected Kaluri V Ranga Rao kaluri@ieee.org
%updated on 26th Jan 2025 @ 9:00am Hyderabad TG
clc; clear all;
close all;
DOAS =[20, -35, 30]; numberOfPhiSamples = 180;
snapShots = 128; NumOfElements = 5;
std = 1; SamplesPerCycle = 8;
D = 2;  dbyl = 0.5;
rcA =[snapShots NumOfElements];
[A SNR] = IQmatrix(DOAS,std,D,rcA,dbyl,SamplesPerCycle);
[muSpk doa En eV] = gMusic(D,dbyl,numberOfPhiSamples,A);
delr = 0.15; B = rootMusic(En,delr);
```

mex commands

Fig. 4.4 MATLAB code Hermitian noisy eigenvectors and $h(\varphi)$

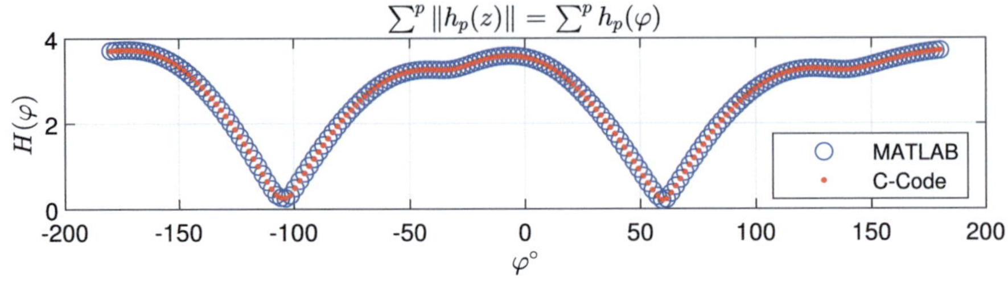

Fig. 4.5 Phase spectrum $H(\varphi)$ for eigenvectors in $\mathbf{E}_n$

4.3 Time and Space Transfer Functions

Digital signal processing, linear systems theory, and direction-finding algorithms share similarities, particularly in their mathematical formulations and notations. Recently, parameter and spectral estimation algorithms have gained significant attention in direction-finding. One notable covariance approach, developed by Prony [1] in 1795 and later by Pisarenko [2], has been incorporated into direction-finding algorithms. It is essential to understand them, and Table 4.1 provides the similarities, which must be understood well, because of the many notations and nomenclature that look similar.

4.3.1 Phasors

Narrowband signals can be understood as phasors, as described by Hayt and Kemmerly [18]. Each signal is created through vector additions at each sensor element as in Eq. 4.4, with each component introducing a phase delay represented by φ^i, as shown in Eq. 4.1. In traditional circuit analysis, this concept is related to time-frequency; however, it pertains to space-phase in this context.

Table 4.1 Time domain and spatial domain comparison

Nomenclature	Time domain $k = 1$ to N	Space domain $i = 1$ to m
Sampling delay operator	$z^{-1} = e^{j\omega}$	$z^{-1} = e^{j\varphi}$
i = ULA element number	$s_{k-1} = z^{-1}s_k$	$s_k^{\varphi} = s_k z^{-1}$ or $s_k^{i-1} = s_k^i z^{-1}$
$s_k = e^{j\omega k}$	$s_{k-1} = e^{j\omega(k-1)}$	$s_k^{\varphi} = e^{j\omega k+\varphi}$
Sampling on unit circle	$\|h(z)\|$ Fourier spectrum	$\|h(z)\|$ phase spectrum
Model	Auto regressive moving average	Only moving average
Type	Poles or zeros or both	Only zeros

4.4 Parameter Estimation Methods

Consider an FIR filter or a moving average process (MA) given as

$$y_k = w_0 x_k + w_1 x_{k-1} + w_2 x_{k-2}$$
$$y_k = \mathbf{w}^T \mathbf{x}_k \tag{4.19}$$

where x_k is the input and y_k is the output of the filter. A simple generic least square solution [19] for min $\|y_k - \mathbf{w}^T \mathbf{x}_k\|$ is given in Chap. 2 as

$$\hat{\mathbf{w}} = \underbrace{\left(\sum_{i=0}^{N} \mathbf{x}_i^t \mathbf{x}_i\right)^{-1}}_{\text{covariance matrix}} \times \left(\sum_{i=0}^{N} \mathbf{x}_i^t y_i\right) \text{ where } N \text{ is number of Eq. 4.19} \tag{4.20}$$

The above equation behaves well when the signal x_k is noise-free and the covariance matrix is accurate. Numerous methods [19–21] are available for estimating $\mathbf{w}$, including Maximum Likelihood (ML), Approximate Maximum Likelihood (AML), Instrumental Variable (IV), and IV-AML. These methods rely on the noise characteristics and statistical properties of the covariance matrix, as outlined in Eq. 4.20, to provide a minimum variance, unbiased estimator. Direction of Arrival (DOA) estimation has effectively implemented these techniques [8].

4.4.1 *Prony's Method*

In this method, we assume that the time series signal x_k is noise-free and can be represented as the sum of several damped sinusoids, a concept that dates back to 1795. It is also assumed that we have prior knowledge of the number of frequencies involved, similar to knowing the model order.

$$\sin(\omega k) = 2\cos\omega \sin(\omega(k-1)) - \sin(\omega(k-2)) \text{ the trignometric identity can be written as}$$
$$x_k = r\left[2\cos\left(2\pi\frac{\varphi^\circ}{360}\right)\right] x_{k-1} - r^2 x_{k-2} \text{ is an AR(2) process [22, 23] with poles at } (r, \varphi)$$
$$y_k = \mathbf{x}_k^T \mathbf{p} \text{ where } y_k = x_k \text{ and } \mathbf{x}_k^T = [x_{k-1}\ x_{k-2}] \text{ and } \mathbf{p}^T = [a_1\ a_2] \tag{4.21}$$

We have a transversal filter defined as $h(z) = [1\ a_1 z^{-1}\ a_2 z^{-2}]$. This is a second-order filter designed for a single frequency. By applying the least squares (LSQ) method, we can solve Eq. 4.21 to determine the coefficient of x_{k-1}. The general least squares solution is outlined in Eq. 4.20 for any specified order. In the context of spectral estimation, the parameter $\frac{\varphi^\circ}{360}$ represents the normalized frequency. For

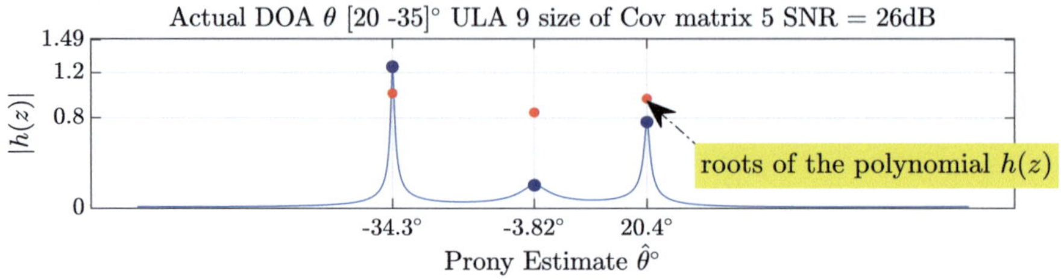

Fig. 4.6 Prony method $\frac{d}{\lambda} = 0.5$

direction of arrival (DOA) estimation, φ is calculated using the formula $2\pi\frac{d}{\lambda}\sin\theta$, where d is the inter element distance and λ is the wavelength. The roots of the polynomial $h(z)$ and the peaks of the frequency response indicate the frequencies that are relevant for time series analysis and the phase angle in case of DOA estimation.

Figure 4.6 shows the solution for emitters at 20° and $-35°$ at SNR 26 dB and model order chosen as 5. The red solid circles represent the roots of the polynomial $h(z) = 0$, and the blue solid circles represent the peaks of the frequency response. This method is sensitive to noise. You can notice that the SNR is 26 dB.

4.4.2 *Pisarenko Harmonic Decomposition*

This method is one of the earliest techniques [2] in subspace analysis and is known for its effectiveness. It is a specific case of the MUSIC algorithm. In this approach, it is assumed that there is only one noise eigenvector, which means that the minimum eigenvalue, denoted as λ_{min}, corresponds to noise energy. As a result, the number of array elements needed is $D + 1$, where D is the number of known sinusoids to be estimated. Kay [24] and Marple explain this concept well on page 1404 in Fig. 12 in their paper. In the noise-free case, the Prony method is optimal. In this method, the amount of noise in the covariance matrix is estimated using the minimum eigenvalue, λ_{min}. The idea is based on the fact that each eigenvalue represents the energy of a sinusoid plus noise, with the last one indicating only noise power.

4.5 Standard Multiple Signal Classification (MUSIC)

In this section, we will review the concepts of the MUSIC spectrum as utilized in [6]. We will assume there are m sensors in an intelligent array and that N snapshots have been collected from the Uniform Linear Array (ULA) sensor. The matrix $\mathbf{S}$, described in Eq. 4.7 and illustrated in Fig. 4.2, represents the $N \times m$ matrix of snapshots in the spatial domain. This $\mathbf{S}$ matrix contains complex values indicating the in-phase and quadrature components of the signals sensed by the array. The covariance matrix $\mathbf{H}$, defined in Eq. 4.10, is a Hermitian matrix. By performing eigenanalysis on **H**, we obtain the eigenvalues **L** and their corresponding eigenvectors **E**.

The matrix **L** contains only positive real values because **H** is positive definite. If there are $D < m$ independent signals, then ideally, $m - D$ of the eigenvalues will be zero in the absence of noise. However, in the presence of noise, these eigenvalues will be close to zero, depending on the signal-to-noise ratio (SNR). By sorting the eigenvalues in **L** in ascending order, we can identify the $(m - D) \times m$ matrix $\mathbf{E}_n$ as shown in Eq. 4.15. This matrix consists of the eigenvectors corresponding to the $m - D$ smallest eigenvalues, representing the noise eigenvectors. Furthermore, the matrix **E** can be expressed as $\mathbf{E} = \{\mathbf{E}_n | \mathbf{E}_s\}$, where $\mathbf{E}_s$ are the signal eigenvectors. The noise eigenmatrix $\mathbf{E}_n$ can be written as

$$\mathbf{E}_n^T = \{\mathbf{v}_1 \ldots \mathbf{v}_i \ldots \mathbf{v}_{m-D}\} \tag{4.22}$$

The magnitude $\|H(z)\|$, as defined by Eqs. 4.15 and 4.16, is evaluated along the unit circle for each value of φ. The spatial delay operator z^{-1} is defined in Eq. 4.6. We consider each eigenvector $\mathbf{v}_i$ from the noise space, as indicated in Eq. 4.10, which acts as a spatial transversal filter. This can be expressed as

$$h_i(\varphi) = \|\mathbf{v}_i(z)\|_{\varphi=\{-\pi,\pi\}} \tag{4.23}$$

Using this expression, we define an objective function as follows:

$$J(\varphi) = \frac{1}{H(\varphi)} \text{ where } H(\varphi) = \sum_{i=1}^{m-D} |h_i(\varphi)| \tag{4.24}$$

Gold univariate minimization is employed to exactly scale the peaks of $J(\varphi)$. The phase φ and direction of arrival (DOA), denoted as θ, are defined through a non-linear relationship

$$\theta = \sin^{-1}\left(\frac{\varphi}{2\pi\frac{d}{\lambda}}\right) \text{ and is illustrated in Fig. 4.7b} \tag{4.25}$$

A simple linear relationship can be expressed as $\theta = \frac{\varphi}{3}$ for the range $-90 \leq \varphi \leq 90$ when $\frac{d}{\lambda} = 0.5$. The factor $\frac{d}{\lambda}$ is crucial for determining the valid range of φ (see Figure in Chap. 2), as the argument in Eq. 4.25 must be less than or equal to one.

The look matrix **S** is generated for $D = 2$ with emitters positioned at 20° and −35° under SNR conditions of 0 dB. The phase φ is sampled, meaning the function $H(\varphi)$ is evaluated on the unit circle at equal intervals $\delta\varphi$. However, it is important to note that the interval $\delta\theta$ is not constant; only the mean value is considered. The function $J(\varphi)$, commonly referred to as the MUSIC spectrum, is computed using Eq. 4.24. We sample the MUSIC spectrum as $J(k\delta\varphi)$, where $\delta\varphi = \frac{2\pi}{N_{mu}}$ or $\frac{360°}{N_{mu}}$, as illustrated in Fig. 4.7a. The Direction of Arrival (DOA) spectrum, also known as the MUSIC spectrum $J(\theta)$, is displayed in Fig. 4.7c.

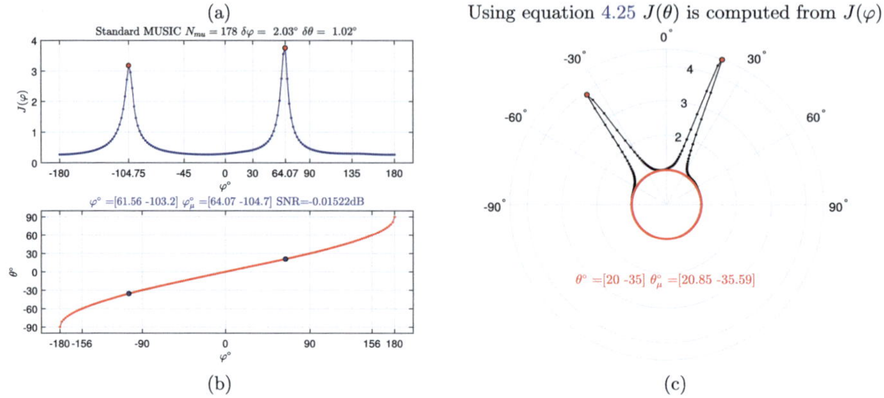

Fig. 4.7 Standard MUSIC phase spectrum $J(\varphi)$ and DOA spectrum $J(\theta)$

$$J(\theta) = J\left[\sin^{-1}\left(\frac{\varphi}{2\pi\frac{d}{\lambda}}\right)\right] \text{ using Eq. 4.25 in Eq. 4.26} \tag{4.26}$$

Estimating the accuracy of peaks depends on the interval $\delta\varphi$; therefore, the accuracy of DOA estimation relies on the choice of this interval.

4.6 *gold*-MUSIC

In this section, we introduce a variation of the MUSIC algorithm, popularly known as *gold*-MUSIC [26]. This method utilizes gold-section univariate minimization [27] to evaluate the peaks of the MUSIC spectrum accurately. The authors have successfully applied this minimization technique in previous work, such as delay estimation [28] and determining Direction of Arrival (DOA) using a spatially tuned filter [29]. The spatial tuned filter approach [29] is based on a method described in the book [30].

4.6.1 Overview of gMUSIC

The *gold*-MUSIC algorithm described in this section is an iterative approach that utilizes gold-section univariate minimization. The process of identifying peaks occurs in two stages. In the first stage, the spectrum is evaluated using the MUSIC method over a range of angles from –90 to 90°, employing coarse intervals. This evaluation helps identify coarse peaks, defined as the maxima of the calculated spectrum. In the second stage, for each coarse peak identified, the algorithm begins by positioning two points to the left and right of the peak. A more precise estimate of the direction of arrival (DOA) for each peak is then obtained through gold-section univariate minimization, applied to the MUSIC spectrum, which serves as the objective function for this minimization process.

4.6.2 Steps Involved in MUSIC, Root-MUSIC, and gold-MUSIC

Figure 4.8 shows the steps involved in arriving at the MUSIC spectrum. We begin with the signal snapshots $\mathbf{S}$. Then, we compute the covariance $\mathbf{H}$. The next step is eigenanalysis, which involves obtaining the eigenvalues $\mathbf{L}$ and the corresponding eigenvectors $\mathbf{E}$. Next, we sort the eigenvalues in ascending order and determine the number of signals D. In this section, we describe a partitioning method in Sect. 4.6.3 on the set of normalized eigenvalues, which provides an estimate of D. We separate the eigenvectors into $M - D$ noise eigenvectors $\mathbf{E_N}$ and the remaining D signal eigenvectors $\mathbf{E_S}$. After this step, the spectrum can be evaluated for different angles. MUSIC, Root-MUSIC and *gold*-MUSIC diverge after this point. In music, the spectrum is evaluated at different angles, and the peaks are selected. In Root-MUSIC, the polynomials associated with $\mathbf{E_N}$ are solved, and the D most common roots are treated as the DOA angles. The *gold*-MUSIC steps are explained in Sect. 4.7. The next section addresses how to estimate D, the number of signals, when prior knowledge of it is lacking.

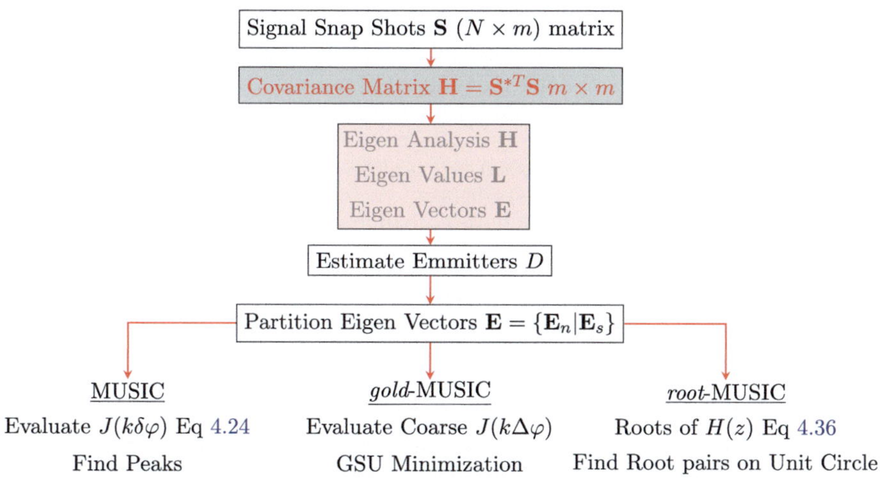

Fig. 4.8 Steps involved in MUSIC, Root-MUSIC, and Gold-MUSIC

4.6.3 Partitioning Algorithm for Estimating the Number of Emitters

In this method, the eigenvalue vector **L** is divided into two parts: dominant values (signal space) and less dominant values (noise space). This partitioning helps identify the number of emitters D. We start with an initial set $P_0 = \{\mathbf{L}\}$, and the proposed partitioning method undergoes several iterations, beginning with $k = 0$.

$$\forall x \in P_{k-1} \;\; p_k = \{x - \mu_{k-1} \geq \sigma_{k-1}\} \text{ and} \tag{4.27}$$

$$P_k = \{x - \mu_{k-1} < \sigma_{k-1}\} \tag{4.28}$$

where $\sigma_{k-1} = \sqrt{\frac{\sum(x-\mu_{k-1})^2}{n-1}}$ $\forall x \in P_{k-1}$ in which $n =$ size$[P_{k-1}]$ and $\mu_{k-1} = E(P_{k-1})$

1. $\{P_0\}$ Initial Set of Normalized Eigen Values
$P_0 = \{3.1608\ 2.4015\ 0.6509\ 0.5491\ 0.5177\ 0.5008\ 0.4426\ 0.3705\ 0.3140\ 0.2912\}$ Initial Set
P_0 (flag 1) (σ_0 1.0031) (μ_0 0.9199) split $\{10\}$
$P_0 - \mu_0 = [2.2409\ 1.4816 - 0.2690 - 0.3708 - 0.4022 - 0.4191 - 0.4773 - 0.5494 - 0.6059 - 0.6287]$

2. $\{P_0\}$ (flag 1) How it is split $10 = \{p_1\}2 + \{P_1\}8$
$p_1 = \{3.1608\ 2.4015\}$ as in Eq. (4.27)
$\chi(0) \longrightarrow P_0([01])$

After each iteration k, the outcome comprises a collection of clusters $\{p_1, p_2, \ldots, p_{k+1}\}$ that have been formed, alongside a remainder set P_k. This remainder set requires further division into additional clusters if possible. Each cluster p_k contains a set of normalized eigenvalues. Similarly, the initial set P_0 and all remainder sets P_k for $k > 0$ consist of normalized eigenvalues.

3. $\{P_1\}$ Eigen Values
$P_1 = \{0.6509\ 0.5491\ 0.5177\ 0.5008\ 0.4426\ 0.3705\ 0.3140\ 0.2912\}$ as in Eq. (4.28)
P_1 (flag 1) (σ_1 0.1238) (μ_1 0.4546) split $\{8\}$
$P_1 - \mu_1 = [0.1963\ 0.0945\ 0.0631\ 0.0462 - 0.0120 - 0.0841 - 0.1406 - 0.1634]$

4. $\{P_1\}$ (flag 1) How it is split $8 = \{p_2\}1 + \{P_2\}7$
$p_2 = \{0.6509\}$ as in Eq. (4.27)
$\chi(1) \longrightarrow P_0([22])$

we note $P_{k-1} = p_k \cup P_k$ and $p_k \cap P_k = NULL$ The choice of the *dynamic* threshold, σ_k(second moment) is *heuristic* [31]. The recursive set of operations as given in Eqs. 4.27 and 4.28 is performed till either set p_k or P_k becomes a NULL set, in which k is an integer. In case p_k is NULL, the set p_k is replaced by P_k. At the end of iterations, we arrive at the χ integer pointer matrix.

5. $\{P_2\}$ Eigen Values
$P_2 = \{0.5491\ 0.5177\ 0.5008\ 0.4426\ 0.3705\ 0.3140\ 0.2912\}$ as in Eq. 4.28
$P_2(flag1)$ $(\sigma_2\ 0.1026)$ $(\mu_2\ 0.4265)$ split $\{7\}$
$P_2 - \mu_2 = [0.1225\ 0.0911\ 0.0742\ 0.0161 - 0.0561 - 0.1126 - 0.1353]$

6. $\{P_2\}$ (flag 1) How it is split $7 = \{p_3\}1 + \{P_3\}6$
$p_3 = \{0.5491\}$ as in Eq. (4.27)
$\chi(2) \longrightarrow \quad P_0([33])$

We can see in the above enumeration 1 to 7 depicted numerically, matrix **L** is partitioned as $\mathbf{L}(\chi)$ where

$$\chi = \begin{pmatrix} 0 & 1 \\ 2 & 2 \\ 3 & 9 \end{pmatrix} \text{ is an integer } \textit{index} \text{ matrix} \tag{4.29}$$

is of size $N_c \times 2$, in which N_c is the number of clusters formed.

7. $\{P_3\}$ Number of Rows 3 sorted on 1st column [0 1] [2 2] [3 9]
Number of rows [flag 1]3 End of Phase 1(10)

8. $[0]\,\sigma(P_0([01]) \rightarrow (0.5369)[1]\,\sigma(P_0([22]) \rightarrow (0.0000)[2]\,\sigma(P_0([39]) \rightarrow (0.1026)$
maximum variance seg 0.5369[0] Row 0 needs to be further partitioned

9. $\{P_0\}P_0 = \{3.1608\ 2.4015\ P_0$ (flag 1) $(\sigma_0\ 0.5369)$ $(\mu_0\ 2.7811)$ split $\{2\}$
$P_0 - \mu_0 = [0.3796 - 0.3796]$

10. $\{P_0\}$(flag –1) How it is split $2 = \{p_1\}0 + \{P_1\}2$
$p_1 = \{\}$ as in Eq. (4.27)
break loop

11. $\{P_0\}$There is Only One Row [flag –1]1 End of Phase 2(2)

12. [0] P_0 [0.1] [σ 0.5369 μ2.7811][1] P_0 [2.2] [σ 0.0000 μ0.6509][2] P_0 [3.9] [σ 0.1026 μ0.4265]

13. [0] P_0 [0.1] [σ 0.5369 μ2.7811][1] P_0 [2.9] [σ 0.1238 μ0.4546]

4.7 DOA Estimation in *gold*-MUSIC

The objective function $J(\theta)$ described in Eq. (4.26) reaches its maximum at each Direction of Arrival (DOA). A brief review of $h(\varphi)$ as shown in Fig. 4.3, along with the content from Sect. 4.2.1, would assist the reader in comprehending the following material.

The *gold*-MUSIC algorithm is an iterative method that employs Gold-Section Univariate(GSU) minimization to identify peaks in the MUSIC spectrum. The process consists of two stages: first, the spectrum is evaluated over angles from –90 to 90° using coarse intervals to find coarse peaks. In the second stage, for each coarse peak, the algorithm employs gold-section univariate minimization on the MUSIC spectrum to obtain a more precise estimate of the direction of arrival (DOA).

4.7.1 *Coarse Peaks*

To demonstrate the *gold*-MUSIC algorithm, we consider two emitters with equal strengths, arriving from angles of 20 and $-35°$, respectively. In the first step, we identify coarse peaks or *energy* clusters by evaluating $J(\varphi)$ at intervals of $\Delta\varphi = 32.7$ degrees within the range of $[-180°, 180°]$ using Eq. 4.24. Following the relationship described in Eqs. 4.25 and 4.26, we obtain the MUSIC spectrum $J(k\Delta\theta)$ from $J(k\Delta\varphi)$, specifically evaluated between -90 and $90°$. This is represented as a line connecting the blue dots in Fig. 4.9, where red solid circles indicate the two coarse peaks. The same figure illustrates the ideal MUSIC spectrum $J(\theta)$ as a dashed line for reference. In Fig. 4.9, we observe that the solid red circles and the bubble red circles align with the ideal MUSIC spectrum. The corresponding peaks of the gold-MUSIC are marked in the figure by red stems, positioned at $\theta_1 = -36.17°$ and $\theta_2 = 20.39°$. It's important to note that the evaluation is linear for φ but non-linear for θ, which contrasts with the conventional frequency response. The phase spectrum can be interpreted as the inverse of the square of the magnitude of the filter's frequency response, as expressed in Eq. 4.24.

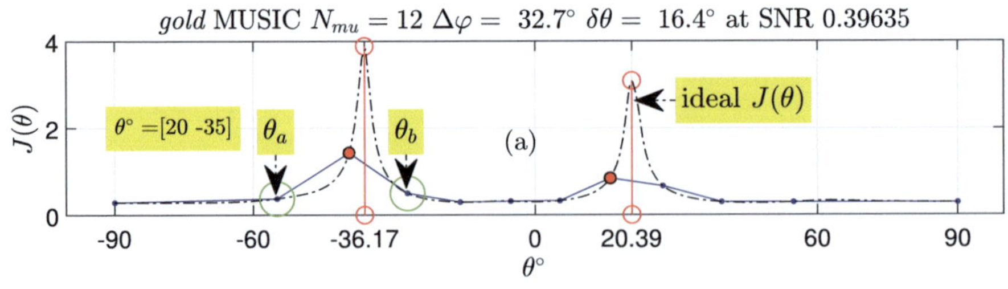

Fig. 4.9 *gold*-MUSIC illustration $J(\theta)$ for eigen vectors in $\mathbf{E}_n$

4.7.2 GSU Minimization

The GSU minimization method [8] accurately identifies the extreme values of a univariate function. The algorithm functions by successively narrowing the range of values where the extremum is known to exist. To find the peaks of $J(\theta)$, we need to consider $-J(\theta)$ as our unimodal function. We require four points, including the endpoints of the interval where the maximum is to be found. Let $[\theta_a, \theta_b]$ represent the defined interval such that $\theta_a < \theta_b$, indicating a potential true peak between them. In Fig. 4.9, the two points, θ_a and θ_b, are highlighted and labeled. The intervals for all potential peaks are established by conducting a coarse sweep across the range of $[-90, 90]°$. The coarse peaks are represented as solid red circles in the same figure.

4.7.2.1 Steps for Minimization

1. In Fig. 4.9, each peak, represented by a red solid circle, has two associated values: θ_a and θ_b. These values are chosen such that they are positioned apart, with the local maximum lying between them. The figure highlights θ_a and θ_b for one of the peaks.
2. We select intermediate points θ_c and θ_d, defined by $\theta_c = \theta_a + g(\theta_b - \theta_a)$ and $\theta_d = \theta_c + g(\theta_b - \theta_c)$, where $g = \frac{3-\sqrt{5}}{2}$, known as the *Golden Ratio*.
3. The objective function represented as $-J(\theta)$, is evaluated at the points θ_a, θ_b, θ_c, and θ_d. If $-J(\theta_c) \leq -J(\theta_d)$, then in the next iteration, θ_b will assume the value of θ_a, and θ_a will adopt the value of θ_d. Conversely, if $-J(\theta_c) > -J(\theta_d)$, θ_a will assume the value of θ_c, and θ_c will adopt the value of θ_d in the subsequent iteration.
4. Typically, a fixed number of iterations $n_F = 16$ is employed to quickly obtain an accurate minimum value, as illustrated in Fig. 4.10a and b, which leads to the determination of the Direction of Arrival (DOA) value. We repeat this process using a straightforward logic defined in step 2 until all peaks and DOA values are estimated.
5. The signal-to-noise ratio (SNR) is approximately 0 dB for this figure. The GSU estimates angles for the peaks are $-36.17°$ and $20.39°$.

4.7.2.2 Quick Convergence of Gold-Section

The fixed number of iterations, $n_F = 16$, is employed for the gold-section search (GSU). Figure 4.10a and b show that the gold-section method requires only a few iterations to converge. Figure 4.10a illustrates the convergence of the first peak, θ_1, at $-35°$, while Fig. 4.10b pertains to the second peak, θ_2, which occurs around $20°$. This indicates that fewer iterations are necessary for accurate results. The figures suggest that a fixed value of 10 iterations would yield reasonably accurate outcomes.

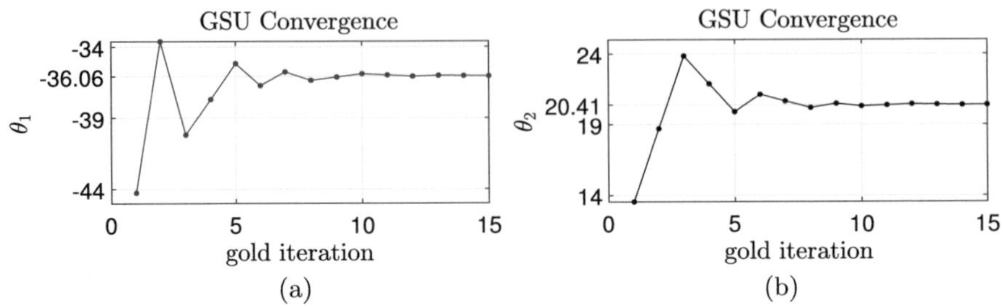

Fig. 4.10 *gold*-MUSIC illustration $J(\theta)$ for eigen vectors in $\mathbf{E}_n$

4.7.3 Sharpness of $J(\theta)$

The *sharpness* of $J(\theta)$ is dependent on three factors

1. N the number of snapshots,
2. m the number of ULA elements,
3. SNR Signal-to-Noise Ratio as given Eq. 4.8.

The resolving power of the MUSIC algorithm is also related to the above parameters. To combat *poor* SNR conditions, parameters N and m are chosen to fit the reality. By evaluating at suitable points, coarse peaks are found. Then, by using the *Gold Section Univariate* (GSU) minimization technique, peaks are located with very high accuracy.

4.7.4 Resolution Technique

Let us consider the scenario where two emitters are positioned very close together, selected at angles of 30° and 27°, which are only 3° apart, and the third target at $-10°$. With a chosen coarse step size of $\Delta\varphi = 30°$, the gold-MUSIC method will yield only one detected peak, primarily within the range of 30° to 27°, along with a spurious peak, as shown in Fig. 4.11a. Instead of observing two distinct peaks, we see a single value of 28.6°. Though we recognize that there are two peaks, denoted as $\theta_1 = 30°$ and $\theta_2 = 27°$, the gold-MUSIC method will detect only one of these peaks when conducting coarse scanning with a step size of $\Delta\varphi = 30°$, as illustrated in Fig. 4.11a. To resolve these peaks, we apply the gold-MUSIC algorithm near each of the two peaks, utilizing a fine sweep with a step size of $\Delta\varphi = 3°$ on either side of the respective peaks. We obtained a closely sampled $J(\theta)$ as shown in Fig. 4.11b for $N = 32$, which accurately identifies the same peak of 28.6°, disappointingly without any further improvement.

For $N = 32$ and a more significant number of sensing elements, $m = 32$, Fig. 4.12 demonstrates the algorithm's capability to resolve closely spaced emitters at angles of 27 and 30° as 27.3° and 30.1°. Additionally, Fig. 4.13b illustrates that increasing

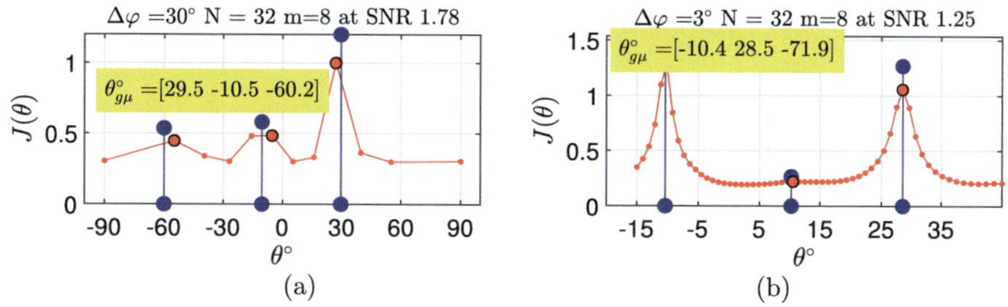

Fig. 4.11 Phase spectrum $h(\varphi)$ for eigenvectors in $\mathbf{E}_n$

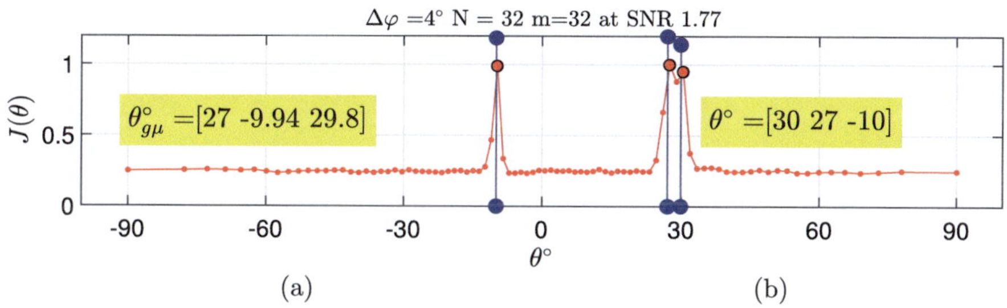

Fig. 4.12 Phase spectrum $h(\varphi)$ for eigenvectors in $\mathbf{E}_n$

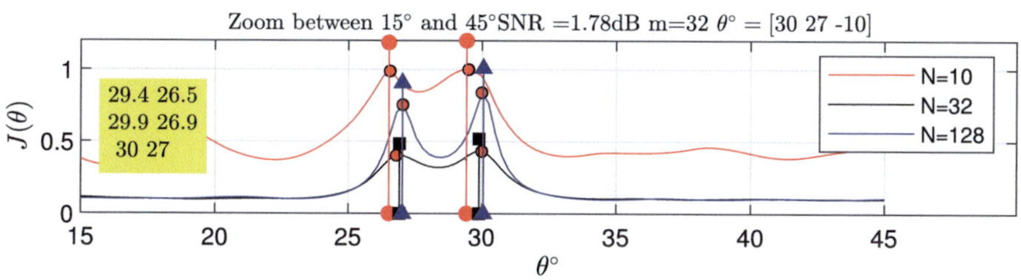

Fig. 4.13 Closely placed targets phase spectrum $h(\varphi)$ for eigenvectors in $\mathbf{E}_n$

the number of snapshots N results in more accurate measurements. We successfully resolved the closely positioned targets with a finer sweep angle of $\Delta\varphi = 4°$ by proper choice of $m = 32$. In Figs. 4.11 and 4.12, the gold estimates $\theta_{g\mu}$ and the true values θ are highlighted in yellow and displayed.

This approach ensures that *gold*-MUSIC maintains high resolution. Simultaneously, the accuracy depends on the number of sensors m, the number of snapshots N, and the SNR conditions, similar to Root-MUSIC, but with less complexity.

4.7.5 *Effect of Number of Snapshots N and Coarseness*

As the number of snapshots, N, is increased, the sharpness of the peaks increases. This effect is depicted in Fig. 4.13. If the sharpness is high, a highly coarse scanning will tend to miss identifying the peak. Therefore, it is preferable to use a smaller number of snapshots. A consequence of increasing the coarse interval is a compromise on the resolving power of the method as seen in Sect. 4.7.4. A unique dual computational advantage is thus achieved by the *gold*-MUSIC method by lowering N and the number of angles to evaluate the spectrum at the same time.

4.8 Computational Time-Complexity of *gold*-MUSIC

gold-MUSIC has some advantages which are mentioned in this section. Till the isolation of the noise eigenvectors $\mathbf{E_N}$, Root-MUSIC and *gold*-MUSIC follow the same steps as depicted in the flow diagram in Fig. 4.8. Till the isolation of the noise eigenvectors $\mathbf{E_N}$, Root-MUSIC and *gold*-MUSIC follow the same steps. The time complexity is that of computing covariance and performing eigendecomposition. The detailed analysis of these steps give

$$\Delta = O(Nm^2 + m^3).$$

4.8.1 *root-MUSIC*

After that, the conventional Root-MUSIC solves $m - D$ polynomials of order $n = m - 1$ and finds D common roots in each of the polynomials close to the unit circle. The time complexity for polynomial rooting is $O(m^n)$ where $n >> 2$ is a relatively large integer for known algorithms. So, the overall complexity of these steps is $\Delta + O((m - D)m^n)$. Finding common roots is not a trivial exercise, but it is a complex and involved process, as illustrated in the root-MUSIC section.

4.8.2 *gold-MUSIC*

In *gold*-MUSIC, the objective function is evaluated once per coarse spectrum sample $J(k\Delta\varphi)$ and a fixed number n_F of times per peak. Let $\Delta\varphi$ degrees represent the coarse angle, and let n_F denote the number of GSU iterations shown in Fig. 4.9b and c, where $n_F = 16$. A coarse spectrum evaluated with a $\Delta\varphi$ value is illustrated in Figs. 4.9a and 4.11a. The time complexity for objective function $H(\varphi) = \|\mathbf{E}_n\mathbf{a}(z)\|_\varphi$ evaluation is that of multiplying a $1 \times m$ matrix with an $m \times (m - D)$ followed by multiplying

$1 \times (m - D)$ matrix. That is $O(m^2)$ ignoring D. Considering evaluating the objective function as a unit of computation (of complexity $O(m^2)$), $\frac{180}{\Delta\varphi}$ units are spent when the spectrum is evaluated with coarse angle of $\Delta\varphi$ degrees. If all the D_1 initial Emitters are scanned finer with a *finer coarse* angle $\delta\varphi$ degrees, the total number of units added for this is $D_1 \times \frac{\Delta\varphi}{\delta\varphi} + D_2 n_F$, where D_2 is the number of new peaks for which the objective function is evaluated n_F times in the *gold*-MUSIC for determining the peaks. Hence, the overall complexity is: $O(Nm^2 + m^3 + m^2 \times [\frac{180}{\Delta\varphi} + D_1 n_F + \frac{D_2\Delta\varphi}{\delta\varphi} + D_2 n_F])$. Assuming n_F, $\Delta\varphi$ and $\delta\varphi$ are fixed values and letting $D = D_1 + D_2$ as the total number of emitters, the overall asymptotic time-complexity is

$$O(Nm^2 + m^3 + Dm^2) = \Delta + O(Dm^2)$$

Let $\Delta\varphi$ degrees be the coarse scanning. Angle of the first pass and let n_F be the number of iterations used. We have demonstrated *gold*-MUSIC with fewer snapshots. $N = 15$ was used in the 3-emitter example. This improves the computational speed of *gold*-MUSIC.

4.8.3 Comparison of Time Complexities

The following table summarizes the time-complexities of MUSIC, Root-MUSIC, and *gold*-MUSIC:

Algorithm	*Complexity*
MUSIC	$\Delta + O(Dm^2 \times \frac{180}{\delta\varphi})$
Root-MUSIC	$\Delta + O((m - D)m^n)$
gold-MUSIC	$\Delta + O(Dm^2)$

If the number of emitters that show up initially is small, *gold*-MUSIC also has an advantage in fewer evaluations of the objective function during acceptable resolution corresponding to fewer initial angles.

4.9 Performance

To evaluate the algorithm, let θ represent the proper direction of arrival (DOA), and let $\hat{\theta}$ denote the corresponding estimate obtained using the *gold*-MUSIC method. The error e_θ for a given Uniform Linear Array (ULA) size, a specified number of snapshots N, and specific signal-to-noise ratio (SNR) conditions is defined as follows:

$$e_\theta = \hat{\theta} - \theta \quad \forall\theta \in \{-90^\circ < \theta < +90^\circ\} \tag{4.30}$$

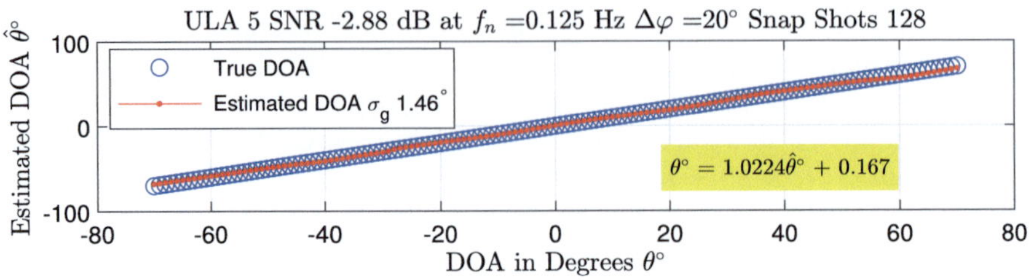

Fig. 4.14 Performnace of *gold*-MUSIC

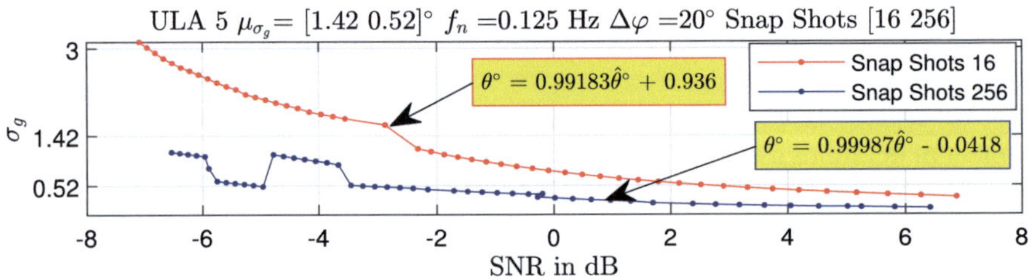

Fig. 4.15 Performnace of *gold*-MUSIC

The formula for the standard deviation of the error e_θ is given by

$$\sigma_g = \sqrt{\frac{\sum_{\theta} (e_\theta - \mu_\theta)^2}{N_\theta - 1}} \quad \text{where } \mu_\theta = E(e_\theta) \tag{4.31}$$

where N_θ is the number of samples for which $\hat{\theta}$ is estimated. The Fig. 4.14 shows $\hat{\theta}$ against the actual DOA θ angles for a single emitter case with DOA values ranging from $-90°$ to $90°$ for a fixed value of SNR. In addition, linear regression is performed between $\hat{\theta}$ and θ, and we get the fit for the above data as

$$\theta = 1.02224\hat{\theta} + 0.167$$

The Fig. 4.15 illustrates the standard deviation σ_g as defined by Eq. 4.31 of the error e_θ across various mean SNR values measured in decibels (dB). Both curves show a decreasing trend at lower SNR levels. The figure indicates that the SNR values range from approximately -6 dB to 6 dB. The mean $\mu_{\sigma_g} = [1.42, 0.52]$ for σ_g consistently remains within 2 degrees for most SNR values. The bias depicted in the inset of Fig. 4.15 represents the intercepts 0.936° and $-0.0418°$ of two linear equations concerning Direction of Arrival (DOA) estimation. This bias is influenced by several factors, including the number of snapshots N, the number of sensors m, the number of sources D, and the Signal-to-Noise Ratio (SNR), as detailed in

[32]. The performance of the *gold*-MUSIC algorithm is at least on par or better with the conventional MUSIC algorithm and asymptotically approaches the Cramer-Rao bound, as noted in [37].

4.10 root-MUSIC

Root-MUSIC is a sophisticated and elegant mathematical approach [37] employed to determine the direction of arrival (DOA) with increased complexity, and explains well the method to obtain the roots [34, 35]. To better grasp this concept, we will reference Fig. 4.17 and Eqs. 4.13 and 4.17. In this context, the roots of the polynomials $\mathbf{v}_p^T\mathbf{a}(z)$ as given in Eq. 4.14 are expressed as $r_i^p e^{j\varphi_i^p}$, where p signifies the index associated with the noise eigenvector $\mathbf{v}_p$. A typical root pair is shown in Fig. 4.16a with zeros and the reciprocal function $J(\omega) = \frac{1}{\|h(z)\|}$ with a sharp peak in Fig. 4.16b. The roots for this second-order polynomial are in the vicinity of the unit circle.

4.10.1 Roots Near the Unit Circle

We examine the roots of a polynomial around the unit circle and their impact. This represents the filter described in Eq. 4.19. Consider a second-order transversal filter $h(z)$ with reciprocal conjugate zeros:

$$h(z) = 1 - \left[\left(r + \frac{1}{r}\right) e^{j\varphi_c}\right] z^{-1} + e^{j2\varphi_c} z^{-2} = (1 - re^{j\varphi_c} z^{-1})(1 - \frac{1}{r} e^{j\varphi_c} z^{-1}) \tag{4.32}$$

To gain deeper insight into the MUSIC spectrum, we analyze the frequency response $\|h(z)\|$ of the filter Depicted in Fig. 4.16a and examine the roots of the

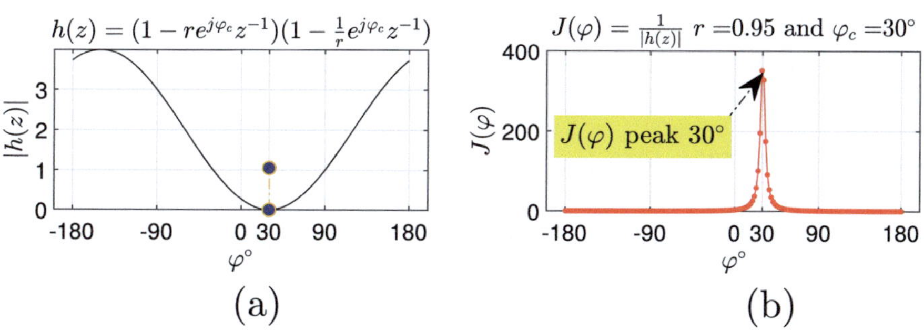

Fig. 4.16 Frequency response $\|h(z)\|$ of reciprocal conjugate zeros filter

equation $h(z) = 0$, shown as two solid blue stems near the unit circle. This analysis offers valuable understanding for Direction of Arrival (DOA) estimation [4].

In particular, the function $J(\varphi)$, illustrated in Fig. 4.16b, exhibits a sharp peak at $\varphi_c = 30°$. This peak directly corresponds to the filter coefficients of $h(z)$, and the location of its roots near the unit circle at magnitudes r and $\frac{1}{r}$, centered at an angle φ_c, as described in Eq. 4.32. Furthermore, the table shown in Fig. 4.19a (under Method B and C) displays reciprocal conjugate roots for a higher-order Polynomial. It is important to note that the sharp peak in the MUSIC spectrum in Fig. 4.16b for this second-order model stems from the roots of $h(z)$ and their proximity to the unit circle. This observation forms the foundation of the *root-MUSIC* algorithm [4].

4.10.2 Analysis of Roots of $Q_p(z)$

Readers are encouraged to consult the foundational paper by Barabell [4]. Particularly Fig. 2 on page 338, to understand the distribution and positioning of the polynomial roots. This section presents a brute-force. Method for estimating signal-related roots from a family of polynomials. While straightforward and illustrative, this approach serves as a Useful baseline before introducing more refined techniques. Let $\{Q_p(z)\}_{p\in\mathcal{P}}$ be a collection of complex polynomials, where each polynomial $Q_p(z)$ has roots represented in polar form as $z_{p,k} = r_{p,k}e^{j\varphi_{p,k}}$. We define the union of all such roots across the polynomials as

$$\mathcal{R} = \bigcup_{p\in\mathcal{P}} \left\{z_{p,k} \mid 1 \le k \le n_p\right\} \tag{4.33}$$

For a uniform linear array (ULA) with $m = 8$ sensors and $D = 2$ sources, we obtain $m - D = 6$ noise-space eigenvectors. Each eigenvector yields a degree-7 polynomial, contributing seven roots. In a total of 42 roots across all six vectors. These roots, denoted $z_{p,i} = r_{p,i}e^{j\varphi_{p,i}}$, are plotted in Fig. 4.17 and listed in Fig. 4.17. Many of these roots lie significantly away from the unit circle. Each function $h_p(\varphi)$ exhibits multiple inflection points (shown as red circles), And the corresponding polynomial roots are visualized as blue squares located at coordinates $(\varphi_{p,i}, r_{p,i})$.

4.10.2.1 Roots Close to Unity

To isolate roots that lie close to the unit circle, we define a proximity set:

$$\mathcal{C}_\varepsilon = \left\{z \in \mathcal{R} \mid \left| |z| - 1 \right| < \varepsilon\right\} \tag{4.34}$$

where $\varepsilon > 0$ is a small tolerance. To understand the relationship between these roots and the norm $\|h_p(z)\|$, refer to Eq. 4.32 and Fig. 4.16, which illustrates a second-order polynomial with Roots near the unit circle and the corresponding local minima.

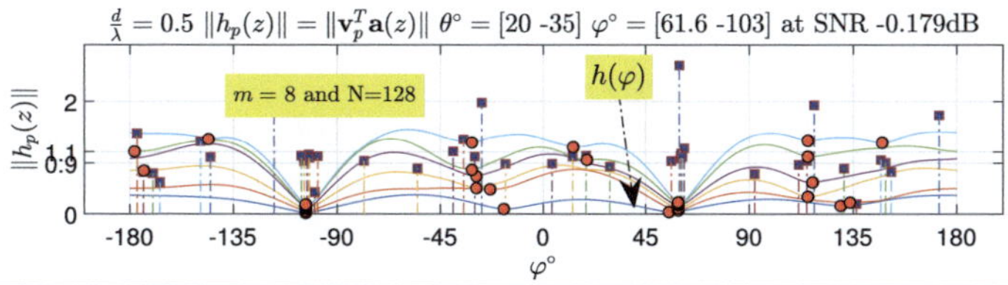

Table 4.17 Section 4.10.2 as in Eq 4.33 $\mathbf{v}_p^T \mathbf{a}(z)$ **Total Roots** 42 for all p					
$2.64e^{(j59.75)^\circ}$	$0.94e^{(j56.22)^\circ}$	$0.89e^{(-j16.44)^\circ}$	$1.03e^{(-j103.13)^\circ}$	$0.81e^{(j131.03)^\circ}$	$0.56e^{(-j167.24)^\circ}$
$0.38e^{(-j99.81)^\circ}$	$1.98e^{(-j26.91)^\circ}$	$1.05e^{(-j102.38)^\circ}$	$0.81e^{(-j55.07)^\circ}$	$0.98e^{(j60.27)^\circ}$	$0.72e^{(-j170.18)^\circ}$
$0.96e^{(j147.17)^\circ}$	$0.87e^{(j111.59)^\circ}$	$2.12e^{(-j117.28)^\circ}$	$1.43e^{(-j176.93)^\circ}$	$0.93e^{(-j104.42)^\circ}$	$1.02e^{(-j30.04)^\circ}$
$1.03e^{(j18.65)^\circ}$	$1.07e^{(j60.51)^\circ}$	$0.94e^{(j115.11)^\circ}$	$1.75e^{(j172.40)^\circ}$	$1.32e^{(-j34.97)^\circ}$	$0.99e^{(-j102.14)^\circ}$
$1.16e^{(j61.83)^\circ}$	$0.84e^{(j29.08)^\circ}$	$0.74e^{(j151.71)^\circ}$	$0.18e^{(j136.44)^\circ}$	$1.93e^{(j118.24)^\circ}$	$1.04e^{(j60.34)^\circ}$
$1.02e^{(j12.76)^\circ}$	$1.11e^{(-j39.54)^\circ}$	$1.03e^{(-j105.55)^\circ}$	$1.29e^{(-j149.34)^\circ}$	$0.74e^{(-j174.21)^\circ}$	$1.01e^{(-j145.08)^\circ}$
$1.02e^{(-j98.53)^\circ}$	$0.94e^{(-j78.24)^\circ}$	$0.89e^{(j3.76)^\circ}$	$0.91e^{(j149.20)^\circ}$	$1.01e^{(j61.02)^\circ}$	$0.71e^{(j92.39)^\circ}$

Fig. 4.17 Phase spectrum $h(\varphi)$ and all the roots of eigenvectors in $\mathbf{E}_n$

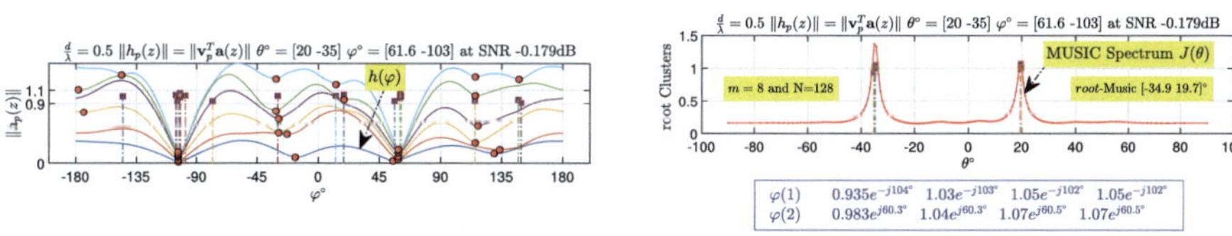

Table 4.18 Section 4.10.2 as in Eq 4.34 **Roots Close to Unit Circle** for $\delta r = 0.1$ is 19					
$0.94e^{(j56.22)^\circ}$	$1.03e^{(-j103.13)^\circ}$	$1.05e^{(-j102.38)^\circ}$	$0.98e^{(j60.27)^\circ}$	$0.96e^{(j147.17)^\circ}$	$0.93e^{(-j104.42)^\circ}$
$1.02e^{(-j30.04)^\circ}$	$1.03e^{(j18.65)^\circ}$	$1.07e^{(j60.51)^\circ}$	$0.94e^{(j115.11)^\circ}$	$0.99e^{(-j102.14)^\circ}$	$1.04e^{(j60.34)^\circ}$
$1.02e^{(j12.76)^\circ}$	$1.03e^{(-j105.55)^\circ}$	$1.01e^{(-j145.08)^\circ}$	$1.02e^{(-j98.53)^\circ}$	$0.94e^{(-j78.24)^\circ}$	$0.91e^{(j149.20)^\circ}$
$1.01e^{(j61.02)^\circ}$					

Fig. 4.18 Phase spectrum $h(\varphi)$ and roots eigenvectors in $\mathbf{E}_n$ close to unit circle

From the 42 roots listed in Fig. 4.17, 19 satisfy the unit-circle proximity criterion and are detailed in Fig. 4.18, also shown in Fig. 4.18. Two clear clusters emerge near angles $\varphi^\circ = [61.6^\circ, -103^\circ]$, corresponding to direction-of-arrival (DOA) estimates at $\theta^\circ = [20^\circ, -35^\circ]$, both located within $\varepsilon = 0.1$ from the unit circle.

However, not all near-unit-circle roots contribute to minima in $|h_p(z)|$. To refine further, we perform an angular analysis. However, not all near-unit-circle roots lead to distinct minima in $|h_p(z)|$. To enhance root selection, we apply *angular clustering*, grouping roots that lie within a small angular distance (e.g., $\delta\theta = 3^\circ$). This eliminates spurious roots and reveals $D = 2$ angular clusters, denoted as $\mathcal{C}_1$ and $\mathcal{C}_2$, each comprising roots with similar phase angles. For cluster $\mathcal{C}_d = \{z_1^{(d)}, \ldots, z_{N_d}^{(d)}\}$, we compute the centroid as

$$\hat{z}_d = \frac{1}{N_d} \sum_{k=1}^{N_d} z_k^{(d)}, \quad \hat{\mathcal{Z}} = \left\{\hat{z}_1, \ldots, \hat{z}_D\right\}$$

The arguments $\arg(\hat{z}_d)$ yield the estimated DOAs. As shown in Fig. 4.18, the final root clusters correspond to mean angle estimates of 19.7° and 34.9°, which align closely with the actual source directions and match the peaks of the standard MUSIC spectrum (also plotted for comparison).

To generalize this idea, we explore the construction of a noise. polynomial $P(z) = \prod_{i=1}^{m-1} h_i(z)$, using noise eigenvector polynomials $Q_p(z) = \mathbf{v}_p^T \mathbf{a}(z)$, whose roots are r_i.

4.10.3 *Methods for Noise Polynomial*

In root music, there are two methods for obtaining polynomials using noise eigenvectors. One is to first create a complex polynomial with the eigennoise vector, then take the conjugate of the polynomial and reverse it—that's one approach. Another approach is to create a matrix and use the sum of the off-diagonal elements, which is an alternative option. Let's consider a numerical example to understand the noise polynomial better as defined in Eq. 4.13 as $Q_p(z) = \mathbf{v}_p^T \mathbf{a}(z)$, a third-order spatial transversal filter for illustration.

$$\begin{aligned} Q_p(z) = \mathbf{v}_p^T \mathbf{a}(z) &= \boxed{3 - 2i + 2iz^{-1} + (1 - i)z^{-2} + z^{-3}} \\ &= \underbrace{[(3 - 2i)\ 2i\ (1 - i)\ 1]}_{\mathbf{v}_p^T} \times \mathbf{a}(z) \end{aligned}$$

4.10.3.1 Reciprocal Conjugate Roots

In this method, we construct the polynomial using a conjugate polynomial as

$$\begin{aligned} Q_p^*(z^{-1}) = \mathbf{v}_p^{*T} \mathbf{a}(z^{-1}) &= (3 + 2i) - 2iz^1 + (1 + i)z^2 + 1z^3 \\ &= \boxed{1 + (1 + i)z^{-1} - 2iz^{-2} + (3 + 2i)z^{-3}} \end{aligned} \tag{4.35}$$

Now, we obtain the noise polynomial [33, 35] as $P(z)$,

$$P(z) = \sum^{p} P_p(z) = Q_p(z) \times Q_p^*(z^{-1}) \tag{4.36}$$

and the following table 4.10.3 in figure presents the roots of the third-order complex polynomial $Q_p(z) = 0$ and the sixth-order polynomial $P_p(z) = 0$. We construct a matrix as

$$\mathbf{H}_n = \sum^{p} \mathbf{v}_p \mathbf{v}_p^T = \begin{pmatrix} 13 & -4 + 6i & 5 - i & 3 + 2i \\ -4 - 6i & 4 & -2 - 2i & -2i \\ 5 + i & -2 + 2i & 2 & 1 + i \\ 3 - 2i & 2i & 1 - i & 1 \end{pmatrix} \tag{4.37}$$

Table 4.10.3 Obtaining Noise Polynomial						
	Method A		Method B Eq 4.36		Method C Eq 4.37	
roots	$Q_p(z) = \mathbf{v}_p^T \mathbf{a}(z)$		$P_p(z)$		$R_p(z)$	
number	r	φ°	r	φ°	r	φ°
1	0.4175	-146.0217	0.4175	-146.0217	0.4175	-146.0217
2	0.7009	66.4659	0.7009	66.4659	0.7009	66.4659
3	0.9477	-66.7541	0.9477	-66.7541	0.9477	-66.7541
4	—	—	1.0551	-66.7541	1.0551	-66.7541
5	—	—	1.4267	66.4659	1.4267	66.4659
6	—	—	2.3951	-146.0217	2.3951	-146.0217

(a)

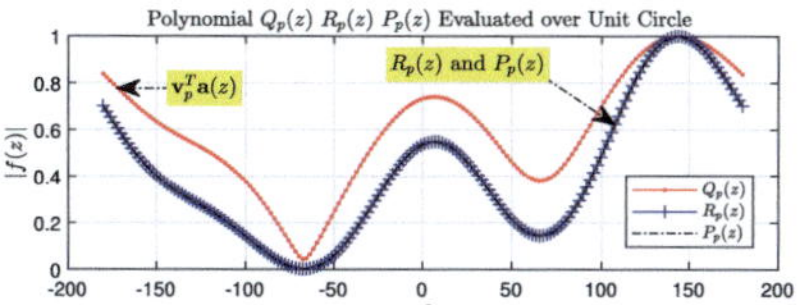

(b)

Fig. 4.19 Root MUSIC methods

And summing the off diagonals or all the traces, we get a polynomial as

$$R(z) = \sum^{p} R_p(z) = \underbrace{(3-2i)z^3 + (5+3i)z^2 - (5+5i)z^1}_{z+} + 20z^0 - \underbrace{(5-5i)z^{-1} + (5-3i)z^{-2} + (3+2i)z^{-3}}_{z^-}$$

and we notice that the polynomials $R_p(z)$ and $P_p(z)$ are identical as it is evident from the roots given in table in the Fig. 4.19a. Approach for arriving at the rooting polynomial using Eq. 4.37 It is very convenient while both lead to the same polynomial. The original paper on *root*-MUSIC uses [37] $P_p(z)$ and evaluates the roots of $P(z)$ and Assigns those roots that are close to the unit circle to signals, and the remaining roots to those farther away. From the unit circle to noise shown as small red solid circles in polar plot Fig. 4.20 and big solid Circles represent the signal sources. The table shown in Fig. 4.20 shows with color coding roots of $P(z)$ exhibiting reciprocal conjugate nature.

4.10.4 Steps in root-MUSIC

There are four distinct steps in the root-MUSIC.

1. Find the roots of the polynomials $P(z) = \sum^{p} P_p(z) = \prod^{i}(1 - r_i e^{j\varphi_i})$. Table in Fig. 4.20
2. Locate all the roots from $r_i e^{j\varphi_i}$ $\forall\, i \;\exists\, |1 - r_i| < \delta r$ in signal space.
3. Locate D Roots close to unit circle $r_i < 1$.
4. Solve for DOA θ using phase $\varphi_i = 2\pi \frac{d}{\lambda} \sin\theta$.

The results of this algorithm are illustrated in Fig. 4.20. In the polar plot, small red solid circles represent noise, while large solid circles indicate the signal sources. The table in Fig. 4.20 uses color coding to highlight the roots of $P(z)$ that are close to the unit circle, as well as two roots that are less than one. All the origins display a reciprocal conjugate nature.

roots of $P(z)$ Eq 4.36		
	r_i	φ_i°
poles $r < 1$	0.438	168.480
	0.520	-165.712
	0.571	121.378
	0.599	-43.924
	0.639	3.069
pole pairs close to unit circle	0.950	61.977
	0.955	-102.488
	1.047	-102.488
	1.053	61.977
poles $\frac{1}{r} > 1$	1.564	3.069
	1.669	-43.924
	1.750	121.378
	1.924	-165.712
	2.285	168.480

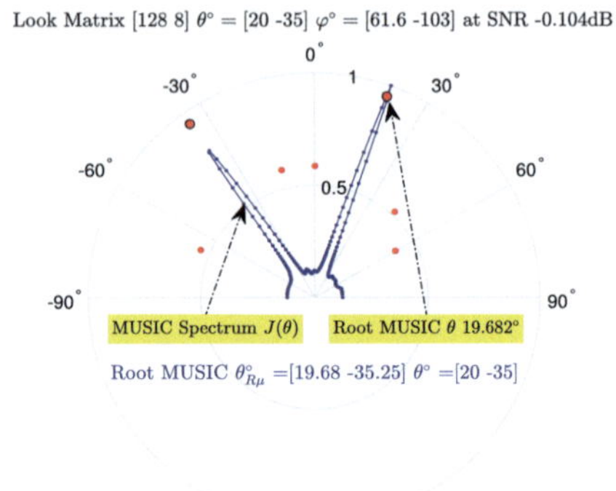

Fig. 4.20 Roots of $P(z) = \sum^p P_p(z) = Q_p(z) \times Q_p^*(z^{-1})$ in $\mathbf{E}_n$ close to unit circle

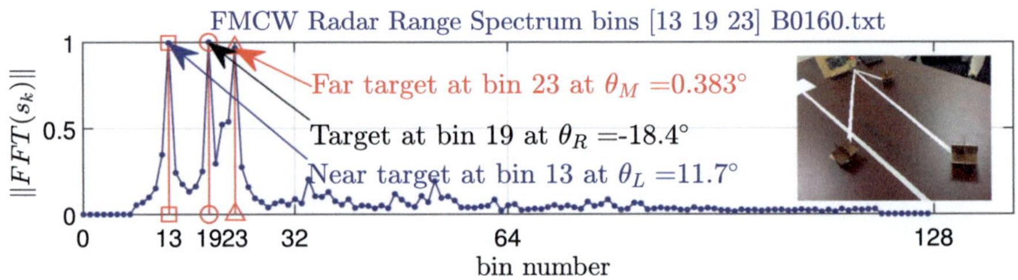

Fig. 4.21 Fourier spectrum of S matrix

4.11 κMUSIC

Broadband signals are typical in FMCW radar and human voice applications. However, direction-finding in these contexts presents a distinct challenge. In applications such as automotive sensing, the Direction of Arrival (DOA) θ uses FMCW radar ($\lambda \approx 4$ mm) using the integrated radar and compute elements in a single chip [38]. This hardware uses four spatially separated sensing elements $m = 4$ with $\frac{d}{\lambda} = 0.5$.

The array configuration and notation, as shown in Fig. 4.1, are used to describe the algorithm. The signal s_k in this application is a broadband signal. The magnitude of Fourier Spectrum for 128 samples of s_k is shown in Fig. 4.21 with three narrow band signals. In the inset image, three targets, referred to as corner reflectors, are positioned at different radial distances: Far, Near, and Mid. The far target is aligned with the bore axis of the radar, while the near target is located to the left of this axis. The mid-range target is situated to the right of the radar's bore axis. The frequency and the target range are uniquely related as $R = f_p \times g_R$ where g_R is constant for a given radar setting.

4.11.1 Range Estimation

Accurately determining the return Doppler frequency is essential for estimating target range. These applications are discussed in references [39–41]. However, conventional Fast Fourier Transform (FFT) methods provide accuracy limited by the number of samples taken. The picture in Eq. (4.38) illustrates each column's Discrete Fourier Transform (DFT) in the look matrix. The row number in this matrix corresponds to the bin number, indicating an approximate peak, with accuracy constrained by the sample size.

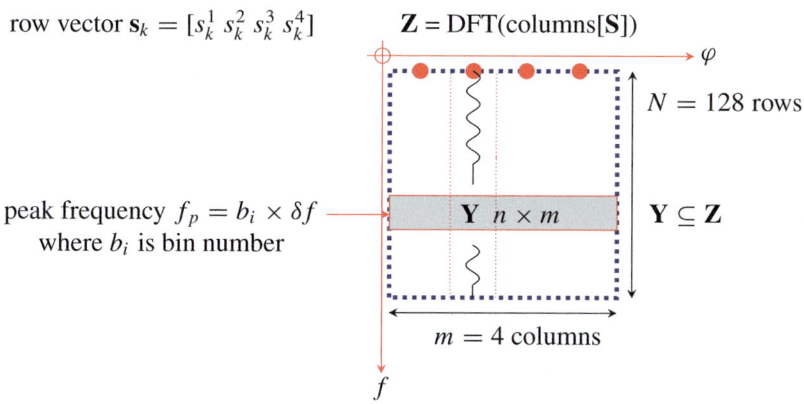

(4.38)

4.11.2 gFK Peaks

The exact spectrum peak or phasor for each integer bin occurs around the same bin frequency (for example, bin number 19). The gold-Fourier Kaluri (gFK) method provides an accurate peak and phase estimate. Addressing this limitation, we get four phasors at bin 19

$$\mathbf{s}_k = 0.87\cos(2\pi fk - 79.5^\circ)\ \ 0.77\cos(2\pi fk + 1.13^\circ)\ \ 0.68\cos(2\pi fk + 27.9^\circ)\ \ 1.0\cos(2\pi fk + 99.1^\circ)$$

This method is detailed in Chap. 2. Figure 4.22 illustrates the fractional bins calculated using gFK for four sensors along with phase. The data triplets A, φ, f are also displayed in the same diagram.

Typically, we generate a spatial transversal filter $h(z)$ with a length of $m = 4$ using this data. For example, the coefficient $w_0 = 0.87e^{-j79.5\frac{\pi}{180}}$ in Eq. 4.39 is calculated based on the data shown in Fig. 4.22, where φ and A are indicated. The peak of $|h(z)|$ corresponds to the direction of arrival (DOA) value for each target bin displayed in Fig. 4.22.

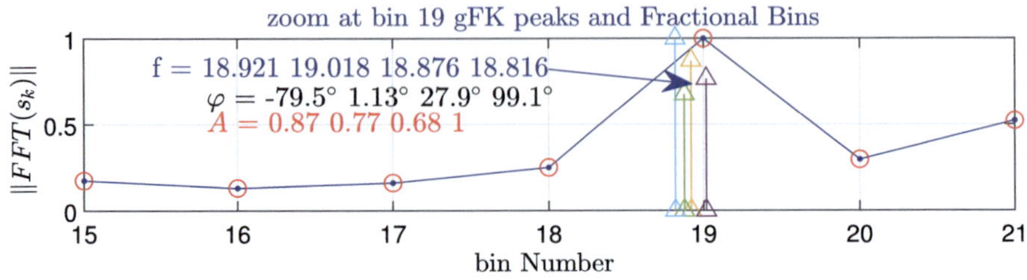

$$h(z) = 0.87e^{-j79.5^\circ} + 0.77e^{j1.13^\circ} z^{-1} + 0.68e^{j27.9^\circ} z^{-2} + 1e^{j99.1^\circ} z^{-3}$$

Fig. 4.22 κMUSIC transversal filter $h(z)$

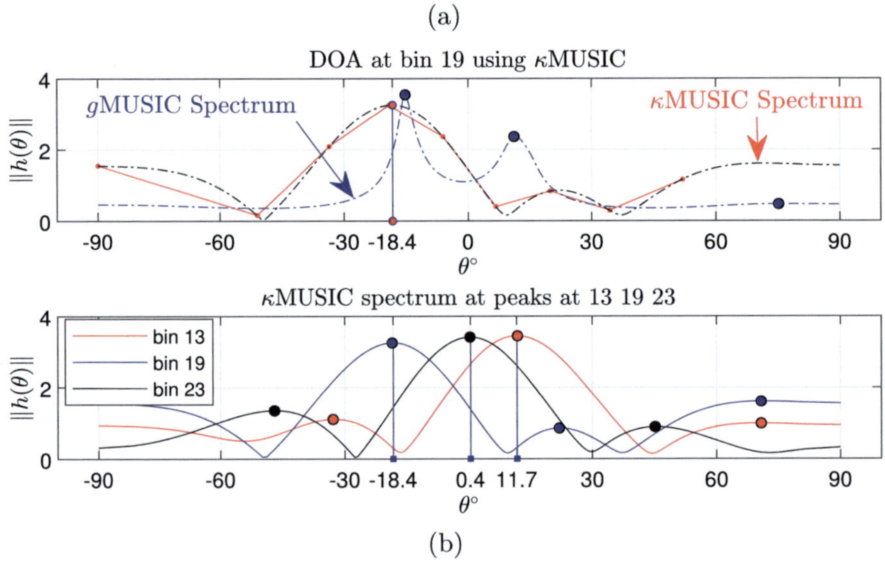

Fig. 4.23 κMUSIC spectrum $\|h(\theta)\|$

$$\begin{aligned} h(z) &= w_0 + w_1 z^{-1} + w_2 z^{-2} + w_2 z^{-3} \\ &= 0.87e^{-j79.5^\circ} + 0.77e^{j1.13^\circ} z^{-1} + 0.68e^{j27.9^\circ} z^{-2} + 1e^{j99.1^\circ} z^{-3} \text{ for bin 19} \end{aligned} \tag{4.39}$$

in Eq. 4.39 spatial delay z^{-1} operator as given in Eq. 4.4 $h(\varphi)$ is evaluated to obtain $h(\theta)$ using the relation ship given in Eq. 4.26 in which $\frac{d}{\lambda} = 0.5$.

The peak of $\|h(\varphi)\|$ is scaled using GSU to arrive at DOA phase, from which DOA is computed. The peak value is shown in Fig. 4.23a as red solid circle at -18.4° for bin 19. For comparison, the corresponding gMUSIC spectrum is shown in the same figure. Figure 4.23b shows the phase spectrum for all the peaks at -18.4°, 0.4°, 11.7° for the targets shown in the inset in Fig. 4.24. The κMUSIC algorithm has been

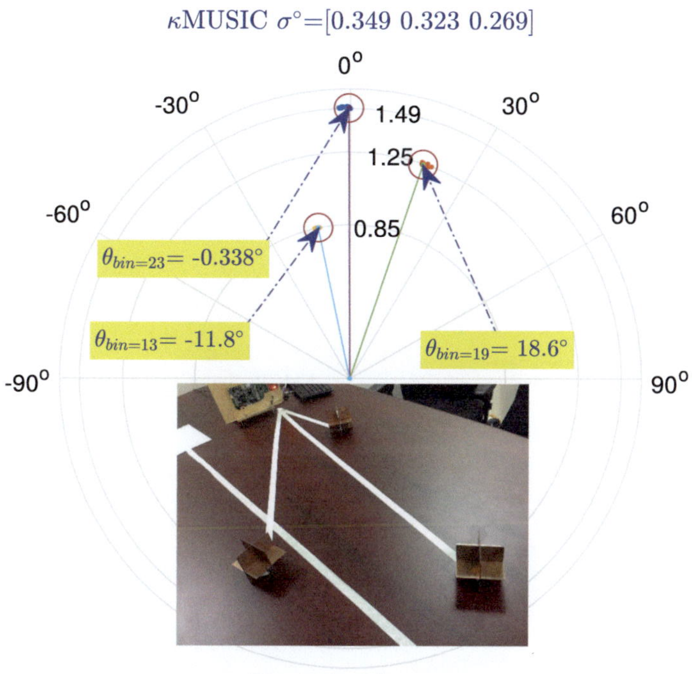

Fig. 4.24 MUSIC spectrum $\|J(\theta)\|$

extensively tested in both laboratory and field settings, and the reported results are reliable.

4.11.3 Experimental Setup

The testing and evaluation of the new algorithm κMUSIC require special attention and a carefully controlled setup. To facilitate this evaluation, gold-MUSIC was implemented simultaneously. The Texas Instruments chip 1642 FMCW radar was used to assess the algorithm's performance. Specific details about the radar parameters can be found in Chap. 6, where a particular example and case study are presented. Each radar chirp generates a complex matrix $\mathbf{A}_k$, which the algorithms use to determine the range r and direction of arrival (DOA) θ. The gold-MUSIC and the κMUSIC spectrum for position r_7 for a chirp are illustrated in Fig. 4.25. The spectra $J_\kappa(\theta)$ and $J_m(\theta)$ are sampled (180) within the interval $[-180, 180]$.

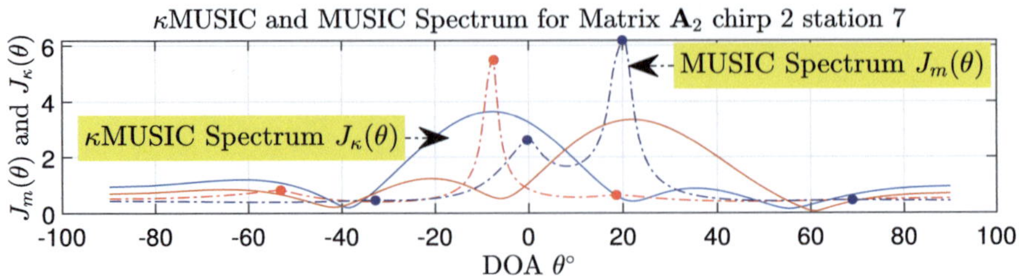

Fig. 4.25 κMUSIC and standard MUSIC

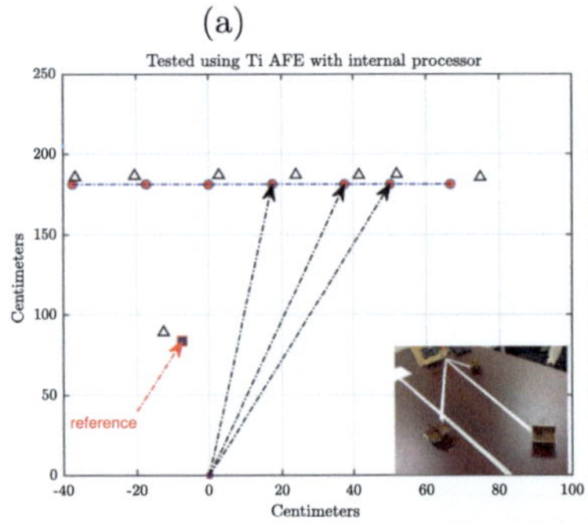

(b)

FMCW Radar Experimental Data					
r_i	θ°_{ref}	Station i	$\hat{r}_i$	θ°_κ	σ°_θ
185	-11.683	1	189.259	-11.179	0.072
182	-5.483	2	187.678	-6.262	0.019
181	0	3	186.952	0.869	0.011
182	5.483	4	188.558	7.296	0.024
185	11.683	5	191.440	12.546	0.011
188	15.494	6	194.437	15.531	0.059
193	20.167	7	199.997	21.960	0.020
84	-5.131	static	90.090	-8.094	0.021

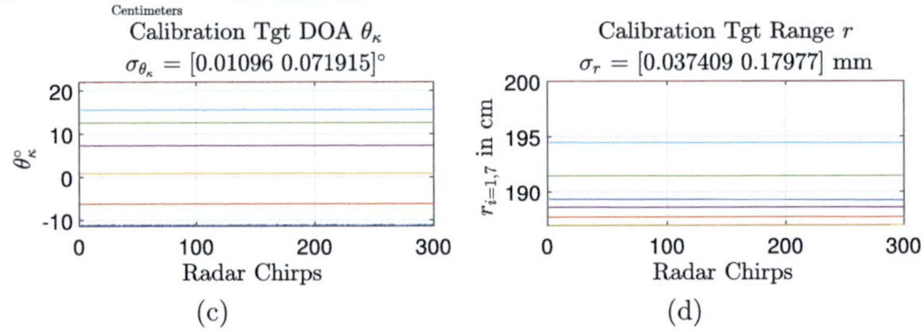

Fig. 4.26 κMUSIC evaluation setup

4.11.4 Test Bed

The test bed depicted in Fig. 4.26a illustrates the geometry of the experiment, with all dimensions measured in centimeters. It is essential to note that the X scale in the figure differs from the Y scale, which can create a misleading perception of angles. Additionally, the same figure shows the range **r** and the direction of arrival (DOA) θ for the target positions. The inset in Fig. 4.26a shows seven positions of the target corner reflector, labeled r_1 to r_7. These positions are indicated by red solid circles and arranged in a straight line. A reference static object shown as a solid red square is located at the coordinates $\{84, -5.13^\circ\}$, as depicted in Fig. 4.26a. The table in columns 4 and 5 of Fig. 4.26b presents the range $\hat{r}_i$ and Direction of Arrival (DOA) θ_κ of the targets, which were obtained from the radar using the κMUSIC method. These values of range r_i and DOA θ_{ref} are calculated based on geometric relationships

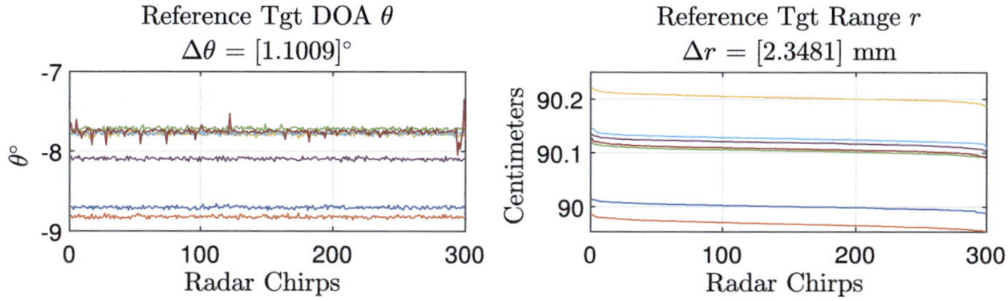

θ	-8.93	-9.11	-7.63	-8.02	-8.8	-7.66	-8.25
σ_θ	0.038	0.054	0.047	0.037	0.045	0.041	0.043

Fig. 4.27 Range r and DOA θ spread of reference target in Fig. 4.26a

instead of angle measurements, which can be prone to errors, as shown in columns 1 and 2 of the table in Fig. 4.26b. By determining the DOA angles geometrically, we reduce the likelihood of errors in angle measurements, thereby minimizing the impact of range errors on these measurements. This approach enhances the accuracy of angle estimates and provides a reliable reference for comparison with the measured radar angles.

4.11.5 Measurements

The target is positioned at seven stations, where a data matrix $\mathbf{A}_k$ with dimensions 128×4 is obtained for each chirp. For each target location r_i, data is collected over $k = 1$ to 300 chirps. Each chirp generates a complex matrix $\mathbf{A}_k$. Using this data, the κMUSIC and MUSIC direction-of-arrival (DOA) estimates are calculated. The results of these computations are presented in the table shown in Fig. 4.26b for this dataset. The estimated DOA $\hat{\theta}_i$ listed in the table of Fig. 4.26 are values obtained using the algorithm being evaluated. The second column provides the angle computed using geometric principles.

4.11.6 Data Measure and Test Results

Objects are not point type, but they are distributed. This must be taken into account when analyzing the results. In our case, the target of 6cm at 100cm subtends an angle of ≈ 3.4 deg. This means DOA value is in this angular window for this target at this distance. In Fig. 4.27 for 200 chirps, the DOA and range are shown, with a spread of $\Delta\theta = 1.5°$ and $\Delta r = 2.44$ mm. In Chap. 6, we utilize this idea to perceive the target, as depicted in the target model in Fig. 6.6. The reader can refer to the figure for a clearer understanding. There are interesting observations in Fig. 4.27. The reference static object DOA and range (in Fig. 4.27a and b) is constant for each station r_i. There are small changes in DOA by 1.4° and a range of 2.438 mm, for each change in $r_{i=1,7}$. The same is presented in the Fig. 4.27. We could infer that radar has moved (human error) during the experiment. The object moved from stations r_1 to r_7 has a min-max of standard deviation $\sigma_r = [0.04812\ 0.2]$ mm and $\sigma_\theta = [0.03\ 0.15]$deg. As can be seen, the DOA and Range variations are well-behaved, as depicted in Fig. 4.26c and d, and are also shown in the table in Fig. 4.26b. Linearity is well exhibited, indicating the accuracy.

4.11.7 Reference Test

In Fig. 4.25, the reference object and the one located at r_7 are represented as two peaks with the appropriate signs. Additionally, the Direction of Arrival (DOA) for all stations, calculated using both methods, is shown. This is further depicted in Fig. 4.28b, which demonstrates excellent linearity and accuracy.

$$\theta_{MUSIC} = 1.0386\theta_{\kappa MUSIC} - 0.0053474 \text{ deg}$$

The κMUSIC algorithm takes approximately 23 μs to run on the same machine, while the standard MUSIC algorithm takes about 254 μs. Both algorithms were implemented in C with $N = 128$. To reduce computational effort without compromising performance, ADC samples of $N = 128$ were utilized. This algorithm achieves a direction of arrival (DOA) accuracy of $\sigma_\theta = 0.15$ degrees and a range accuracy of $\sigma_r = 0.2$ mm, all while maintaining lean computing. We have compared the results of κMUSIC with the standard MUSIC, which is computationally intensive and has other limitations. The current κMUSIC algorithm is approximately 11 times faster than the standard MUSIC. The angular accuracies are measured to be within a fraction of a degree. This work presents a novel approach for both direction-of-arrival (DOA) estimation and range measurement. Additionally, a calibration procedure for the radar is discussed. Results for DOA, utilizing the κMUSIC algorithm, and range

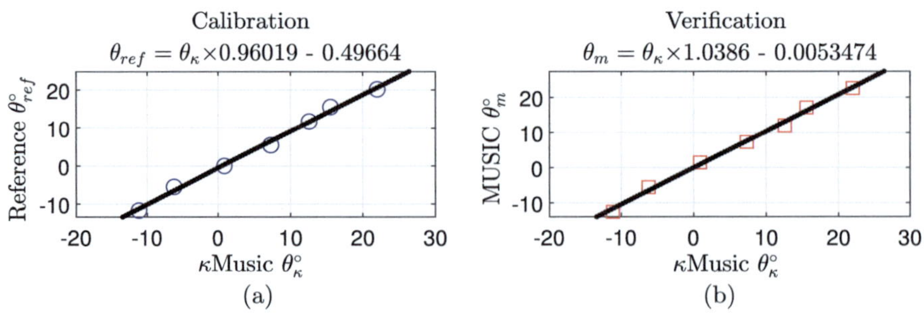

Fig. 4.28 Calibration of κMUSIC compare MUSIC

measurements, employing gFK, are presented in the table shown in Fig. 4.26b. Field tests conducted outside the laboratory demonstrated improved outcomes with the same algorithm using $N = 512$ samples, while in the laboratory, $N = 128$ samples were used.

4.12 *easy* MUSIC

The data used is real-time data obtained from the AWR1642 Evaluation module. Applying gMUSIC for broadband signals poses a challenge [41] that has been overcome by choosing the data matrix as $\mathbf{Y}$ of size $n \times m$ given in the picture in Eq. (4.38), near peak bin frequency. The starting and ending rows are $\lfloor b_i \pm \frac{n}{2} \rfloor$ where b_i is the bin number of the peak. The number of snapshots n is small, and the number of targets D is chosen as two for each peak in the MUSIC perspective. For each peak we choose a matrix $\mathbf{Y}$ of size 10×4 from $\mathbf{Z}$ for each peak bin. The covariance matrix would be $\mathbf{H} = \mathbf{YY^T}$. We perform eigenanalysis on covariance matrix as in Eq. 4.22 and obtain $H(\varphi)$ as in Eq. 4.24 to obtain MUSIC spectrum $J(\varphi)$. We use gMUSIC to obtain DOA value for each peak frequency.

4.13 Estimating Signal Parameters *via* Rotational Invariance Techniques

The origins of Estimating Signal Parameters via Rotational Invariance Techniques (ESPRIT) [36] lie in the field of Direction of Arrival (DOA) estimation, a key problem in array signal processing. However, for illustration and clarity, we begin with a simplified one-dimensional time series model. This approach captures the essential structure of the problem while avoiding the initial complexity of Spatial array configurations. Later, we will demonstrate ESPRIT using data from a uniform linear array (ULA). ESPRIT has evolved to overcome the calibration of the sensor array. Consider a time series x_k with a signal-to-noise ratio (SNR) of 7 dB. We assume that this signal is composed of a sum of complex exponentials, which can be modeled as

$$x_k = \sum_{i=1}^{n_s} A_i e^{j2\pi f_i k} + N(0, \sigma^2) \text{ where } f_i \text{ is normalized frequency of the form } \left| \frac{\varphi_i^\circ}{360} \right| < 0.5 \tag{4.40}$$

The time series x_k can be viewed as an ARMA process, characterized by poles that are very close to the unit circle. For example, consider the angles φ_i at 18°, 72°, 108°, and 162°. These angles correspond to normalized frequencies f_i of 0.05 (which is $\frac{18^\circ}{360}$), 0.2 (or $\frac{72^\circ}{360}$), 0.3 (which is $\frac{108^\circ}{360}$), and 0.45 (or $\frac{162^\circ}{360}$). The Fourier spectrum of the signal x_k is illustrated in Fig. 4.30, which shows these frequencies. When poles

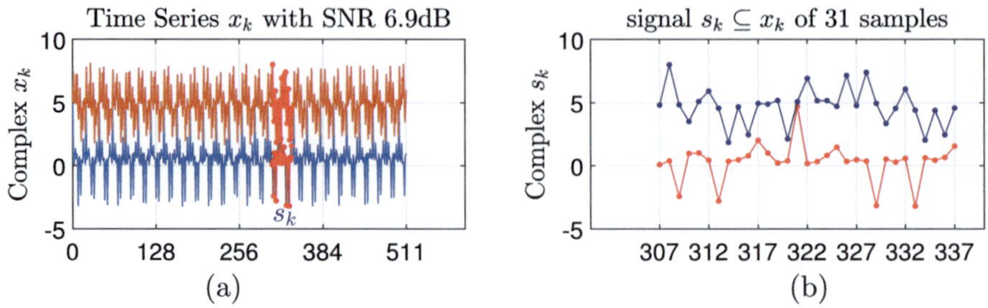

Fig. 4.29 ESPRIT method for time series x_k and s_k

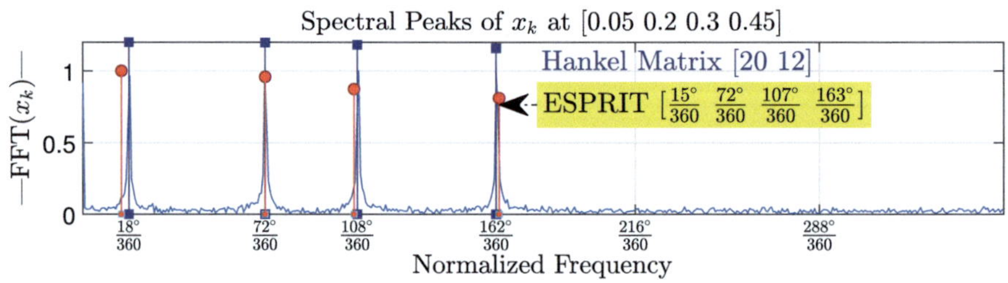

Fig. 4.30 ESPRIT method for time series spectral peaks

are positioned near the unit circle, they create a sharp peak in the Fourier spectrum, represented by the blue solid squares in Fig. 4.30. The time series x_k is depicted in Fig. 4.29a.

4.13.1 Short Data Length

Accurately estimating sinusoidal frequencies and identifying peaks in the spectrum is a significant area of interest that numerous authors have researched extensively. The challenge is further complicated by the fact that the available data lengths are often short, adding to the complexity of finding a solution. In this context, the ESPRIT method proves to be highly effective, as demonstrated in this section. A small segment, s_k, with a length of 31, is extracted from the time series x_k. This process is illustrated in Fig. 4.29a and b, where the extracted segment s_k is highlighted in bright red in Fig. 4.29a.

4.13.2 Covarinace Matrix

Estimating the spectral peaks from a short data sequence s_k requires a different approach. The Prony method is effective in the absence of noise and is quite elegant. However, when noise is present, the covariance matrix becomes biased. We follow a series of steps to address this issue. First, we construct a complex Hankel data matrix **D** with dimensions $12(m) \times (n)20$. To do this, we need a time series s_k with a length of $(m+n-1)31$. This Hankel matrix is illustrated in Eq. 4.41. The length of the time series is determined using the formula $12+20-1$. In general, to create a data matrix of size $m \times n$, a time series of length $m+n-1$ is required. This requirement poses a significant limitation of this method, especially in DOA estimation. In this example, we specifically consider the case where $m \neq n$. It would be appropriate to recollect the relationship $s_{k-1} = z^{-1}s_k$ where z^{-1} is a space or time delay operator.

$$\mathbf{D} = \begin{pmatrix} s_1 & s_2 & \cdots & s_{20} \\ s_2 & s_3 & \cdots & s_{21} \\ \vdots & \vdots & \vdots & \vdots \\ s_{12} & s_{13} & \cdots & s_{31} \end{pmatrix} \text{ is a Hankel matrix of size } 12 \times 20$$

$$\text{if } m < n \;\; \mathbf{S} = \mathbf{D}^T \text{ else } \mathbf{S} = \mathbf{D} \text{ this is required for economy model SVD and makes } \lambda_{min} > 0 \tag{4.41}$$

4.13.3 Algorithm

The time or space-sampled data is used to generate the Hankel matrix, as described in Eq. 4.41. The steps for this process are outlined in algorithm 4.13.3 and depicted in Fig. 4.31. There are nine distinct steps for obtaining the direction of arrival (DOA) or frequency peaks. Steps 1 to 4 yield the left eigenvectors **U** of the Hankel matrix **S**. Step 5 partitions the matrix into two parts: the signal and noise, represented in green and red, respectively, based on a priori knowledge of the number of signals. The step 3 in the algorithm 4.13.3 is numerically sensitive due to fact term $\frac{1}{\sqrt{\lambda_i}}$ numerically indeterminate when λ_i is very close to zero. We must take special approaches given by Golub [25]. Alternatively, we need to seek other approaches.

4.13.4 Left Eigenvectors of S

The singular value decomposition of the matrix $\mathbf{S} = \mathbf{U}\Sigma\mathbf{V}$ is performed elegantly using a simple method described below to obtain left eigenvectors of **S**. We obtain Hermitian matrix **H** as

Algorithm ESPRIT Algorithm 4.13.3

1: Create a data matrix $\mathbf{S}$ of dimensions $m \times n$. if $m < n$ *only* transpose $\mathbf{S}$. We need a time series s_k of length $m + n - 1$.
2: Compute $\mathbf{H} = \mathbf{S}\mathbf{S}^T$ and perform an eigenvalue analysis of $\mathbf{H}$. Obtain the eigenvectors $\mathbf{V}$ and the eigenvalues λ_i.
3: Construct a diagonal matrix $\mathbf{\Sigma}^{-1}$, where the diagonal elements are the values $\frac{1}{\sqrt{\lambda_i}}$.
4: Calculate the left eigenvectors of $\mathbf{S}$ as $\mathbf{U} = \mathbf{S}\mathbf{V}\mathbf{\Sigma}^{-1}$.
5: Partition $\mathbf{U}$ as $\{\mathbf{U}_s|\mathbf{U}_n\}$ using the prior knowledge of signal sources n_s.
6: Obtain the matrices $\mathbf{A}$ and $\mathbf{y}_i$ from $\mathbf{U}_s$.
7: Solve the system of equations $\mathbf{A}\mathbf{\Phi}_i = \mathbf{y}_i$ using the equation: $\mathbf{\Phi}_i = [\mathbf{A}^T\mathbf{A}]^{-1}\mathbf{A}^T\mathbf{y}_i$ for n_s sources.
8: The matrix $\mathbf{\Theta} = [\mathbf{\Phi}_1, \mathbf{\Phi}_2, \ldots, \mathbf{\Phi}_{n_s}]$ is a square matrix of size n_s.
9: The phase angles of the eigenvalues of $\mathbf{\Theta}$ provide the desired values φ_i.

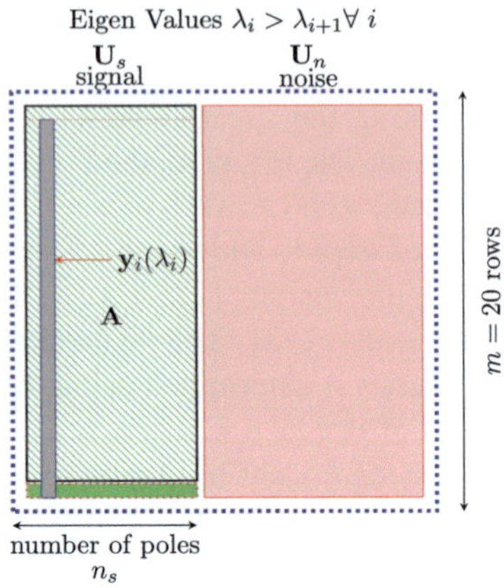

Eigen Values H											
Signal Space λ_i				5	6	7	8	9	10	11	12
5.197	4.983	4.539	4.214	2.233	0.754	0.647	0.494	0.425	0.379	0.306	0.120

Fig. 4.31 ESPRIT algorithm understanding

$$\mathbf{H} = \mathbf{S}^T\mathbf{S} \text{ and solve } \mathbf{H}\mathbf{v}_i = \lambda_i \mathbf{v}_i \text{ obtain } \mathbf{V} = [\mathbf{v}_1, \mathbf{v}_2 \ldots \mathbf{v}_m] \text{ such that } \lambda_i > \lambda_{i+1} \forall\, i \quad (4.42)$$

The Eq. 4.42 describes the eigenvalue analysis of the matrix $\mathbf{H}$. Through this analysis, we derive the diagonal matrix Σ^{-1}, where the diagonal elements take the form $\frac{1}{\sqrt{\lambda_i}}$. Additionally, we obtain the left eigenvectors of the matrix $\mathbf{S}$, as indicated in Eq. 4.43. The matrix $\mathbf{U}$, which consists of these left eigenvectors of $\mathbf{S}$, is calculated using Eqs. 4.41 and 4.42.

$$\mathbf{U} = \mathbf{S}\mathbf{V}\Sigma^{-1} \quad (4.43)$$

The above process is for obtaining Singular Value Decomposition of the matrix $\mathbf{S}$ as described in Chap. 2, Sect. 2.5.1 steps.

4.13.5 Least Squares Estimate $\mathbf{\Theta}$

The Total Least Squares is approximated by Least Squares for ease. From the signal space $\mathbf{U}_s$, we extract a matrix $\mathbf{A}(m - 1 \times n_s)$, represented by a green hatched box depicted in Fig. 4.31. It is important to note that the last row of the signal space is omitted. For each λ_i in the signal space, we select a column vector, denoted as $\mathbf{y}_i$. This is illustrated as a slender black box in Fig. 4.31. Additionally, the first row of the signal space is not included in $\mathbf{y}_i(m - 1 \times 1)$. We then formulate an overdetermined set of simultaneous equations as follows:

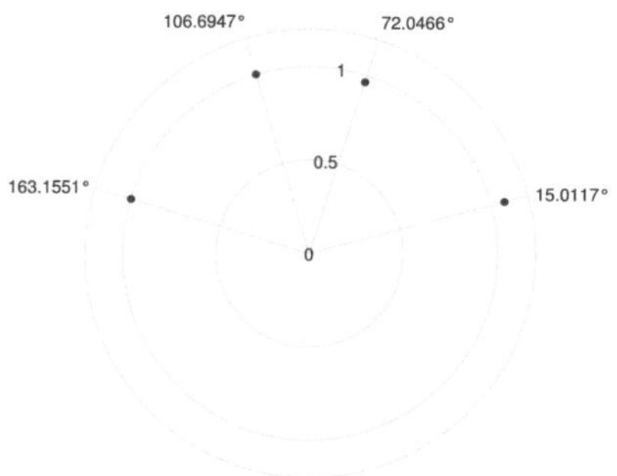

Estimated $re^{j\varphi}$ of the ARMA using ESPRIT

(a)

$n_s = 4$ Eigen Values $\boldsymbol{\Theta}$				
Complex	λ_1^{φ}	λ_2^{φ}	λ_3^{φ}	λ_4^{φ}
Magnitude(r)	1.015	0.955	0.964	1.023
Argument(φ)	13.54°	69.6°	107.51°	161.2°

(b)

Fig. 4.32 ESPRIT outcome for time series and eigenvalues of Θ

$$\mathbf{A}\Phi_i = \mathbf{y}_i \text{ where } \Phi_i \text{ is a column vector of size } n_s \tag{4.44}$$

The least squares solution for Φ_i is expressed as $[\mathbf{A}^T\mathbf{A}]^{-1}\mathbf{A}^T\mathbf{y}_i$. We construct a matrix $\Theta = [\Phi_1, \Phi_2, \ldots, \Phi_{n_s}]$, which is a square matrix of size $n_s \times n_s$.

4.13.6 Eigenvalues of $\boldsymbol{\Theta}$

The complex eigenvalues of Θ are computed and illustrated in Fig. 4.32a as a polar plot in the z-plane. As shown, the poles are situated close to the unit circle, indicating oscillators with strengths that are proportional to the eigenvalues of Θ.

Additionally, the argument of the complex eigenvalues of Θ indicates the pole positions of the ARMA model, as shown in the table in Fig. 4.32b. This represents the locations of the peaks in the spectrum depicted in Fig. 4.30.

4.13.7 ESPRIT for Time Series s_k

The ESPRIT algorithm, as detailed in 4.13.3 and illustrated in Fig. 4.31, was tested using 31 data samples. The eigenvalues associated with the left eigenvectors of the Hankel matrix are presented in a table within the same figure. Steps 1 to 9 of the algorithm have been implemented, and the results are summarized below. The table shows that the rank of the matrix is 12, with all other eigenvalues equal to zero.

We present the outcomes of the algorithm in Fig. 4.30, which compares the original frequencies with the ESPRIT estimates. Furthermore, Fig. 4.32a displays a polar diagram illustrating the four poles, and the table in Fig. 4.32b enhances readability of the results.

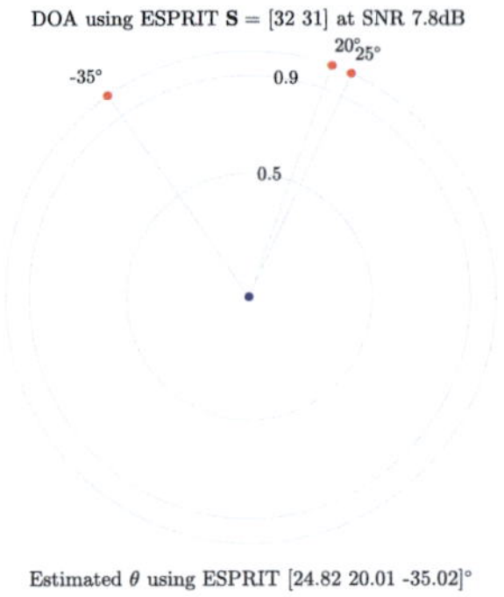

(a)

(c)

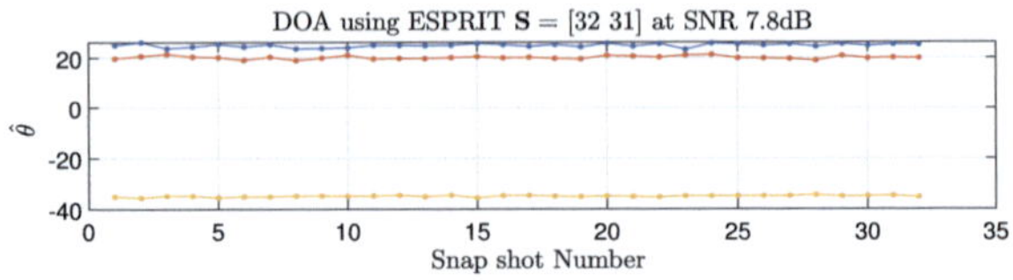

θ Values							
0	1	2	3	4	5	6	7
24.955	26.082	23.676	24.330	25.278	24.313	25.198	23.538
19.658	20.635	21.369	20.339	20.088	18.971	20.263	18.857
-35.113	-35.584	-34.831	-34.882	-35.541	-35.110	-35.129	-34.899

(b)

Fig. 4.33 ESPRIT solution using ULA

4.13.8 DOA Using ESPRIT with ULA

In the context of spatial sampling using a Uniform Linear Array (ULA), we have selected an array consisting of 31 elements. The same algorithm described in steps 1 to 9 of Algorithm 4.13.3, as illustrated in Fig. 4.31, is applied within this ULA framework. Each snapshot from the look matrix is used to construct a Hankel matrix of size 16×16. Each row of this matrix is formed using subarrays of data. In this case, we have set $m = n$. For the MUSIC algorithm's m-array equivalent, a sample array of size $2m - 1$ is required. In this numerical example, we used a complex look matrix of size 4×31. Each snapshot serves as input to the ESPRIT algorithm, yielding Direction-of-Arrival (DOA) results. We have considered three narrowband emitters located at angles of $[-35°, 20°, 25°]$. The results are presented in Fig. 4.33b for the four snapshots. Figure 4.33a offers a diagrammatic approach to enhance understanding.

4.14 Summary

In this chapter, we discuss subspace methods. We provide a brief overview of the Uniform Linear Array (ULA) data model and introduce the concept of signal-to-noise ratio. The decomposition of a rectangular data matrix is revisited for clarity. Key methods such as standard MUSIC, *root*-MUSIC, Prony Method, *gold*-MUSIC, κMUSIC, *easy*-MUSIC, and ESPRIT are explained with the aid of numerical examples. Each figure included offers additional clarification and contains self-contained data.

4.14.1 MEX File Generation

The C source files and MATLAB scripts used to generate MEX files in this chapter are located in the following directories for generating MEX code.

```
chap4\figures\esprit\esprit;      chap4\figures\musicAndGmu\musicAndGmu
chap4\figures\myMexGetRgD;        chap4\figures\myMexInitR
chap6\figures\dOfVoice\dOfVoice; chap6\figures\fmcwRadar\fmcwRadar
```

Each of the MATLAB `.m` files listed contains a `mex` compile directive that links the corresponding C source code and generates a platform-specific MEX file. Because MEX files are platform-dependent, the portability of precompiled binaries across different systems is not assured. Therefore, it is necessary to regenerate the MEX files on the target machine to ensure compatibility. This process requires a MATLAB environment that supports MEX compilation. A basic or trial version of MATLAB, without any toolboxes, is sufficient for this purpose, as the code relies only on core MATLAB functionality and standard C compilers. The table below lists the resulting `.mex` files (first column), their respective file locations (second column), and the MATLAB `.m` files containing the `mex` command (third column).

This chapter C files for MEX		
MEX File	Location of C Files	Command
gMusik.mexw64	chap6 \ figures\ dOfVoice\ dOfVoice	mexGmusik.m
LatexFileMatrix.mexw64	chap6\ figures\ fmcwRadar\ fmcwRadar	myMexLatexFileMatrix.m
clusterLin.mexw64	chap6\ figures\ fmcwRadar\ fmcwRadar	myMexClst.m
espritUla.mexw64	chap4\ figures\ esprit\ esprit	mexEspritUla.m
IQmatrix.mexw64	chap4\ figures\ musicAndGmu\ musicAndGmu	mexIQmatrix.m
gMusic.mexw64	chap4\ figures\ musicAndGmu\ musicAndGmu	mexGmusic.m
sweepFine.mexw64	chap4\ figures\ musicAndGmu\ musicAndGmu	mexSweepFine.m
rootMusic.mexw64	chap4\ figures\ musicAndGmu\ musicAndGmu	mexRootMusic.m
getRgD.mexw64	chap4\ figures\ myMexGetRgD	myMexGetRgD.m
initR.mexw64	chap4 \ figures\ myMexInitR	myMexInitR.m

4.14.2 File Organization

This subsection presents the list of program files associated with the chapter *Subspace Methods*. The program files are organized into a total of 15 directories, which are presented in the two tables below. The first table lists six directories, and the second table lists an additional nine directories. Each directory name is highlighted in yellow at the top of its respective column for easy identification.

This chapter program files Table A

figESPRIT	figEspritArray	figStdMu	figPerformance	figSharpSpec
ds2nfu.m	ds2nfu.m	figStdMu.eps	figPerformance.eps	figSharpSpec.eps
EigenValues.tex	espritDoa.m	figStdMu.m	figPerformance.m	figSharpSpec.m
espritUla.mexw64	espritDoa.tex	figStdMuPolar.eps	figPerformanceSnr.eps	gMusic.mexw64
figESPRIT.eps	espritUla.mexw64	gMusic.mexw64	figPerformanceSnr.m	gMuSpec.m
figEsprit.m	figEspritArray.eps	IQmatrix.mexw64	gMusic.mexw64	IQmatrix.mexw64
figEspritPolar.eps	figEspritArray.m	labelStdMu.m	gMuStd.m	labelSubplot.m
figEsprtReslts.eps	figEspritSnapshots.eps		IQmatrix.mexw64	labelSubplotZoom.m
labelARMAspk.m	IQmatrix.mexw64			plotPeaks.m
labelEsprit.m	labelPolarEsprit.m	equations		sweepFine.mexw64
LatexFileMatrix.mexw64	LatexFileMatrix.mexw64	gMusik.mexw64		
poles.tex		obj.csv		
timeData.m		tstMuEqns.m		

The code itself is provided separately in the repository and is not embedded in this document.

This chapter program files Table B

figJphi	figKmuPerformance	figKmusic	figRootMu	figGspectrum
clusterLin.mexw64	A0166-01.txt	B0160.txt	clusterLin.mexw64	ds2nfu.m
ds2nfu.m	A0166-02.txt	cr3.jpg	ds2nfu.m	figGspectrum.eps
eigenV.m	A0166-03.txt	dsxy2figxy.m	figRootMu.eps	figGspectrum.m
figHphi.eps	A0166-04.txt	figKmusic.eps	figRootMu.m	figGspectrum32.eps
figJphi.eps	A0166-05.txt	figKmusic.m	figRootMuNew.m	
figJphi.m	A0166-06.txt	figKmusicMu.eps	figRootMuNewEx.m	
figJphiEigen.tex	A0166-07.txt	figKmusicPolar.eps	figRootMuAllpoles.eps	gMusic.mexw64
figJphiPoly.tex	cr3.jpg	figKmusicPolar.m	figRootMuUnit.eps	gMuSpec.m
figJphiRoots.tex	ds2nfu.m	figKmusicSpk.eps	gMusic.mexw64	IQmatrix.mexw64
gMusic.mexw64	dsxy2figxy.m	figKmusicZoom.eps	IQmatrix.mexw64	labelSubplot.m
IQmatrix.mexw64	ExpTestBed.tex	getRgD.mexw64	labelPlot.m	sweepFine.mexw64
labelPlot.m	figCalibrate.eps	initR.mexw64	labelRootMu.m	
labelPoly.m	figExpTestBed.eps	label211.m	phiSpek.m	figPisarenko
musicProof.m	figFixedTgt.eps	labelFig1.m	rootclusters.tex	covSig.m
obj.csv	figKmuCal.eps	labelFig2.m	rootMusic.mexw64	figPisarenko.m
phiSpek.m	figKmuCalSpk.eps	labelFig3.m	rootsInpolarVec.m	IQmatrix.mexw64
rec2polar.m	figKmuPerformance.m	labelFig3a.m	sweepFine.mexw64	mysvd.m
rootclusters.tex	getRgD.mexw64	labelFig4.m	totalroots.log	
rootMusic.mexw64	initR.mexw64	polarDS2nfu.m	totalroots.tex	
rootsInpolar.m	labelCalibrate.m	rcon.txt	UnitCircle.tex	
totalroots.tex	labelFixedTgt.m	sweepFine.mexw64		figPronyArray
UnitCircle.tex	labelKmuAndMu.m		figGmusic	covSig.m
	labelLinearFit.m		ds2nfu.m	ds2nfu.m
	labelTestBed.m		figGmusic.eps	figProny.m
	LatexFileMatrix.mexw64	figPartition	figGmusic.m	figPronyArray.eps
	makeTable.m	clusterLin.mexw64	figGmusicGsu.eps	figPronyArray.m
figZeros	rcon.txt	figPartition.m	gMusic.mexw64	IQmatrix.mexw64
ds2nfu.m	TrueRgDoa.m	gMusic.mexw64	IQmatrix.mexw64	labelProny.m
figZeros.eps		IQmatrix.mexw64	labelGmu.m	pronyDoa.m
figZeros.m		partition.tex	sweepFine.mexw64	timeData.m

Disclaimer
These demo programs are intended solely for academic and illustrative purposes in connection with the book *Direction Finding Algorithms for Practicing Engineers*, published by Springer Nature. Authored by Dr. Venkata Ranga Rao Kaluri (kaluri@ieee.org) this material is protected under copyright © 2025. All rights are reserved. Unauthorized reproduction, distribution, or use of the code in any form is strictly prohibited without prior written permission. The author assumes no responsibility or liability for any outcomes resulting from the use of this code.

References

1. Prony, R. (1795). *Essai experimentale et analytique*, J. Ecole Polytechnique, 2, 24–76.
2. Pisarenko, V. F. (1973). *The retrieval of harmonics from a covariance function*, Geophys. J. Roy. Astronom. Soc. 33, 347–366.
3. R. Kumaresan and D. W. Tufts, *Estimating the Angles of Arrival of Multiple Plane Waves*, in IEEE Transactions on Aerospace and Electronic Systems, vol. AES-19, no. 1, pp. 134–139, Jan. 1983.
4. A. Barabell, *Improving the resolution performance of eigenstructure-based direction-finding algorithms*, ICASSP '83. IEEE International Conference on Acoustics, Speech, and Signal Processing, Boston, MA, USA, 1983, pp. 336–339.
5. Bjorn Ottersten and Thomas Kailath; *Direction-of-Arrival Estimation for Wide-Band Signals Using the ESPRIT Algorithm*, IEEE Transactions on Acoustics, Speech, and Signal Processing, Vol. 38, No. 2, February 1990 317.
6. Ralph O. Schmidt; *Multiple Emitter Location and Signal Parameter Estimation*, IEEE Transactions on Antennas and Propagation, Vol. AP-34, No. 3, March 1986.
7. P. Stoica and A. Nehorai, *MUSIC, maximum likelihood, and Cramer-Rao bound: further results and comparisons*, in IEEE Transactions on Acoustics, Speech, and Signal Processing, vol. 38, no. 12, pp. 2140–2150, Dec. 1990.
8. P. Stoica and A. Nehorai, *MUSIC, maximum likelihood and Cramer-Rao bound*, ICASSP-88., International Conference on Acoustics, Speech, and Signal Processing, New York, NY, USA, 1988, pp. 2296–2299 vol. 4.
9. B. Ottersten and M. Viberg, Analysis of subspace fitting based methods for sensor array processing, International Conference on Acoustics, Speech, and Signal Processing,, Glasgow, UK, 1989, pp. 2807–2810 vol. 4.
10. J. A. Cadzow, Young S. Kim and Dong C. Shiue, *General direction-of-arrival estimation: a signal subspace approach*, in IEEE Transactions on Aerospace and Electronic Systems, vol. 25, no. 1, pp. 31–47, Jan. 1989.
11. J. A. Cadzow, *Direction finding: a signal subspace approach*, in IEEE Transactions on Systems, Man, and Cybernetics, vol. 21, no. 5, pp. 1115–1124, Sept.-Oct. 1991.
12. J. A. Cadzow, *Direction-of-arrival estimation using signal subspace modeling*, in IEEE Transactions on Aerospace and Electronic Systems, vol. 28, no. 1, pp. 64–79, Jan. 1992.
13. Bhaskar D Rao and K V S Hari, *Analysis of subspace-based direction of arrival estimation methods*, Sadhana, Vol. 16, Part 3, November 1991, pp. 183–194. ©Printed in India.
14. N. K. Bose and C. R. Rao, eds., Chap 16, A. Paulraj, B. Ottersten, R. Roy, A. Swindlehurst, G. Xu and T. Kailath, *Subspace Methods for Directions-of-Arrival Estimation*, Handbook of Statistics, Vol. 10, 1993 Elsevier Science Publishers.

15. T. Soderstrom and P. Stoica, *On the accuracy of high-order Yule-Walker methods for cisoids*, [Proceedings] ICASSP 91: 1991 International Conference on Acoustics, Speech, and Signal Processing, Toronto, ON, Canada, 1991, pp. 3573–3576 vol. 5.
16. Qi Cheng and Yingbo Hua, *Detection of cisoids using least square error function*, in IEEE Transactions on Signal Processing, vol. 45, no. 6, pp. 1584–1590, June 1997.
17. Bienvenu, G. and L. Kopp (1979). *Principle de la goniometrie passive adaptive*, In: Proc. 7'eme Colloque GRESIT. Nice, France, 106/1–106/10.
18. W. H. Hayt and J. E. Kemmerly, *Engineering Circuit Analysis*, McGraw-Hill, New York, 1993.
19. Peter C. Young *Recursive Estimation and Time-Series Analysis—An Introduction for the Student and Practitioner* Second Edition 2011, Springer Heidelberg Dordrecht London New York.
20. T. Söderström and P. Stoica: *System Identification*, Prentice-Hall, London, United Kingdom, 1989 (Paperback Edition 1994, Polish Edition 1997).
21. T. Söderström and P. Stoica: *System Identification Solutions Manual*, Prentice-Hall International, London, United Kingdom, 1989.
22. Kaluri V. Rangarao, Atul Negi, *A Novel Method of Generating Complex Sine Wave in Automotive Sensing Application*, IEEE APSCON 2025 20–22, 2025 IIT Hyderabad, India.
23. P. A. Janakiraman and Kaluri. V. Ranga Rao, *Identification of linear modulated FM signal via a new recursive modified response error method (REM)*, in IEEE Transactions on Acoustics, Speech, and Signal Processing, vol. 36, no. 10, pp. 1675–1679, Oct. 1988.
24. S. M. Kay and S. L. Marple, Spectrum analysis—A modern perspective, in Proceedings of the IEEE, vol. 69, no. 11, pp. 1380–1419, Nov. 1981.
25. Gene H. Golub and Charles F. Van Loan fourth edition, *Matrix Computations*, Publication Date February 15, 2013 The Johns Hopkins University Press, Baltimore.
26. Kaluri V. Rangarao and Shridhar V. Narasimhan *gold-MUSIC: A variation on MUSIC to accurately determine peaks of the spectrum*, IEEE Trans Antenna and Propagation Vol 61 issue 4, April 2013 pp 2263–2268.
27. Richard Brent, *Algorithms for Minimization without Derivatives.* Prentice-Hall, Inc. (1973).
28. Kaluri V. Rangarao and Shridhar V.; *An Accurate Numerical Method for Estimating the Delay Between Two Omni-Directional Receiving Elements* IEEE 30th Digital Avionics Systems Conference 2011, Seattle, Washington, U.S.A., October 2011, pp 8C3-4–8C3-7.
29. Kaluri V. Rangarao, Shridhar V., V. Prathyusha, T. Neela Pavani; *Estimating the Directions of Arrival of Narrow Band Signals using Spatial Tuned Filter* IEEE International Conference on Radar 2011, Chengdu, China, 24–27 October 2011, pp 619–622.
30. Kaluri V. Rangarao and Ranjan K. Mallik; *Digital Signal Processing: A Practitioner's Approach* Wiley.
31. Harry L. Van Trees; *Detection, Estimation, and Modulation Theory, Part 1* John Wiley & Sons.
32. Fu Li and Yang Lu; *Unified bias analysis for DOA estimation algorithms* IEEE International Conference on Acoustics, Speech, and Signal Processing, 1993, Volume: 4, pp: 376–379.
33. D. Wang, R. Chai and F. Gao, *An improved root-MUSIC algorithm and MSE analysis*, 2016 International Conference on Computer, Information and Telecommunication Systems (CITS), Kunming, China, 2016, pp. 1–4.
34. P. Stoica and R. L. Moses, *Introduction to Spectral Analysis*. Upper Saddle River, NJ: Prentice Hall, 1997.
35. R. De Silvaa, A. Antoniria, A. Ignjatovica, and C. Wijenayakeb, *MUSIC algorithm for Young Mathematicians and Engineers*, in *Proc. 33rd Australasian Association for Engineering Education Conference (AAEE)*, Sydney, Australia, Dec. 4–7, 2022.
36. H. Krim and M. Viberg, *Two decades of array signal processing research*, IEEE Signal Processing Magazine, vol. 13, no. 4, pp. 67–94, Jul. 1996.
37. Rao, B.D.; Hari, K.V.S.; *Performance analysis of Root-Music* IEEE Transactions on Acoustics, Speech and Signal Processing Volume: 37, Issue: 12 1989, pp: 1939–1949.
38. Texas Instruments User Guide *AWR1642 Evaluation Module Single-Chip mmWave Sensing Solution User's Guide* (Rev. C) May 2020.
39. Kaluri V. Rangarao, and Balaji Kanigicherla, *DOA Estimation via kMUSIC in* FMCW Radar Application, in Proc IEEE Aug ICSP2018, pp 903–908, Beijing, China.

40. Kaluri V. Rangarao, Atul Negi, *A Perception Engine in Automotive FMCW Radar*, 2023 IEEE International Workshop on Technologies for Defense and Security (TechDefense), Rome, Italy, 2023, pp. 234–239.
41. Kaluri V Rangarao and A. Negi, *Formant Based Direction of Voice for Smart Microphone Array*, 2024 IEEE International Workshop on Technologies for Defense and Security (TechDefense), Naples, Italy, 2024, pp. 363–367.
42. A. Paulraj, R. Roy and T. Kailath, *Estimation Of Signal Parameters Via Rotational Invariance Techniques- Esprit*, Nineteenth Asilomar Conference on Circuits, Systems and Computers, 1985., Pacific Grove, CA,USA, 1985, pp. 83–89.

Chapter 5
Beam Steering Methods

Beam steering originates from antenna design and adaptive array processing [1–3], and is mainly focused in this direction [4–6]. In the early days, it was used in radio sounding [7]. At millimeter waves, mechanical rotation with fixed beams remains practice [8]. It makes it difficult to find references, as direction finding is challenging. The digital revolution and subspace [9] methods have surpassed this approach. Monopulse radar is one example [2]. A wide range of literature exists across various domains. In this chapter, we focus on the spatial filtering method.

5.1 Beam Steering

The main beam of an antenna can be steered, which involves changing the direction of the main lobe in its radiation pattern. There are two methods for directing the beam: mechanical steering and electronic steering. Mechanical steering entails physically moving the antenna array to alter the beam direction. In contrast, electronic beam steering adjusts the direction without physical movement by delaying signals before they are combined. The movement of an antenna beam can be accomplished electrically using a phased array, eliminating the need for mechanical motion. This delay can be introduced using phase shifters or modifying the signal's gain before combining. Conventional electronic beam steering typically relies on phase delays among the elements of a uniform linear array (ULA).

5.1.1 Mechanical Steering

The standard air-surveillance radar system [10–13] uses a mechanically rotated reflector antenna that creates a fan-shaped beam. This fan beam has a narrow angular

V. R. Kaluri, *Direction Finding Algorithms for Practicing Engineers*,
https://doi.org/10.1007/978-3-032-06997-9_5

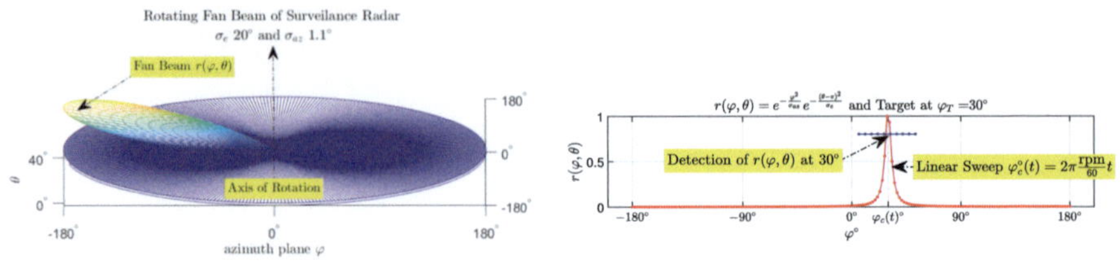

(a) (b)

Fig. 5.1 Early days of beam steering in radar $r(\varphi, \theta) = e^{-\frac{\varphi^2}{\sigma_{az}}} \times e^{-\frac{(\theta-\pi)^2}{\sigma_e}}$

width in the azimuthal plane, typically measuring around 1°, while showing a wider angular spread in the elevation plane of approximately 20° as depicted in Fig. 5.1a. Choosing the scanning rate for the fan beam antenna is a crucial balance between rapidly obtaining target position data and the radar's capacity to detect weak targets. A slower scanning rate allows more pulses to accumulate, thereby enhancing the integration of received signals and increasing the likelihood of detection, especially for faint targets. However, this slower rate leads to longer gaps between successive observations of a target, which could delay threat responses. In practice, air surveillance radars typically operate with scanning rates ranging from 1 to 60 revolutions per minute (rpm). This enables the effective filtering of signals, allowing them to be distinguished from background noise. The mechanical motion of the radar beam creates relative motion, as shown in Fig. 5.1b, along with the detection threshold for the target, which is crucial for accurately detecting and identifying aerial objects. This combination of scanning dynamics and signal processing techniques is essential for optimizing radar performance in complex airspace environments.

5.1.2 Phased Array Weighting

When a plane wave strikes an antenna array, the phase of the signal at each antenna depends on the angle at which the wave arrives. When these signals are combined, they can either add constructively or destructively, based on their respective phases. Applying a complex phase shift (the weights of the phased array) to each antenna's signal, which counteracts the phase change caused by wave propagation, allows them to be summed coherently when combined. This process is the fundamental principle underlying the operation of phased arrays. The phased weighting scheme is considered the simplest among all weighting methods.

5.1.3 Adaptive Weighting Algorithm

Adaptive weighting algorithms recalibrate their weights based on the signals they receive to enhance the array's performance. One example of such an algorithm is the

Least Mean Squares (LMS) algorithm [14, 15]. This algorithm incrementally updates the weights by moving toward the negative gradient of the Mean Square Error (MSE) function. Following this negative gradient reduces the overall MSE with each time step. In this chapter, we will implement beam steering using a spatially tuned filter, where the weights are adjusted based on the angle of observation.

5.2 Capon's Method

This method is historically the oldest approach [16, 17]. We focus on traditional beamforming with Capon, also known as minimum-variance distortionless response beamforming, for estimating direction. It has been demonstrated that any vector-sensor array, such as the widely used linear array, can accurately and distinctly determine the direction of arrival (DOA). Additionally, we highlight that the challenges of the Capon method have been addressed in the Spatial Tuned Filter, as detailed in Sect. 5.4.2 of this chapter.

5.2.1 *Capon Spectrum*

The Capon method is closely related to the Linear Prediction (LP) method used in parameter estimation and has roots in spectral analysis. To better understand the Capon method, it is helpful to review Eqs. (5.15) and (5.16), which utilize the covariance matrix $\mathbf{H}$ to obtain the Direction of Arrival (DOA) spectrum $J(\theta)$. It is important to note that the weighting vector $\mathbf{c}$ remains constant in the Capon method, and this was chosen as $1 + 0.5\sin(2\pi\frac{i}{m})$ for $i = 1 \ldots m$ by Peter Stoica [18]. The Capon estimates of the DOA θ correspond to the locations of the minor minima or prominent maxima of the following function,

$$J(\theta) = \mathbf{a}^{*T}\mathbf{H}^{-1}\mathbf{a}(z)\Big|_{\varphi=2\pi\frac{d}{\lambda}\sin\theta} \text{ in case of maximization we use } \boxed{\mathbf{a}^{*T}\mathbf{H}\mathbf{a}(z)\Big|_{\varphi=2\pi\frac{d}{\lambda}\sin\theta}} \tag{5.1}$$

Evaluated over the domain of interest. Here, $\mathbf{H} = \mathbf{S}^{*T}\mathbf{S}$ represents the covariance matrix. This method requires a larger array size compared to the STF, and most importantly, the problem area spectrum has many peaks. The choice of the weighting vector, such as the Hanning window, would reduce the ripple; however, the demand for array size remains unchanged. Figure 5.2 shows the STF spectrum and Capon Spectrum at an SNR of –10dB. The demand for a higher number of sensing elements is evident in Fig. 5.6.

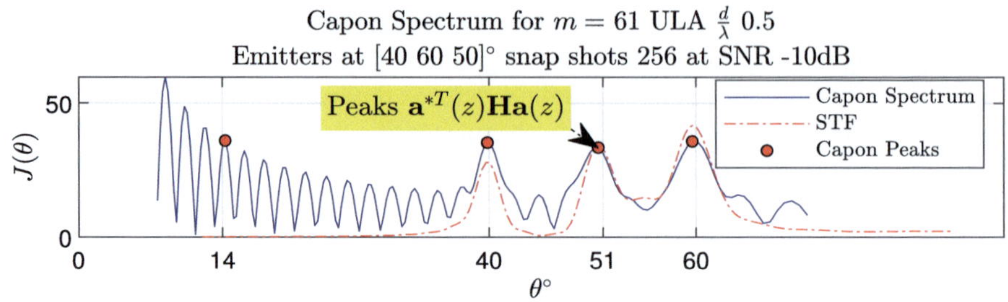

Fig. 5.2 Capon spectrum as in Eq. 5.1

5.3 Squint Beams and Adcock/Watson-Watt

Before World War II, various vintage techniques [19] were employed for communication and radar frequencies. Significant research took place in both New York and Tokyo. The method of direction finding for communication frequencies is well explained by Terman [20], specifically the Watson-Watt method, which utilizes the Adcock antenna system [21]. In this approach, target signals are received in two beams separated by a slight angle, as described by Sharenson [22]. The twin beams are produced using a Cassegrain antenna system [23].

In the Watson-Watt method, the received signals can be expressed as

$$x(t) = g\frac{D}{\lambda}m(t)\cos\theta \text{ and } y(t) = g\frac{D}{\lambda}m(t)\sin\theta \text{ where } m(t) \text{ low frequency demodulation} \tag{5.2}$$

The plot of $x(t)$ and $y(t)$ on an oscilloscope reveals the signal's direction as shown in Fig. 5.3a. This method involves analog computation, which requires extensive calibration. The constant g is a factor that depends on the type of modulation and circuit parameters, while the term $\frac{D}{\lambda}$ represents the antenna configuration and frequency-dependent characteristics. In the early days, Rhode and Schwartz developed the direction finding (DF) system based on this principle. The twin beam technique is primarily used in monopulse radar for tracking purposes. This technique utilizes sum and difference channels for angular tracking; a typical sum and difference is shown in Fig. 5.3b and c.

5.4 Weighted Beam Steering

In this method, we determine the Uniform Linear Array (ULA) weights to maximize energy in the direction of the search, represented by θ. This method is a marked improvement over Capon's method, as shown in Fig. 5.2. Using real coefficients for weights reduces range from $-90°$ to $-90°$. Over the past few decades, the directions of arrival (DOA) for narrowband signals have been computed using super-resolution

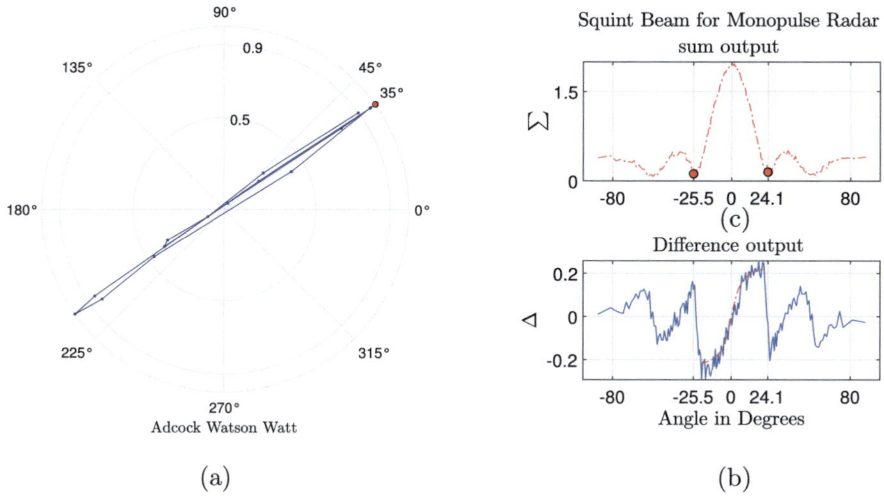

Fig. 5.3 Monopulse radar and adcock watson watt

algorithms, as discussed in [24, 25]. This section introduces a competing concept of a Spatial Tuned Filter (STF) for determining the DOA of narrowband signals.

5.4.1 Two Step Approach

Determining the Direction of Arrival (DOA) involves two main steps. In the first step, we conduct coarse beam steering to estimate the approximate locations of the emitters. In the second step, we utilize a non-gradient gold section univariate minimization method to address the min-max problem. This allows us to achieve a more accurate estimate of the DOA.

5.4.2 Spatial Tuned Filter (STF)

We connect the temporal domain filter to the spatial domain filter using the award-winning paper [26]. Spectral Angular Frequency ω is mapped into φ, the phase shift due to spatial sampling. The Spatial Tuned Filter (STF) refers to an autoregressive (AR) second-order filter that operates in the spatial dimension, i.e., across the indices $1, 2, \ldots, m$ of sensors in a ULA. The STF output is maximized when the spatial angle corresponds to an emitter's DOA. Therefore, the AR(2) filter is IIR and cannot be realized in the spatial domain. However, we derive an equivalent FIR filter, obtaining coefficients $c_1, c_2, \ldots, c_m$. These coefficients are used as weights for beam steering. Consider an AR(2) narrow-band filter given by the following difference equation:

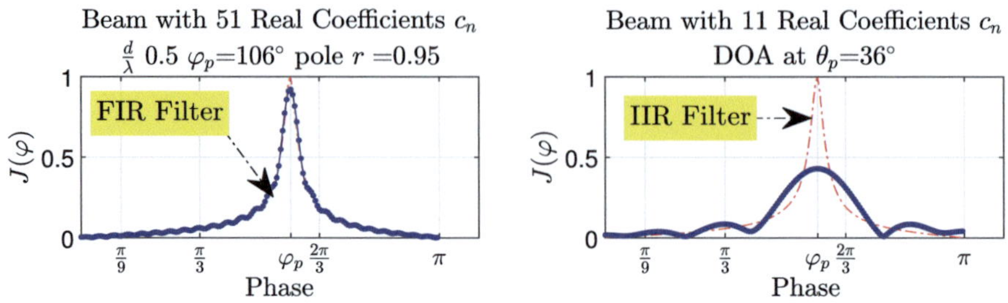

Fig. 5.4 IIR filter Eq. 5.3 to FIR filter Eqs. 5.7 and 5.8

$$x_k = rpx_{k-1} - r^2x_{k-2} + g(u_k - u_{k-2}) \tag{5.3}$$

where r is the pole position. For stability, r is chosen such that $|r| < 1$. The gain is given by $g = \frac{1-r^2}{2}$. The frequency response peaks [7] at φ_p given as

$$\varphi_p = \cos^{-1}\left(0.25p\left[r + \frac{1}{r}\right]\right)$$

u_k is the input sequence and x_k is the output sequence. $p = 2\cos\varphi$ for some angle φ. The values of r and φ determine the *impulse response* of the filter (Fig. 5.4).

5.4.3 Spatial Filter Using AR (2) Process

Spatial equivalent of this Infinite Impulse Response (IIR) filter as in Eq. 5.3 cannot be realized in this form. We get an equivalent Finite Impulse Response (FIR) filter [16, 18], which can be implemented using a ULA. Equation (5.3) can be rewritten using the delay (z^{-1}) operator as

$$x_k = \frac{g(1 - z^{-2})}{(1 - rpz^{-1} + r^2z^{-2})}u_k = \frac{g(z^2 - 1)}{(z - \alpha)(z - \beta)}u_k \tag{5.4}$$

where α and β are *complex conjugates* as

$$(\alpha, \beta) = \frac{r}{2}[p \pm \sqrt{p^2 - 4}] = re^{\pm j\varphi} \tag{5.5}$$

Using α and β, Eq. (5.4) can be expressed as

$$x_k = \frac{(1 - r^2)(z^3 - z)\sum_{n=1}^{\infty}(\alpha^n - \beta^n)z^{-n}}{2(\alpha - \beta)}u_k \tag{5.6}$$

We can re-write Eq. (5.6) as

$$x_k = \sum_{n=1}^{\infty} c_n u_{k-n}$$

.

$$c_1 = \frac{1-r^2}{2} \quad c_2 = \frac{1-r^2}{2}(\alpha+\beta) \tag{5.7}$$

and for $n > 2$.

$$c_n = \frac{1-r^2}{2\sin\varphi} r^{(n-3)}(r^2 \sin n\varphi - \sin((n-2)\varphi)) \tag{5.8}$$

It is evident that all the coefficients are real since α and β are complex conjugates. We truncate this series to match the length of the ULA. The coefficient vector $\mathbf{c}$ can be written as

$$\mathbf{c}^T(\varphi) = [c_1, c_2 z^{-1}, c_2 z^{-2} \ldots c_m z^{-m+1}] \text{ or } \mathbf{c}^T(\theta) \text{ or } \mathbf{c}^T(z)$$

where z^{-1} is the spatial delay operator.

5.4.4 *Signal Model*

We assume that the signals received at the ULA are coherent, narrowband signals sharing the same center frequency.

$$\varphi^i_m = m \times \varphi^i \text{ where } \varphi^i = 2\pi \frac{d}{\lambda} \sin\theta_i$$

$$s_k^{m\varphi^i} = A_k^i \left[\underbrace{\cos(2\pi f_n k + \varphi^i_m)}_{\tilde{s}_k^{m\varphi^i}} \right] \tag{5.9}$$

$$s_k^{m\varphi} = \sum_i^D s_k^{m\varphi^i} = \boxed{a_k[e^{j\varphi}]^m = a_k z^{-m}} \tag{5.10}$$

$$\text{where } e^{j\varphi} = z^{-1} \text{ spatial delay operator}$$

$$\begin{aligned} \mathbf{s}_k &= [s_k \; s_k^{\varphi} \; s_k^{2\varphi} \; s_k^{3\varphi} \; s_k^{4\varphi}] \\ &= s_k[1 \; z^{-1} \; z^{-2} \; z^{-3} \; z^{-4}] = s_k \mathbf{a}^T(z) \end{aligned} \tag{5.11}$$

The signals discussed are narrowband and coherent, as described in Eq. 5.9. Equation 5.10 represents the sum of D narrowband signals, which corresponds to the sum of phasors incident on each sensor element. This means that all signals share the same frequency, $f_p = 0.1$, as depicted in Fig. 5.5b. In Fig. 5.5c, we notice two signals, $s_k^{(1)}$ and $s_k^{(2)}$, at two adjacent sensor elements. Although they share the same frequency,

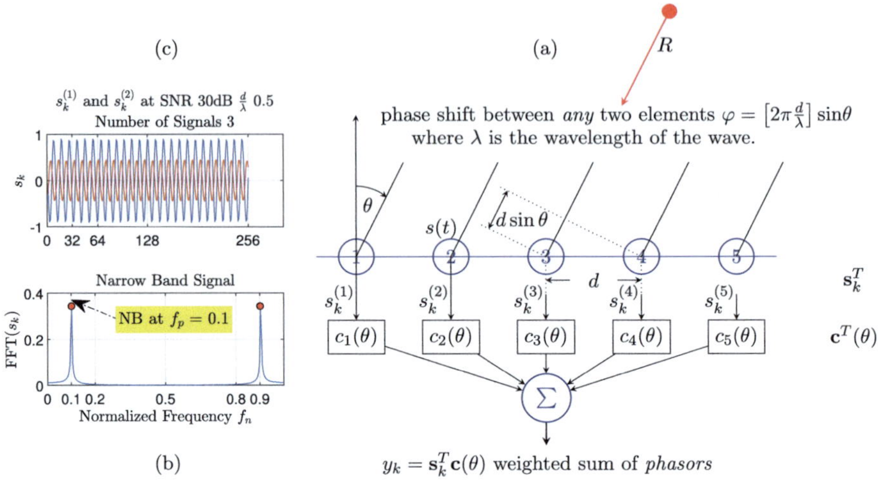

Fig. 5.5 Understanding beam steering

their amplitudes differ because of the additive nature of the signals described in Eq. 5.10, with varying phases. Spatial sampling by the Uniform Linear Array (ULA) is described by Eq. 5.11 and is mathematically represented as the spatial sampling vector $\mathbf{a}^T(z)$.

5.5 Beam-Steering Using STF

Consider the Uniform Linear Array (ULA) depicted in Fig. 5.5a. The array comprises five isotropic antenna elements. A narrowband emitter with a center frequency of f_c strikes the ULA at an angle θ. We define a snapshot at the kth instant in time as follows:

$$\mathbf{s}_k = [s_k^1, s_k^2, \ldots s_k^m]^T \tag{5.12}$$

The relationship between the phase shift, φ, and the angle of arrival, θ, for a Uniform Linear Array (ULA) is expressed by the equation $\varphi = 2\pi\frac{d}{\lambda}\sin\theta$. In this equation, λ represents the wavelength corresponding to the carrier frequency f_c, and d is the spacing between the antenna elements in the ULA. The coefficients derived from Eqs. (5.7) and (5.8) as functions of θ are represented as $\mathbf{c}(\theta) = [c_1, c_2, \ldots, c_m]^T$. The Spatial Tuned Filter (STF) is depicted in Fig. 5.5. The output of the STF is:

$$y_k(\theta) = \mathbf{s}_k^T\mathbf{c}(\theta) \tag{5.13}$$

Let N be the number of snapshots. We define the *data matrix* $\mathbf{S} = [\mathbf{s}_1, \mathbf{s}_2, \ldots, \mathbf{s}_N]$, which has a size of $m \times N$. The energy $\sum y_k^2$ is calculated using Eq. 5.14 for a specific spatial angle θ.

$$\sum_{k=1}^{N} y_k^2 = \mathbf{c}(\theta)^T \left(\sum_{k=1}^{N} \mathbf{s}_k \mathbf{s}_k^T \right) \mathbf{c}(\theta) \tag{5.14}$$

5.5.1 Cost Function

The energy spectrum $J(\theta)$, and this can be written using Eq. 5.14 as

$$J(\theta) = \mathbf{c}(\theta)^t \mathbf{H}\mathbf{c}(\theta) \text{ where } \mathbf{H} = \sum_{k=1}^{N} \mathbf{s}_k \mathbf{s}_k^T \text{ is the covarinace matrix} \tag{5.15}$$

We can visualize Eq. 5.15 by expressing $\mathbf{H}$ as $[\mathbf{v}_1 \ldots \mathbf{v}_i \ldots \mathbf{v}_m]$, where $\mathbf{v}_i$ are the column vectors of the covariance matrix $\mathbf{H}$. This creates a symmetric matrix with correlation coefficients R_τ.

$$J(\theta) = \sum_{i=1}^{m} |h_i(z)| \Big|_{\varphi = 2\pi \frac{d}{\lambda} \sin\theta} \quad \text{where } h_i(z) = |\mathbf{v}_i^T \mathbf{c}(z)| \tag{5.16}$$

5.5.2 Peaks of Energy Spectrum

The Eq. 5.16 for $h_i(z)$ describes a transversal filter. The magnitude frequency responses from all columns are combined to create $J(\theta)$. Since all coefficients are real numbers, $J(\theta)$ is an even function. Beam steering is achieved by calculating the angle $\varphi = 2\pi \left(\frac{d}{\lambda}\right) \sin\theta$ for a given angle θ. The steering vector $\mathbf{c}(\theta)$ is then derived using Eqs. (5.7) and (5.8). The function $J(\theta)$, which represents the energy spectrum, is illustrated in Fig. 5.6. It shows several distinct peaks corresponding to the number of emitters, marked by red solid circles. The position of each peak indicates a direction of arrival (DOA). We can accurately estimate these peaks using the proposed algorithm as DOA values. It is important to note that the function $J(\theta)$ is even and has a period of π, as shown in Fig. 5.6. Due to this property, the DOA can be identified within the range $[0, \frac{\pi}{2}]$ using a single uniform linear array (ULA) of size $m = 21$.

5.6 3-ULA Topology

To get the full coverage, we employ the 3-ULA configuration as given in Fig. 5.7 to find DOA in the range $[-\frac{\pi}{2}, +\frac{\pi}{2}]$. The signals are modeled taking into account the geometry. We have considered two types of NB signals at the center of the ULA system, O, in our simulation, given by

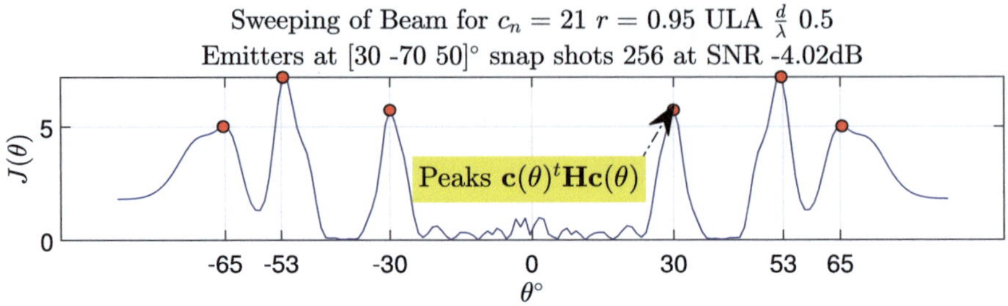

Fig. 5.6 Energy spectrum $J(\theta)$ given by Eq. 5.15

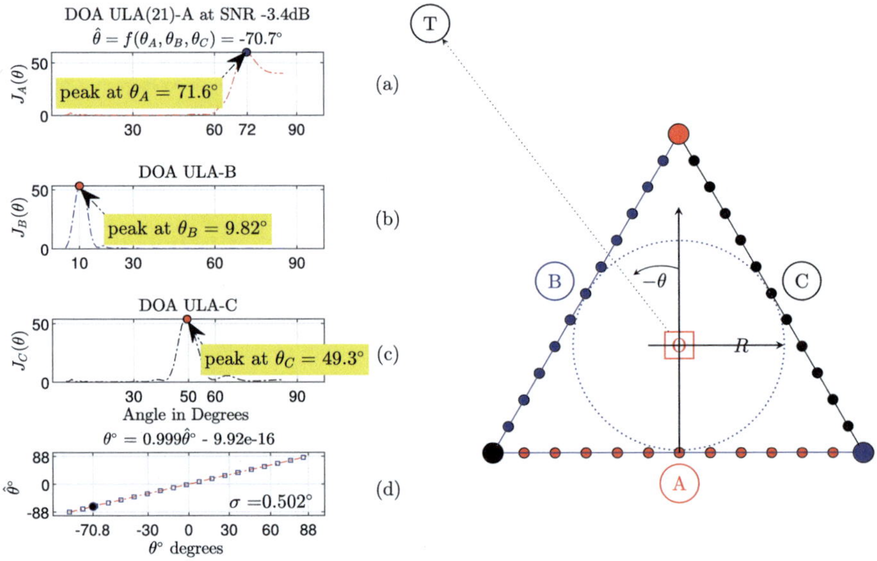

Fig. 5.7 3-ULA topology covering $-\frac{\pi}{2}$ to $\frac{\pi}{2}$ using single ULA Fig. 5.5

$$
\begin{aligned}
s_O &= A_s \sin(2\pi f_n k + \phi_0) + \gamma_k^O \\
s_O &= A_s \sin(2\pi f_n k + \phi_0) + A_m \sin(2\pi f_m k) + \gamma_k^O
\end{aligned}
\tag{5.17}
$$

where ϕ_0 is an initial arbitrary phase and γ_k^O is a zero mean White Gaussian Noise of $N(0, \sigma^2)$. Let f_n be the normalized frequency and $k = 1, 2, 3, \ldots, N$. The DOA concerning *true North*, which is the same as normal to ULA$_A$, is θ_s. The signals received at m^{th} sensor of ULAs as in Eq. 5.12 A, B, and C due to D emitters are given as

$$s_m^A(k) = \sum_{s=1}^{D} A_s \sin(2\pi f_n k + \phi_A^m(s)) \tag{5.18}$$

$$s_m^B(k) = \sum_{s=1}^{D} A_s \sin(2\pi f_n k + \phi_B^m(s)) \text{ and } s_m^C(k) = \sum_{s=1}^{D} A_s \sin(2\pi f_n k + \phi_C^m(s)) \tag{5.19}$$

The phases in Eqs. 5.18 and 5.19 $\phi_A^m(s)$, $\phi_B^m(s)$ and $\phi_C^m(s)$ are functions of $\frac{d}{\lambda}$, $\frac{R}{\lambda}$, θ_s and m. Solely based on the *geometric* properties, a simple trigonometric formulation can be arrived at easily as follows:

$$\phi_A^m(s) = A_m \sin\theta_s + \boxed{2\pi\frac{R}{\lambda}\cos\theta_s}$$

$$\phi_B^m(s) = A_m \sin\left(\theta_s + \frac{\pi}{3}\right) - \boxed{2\pi\frac{R}{\lambda}\cos\left(\theta_s + \frac{\pi}{3}\right)}$$

$$\phi_C^m(s) = A_m \sin\left(\theta_s - \frac{\pi}{3}\right) + \boxed{2\pi\frac{R}{\lambda}\cos\left(\theta_s - \frac{\pi}{3}\right)}$$

where A_m is given as $A_m = 2\pi\frac{d}{\lambda}(m - \lfloor\frac{m}{2}\rfloor)$, we assume m is the same odd number of elements in each ULA. The quantities in the boxed region contribute only as a constant phase and do not vary with the element number, so they do not affect the DOA accuracy. The accuracy and resolving power of DOA is dependent on the choice of *pole position* r, $\frac{d}{\lambda}$, and M.

5.6.1 DOA from Multiple Peaks

The objective function $J(\theta)$ as given by Eq. (5.15) peaks at each DOA. Using *Gold Section Univariate* (GSU) minimisation technique, peaks are located very accurately. Using the 3-ULA topology and GSU method, we obtain the peaks of $J_A(\theta)$, $J_B(\theta)$, and $J_C(\theta)$ in the interval $[0, \frac{\pi}{2}]$. The number of peaks in each function may not be the same. The union of all peaks positions are given as

$$\Theta = \{\theta_a^1, \theta_a^2 \ldots, \theta_a^I, |\theta_b^1, \theta_b^2 \ldots, \theta_b^J, |\theta_c^1, \theta_c^2 \ldots, \theta_c^K\}$$

Any peak pair $< \theta_i, \theta_j >$ for $i \neq j$ Is a member of the cartesian product $\Theta \times \Theta$. Using a simple logic based on the expected geometric relationship between angles in $\Theta \times \Theta$, we are Able to identify the accurate DOA angles in the range $[-90°, +90°]$.

5.6.2 Single Emitter

Figure 5.7 illustrates the Direction of Arrival (DOA) estimation for a single emitter by combining the spectra from 3-ULA. The target T, shown in Fig. 5.7, moves from –90 to +90° around the 3-ULA system depicted in Fig. 5.7. At a specific angle of $\theta = 70.8°$, indicated by the blue solid circle in Fig. 5.7d, the spectra are captured and presented in sub-figures (a), (b), and (c) of Fig. 5.7. As mentioned earlier, a coarse sweep of three Uniform Linear Arrays (ULAs), labeled A, B, and C, is conducted, generating the functions $J_A(\theta)$, $J_B(\theta)$, and $J_C(\theta)$ (as shown in Eq. 5.15). These functions are illustrated in sub-figures (a), (b), and (c) of Fig. 5.7. The Gold Section Univariate (GSU) method is then employed to pinpoint the exact peak, as indicated in the subfigures (a, b, c), highlighted in yellow. This method is explained in detail in the previous Sect. 2.10.5.

Using a coarse peak interval $[\theta_a, \theta_b]$ around any coarse peak θ, the exact peak is determined for each ULA as given in Fig. 4.9. A peak vector $\Theta = [71.6°, 9.82°, 49.3°]$ is obtained from all 3-ULAs and are shown Fig. 5.7(a, b, c), leading to a DOA estimate of $-70.7°$ in the interval $[-90°, +90°]$, as illustrated in Fig. 5.7a. As the target T is traversed, covering the range –90 to 90, the estimate is shown as a straight line.

$$\theta = 0.999\hat{\theta} - 9.92 \times 10^{-16}$$

In the subfigure (d). The slope is very close to unity, and the intercept is close to zero. The signal under analysis is a narrowband signal with additive noise modeled as in Eq. 5.17 at a signal-to-noise ratio (SNR) of -3 dB. The DOA estimate has a standard deviation σ of 0.5°.

5.6.3 Combining 3-ULA Peaks

Combining the 3-ULA peaks can be better understood by referring to the Fig. 5.8. Each ULA peak is divided into three bands as given in the first row of the table. Peaks can be any of these bands. In Fig. 5.6(a, b, c), θ_a has a weight of 3 since it is in band 3, θ_b is in band one and has a weightage of 1, and θ_c is in the mid-band with a weightage of two. This combination is in zone 32 = $(3\times 9 + 1\times 3 + 2)$. We can see in Fig. 5.8d that there are six zones (32, 24, 18, 20, 28, 34); the rest are not valid zones. In zone 32 we use the θ_c value to construct the output as $\hat{\theta} = 49.3 - 120$ which is equal to –70.7. The total logic is presented in Table 5.1 for reference in conjunction with Fig. 5.8d.

Three emitters were considered with equal power at 40°, $-70°$, and $+50°$ *wrt* true north. The 3-ULA output is shown in Fig. 5.8. Peaks were estimated using GSU and using the peak vector Θ. DOA is estimated as $-31.32°$, -71.618, and $+54.99°$ at an SNR of 0 dB for an NB signal.

Table 5.1 Full Azimuth Coverage

Band	$60 < \theta_{a,b,c} < 90$		$\psi = 30 < \theta_{a,b,c} < 60$		$0 < \theta_{a,b,c} < 30$	
Weight $w^{\theta}_{a,b,c}$	3		2		1	
Compute zone	$w^{\theta}_a \times 9 + w^{\theta}_b \times 3 + w^{\theta}_c \times 1$					
Zone	34	24	18	20	28	34
$\hat{\theta}$	$\psi - 120$	$-\psi$	$\psi - 60$	$\psi + 60$	ψ	$120 - \psi$
Sign of $\hat{\theta}$	Negative			Positive		

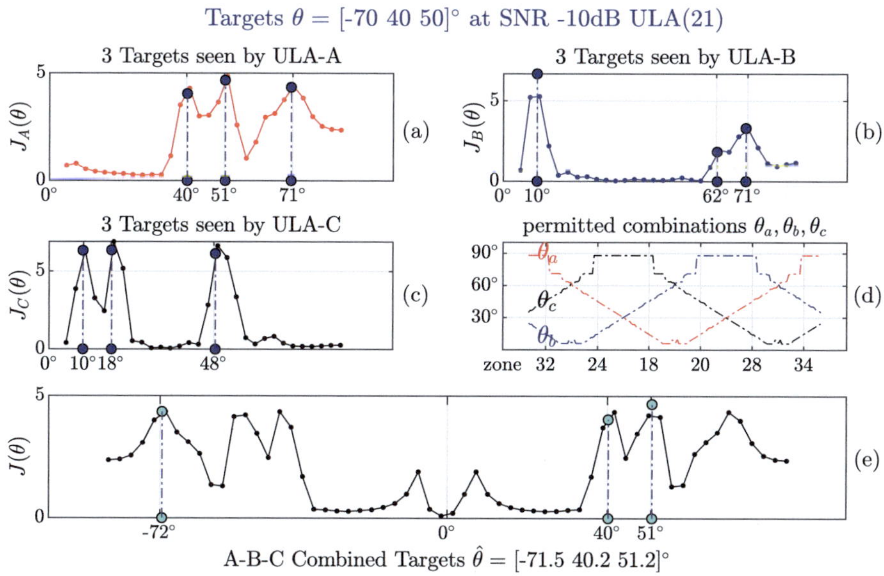

Fig. 5.8 Beam steering multiple targets 3-ULA

5.6.4 Rotation Matrix Method

In this method, peaks are transformed to the base ULA by a rotation matrix.

$$\begin{bmatrix} x \\ y \end{bmatrix} = \begin{bmatrix} \cos\theta_{rot} & -\sin\theta_{rot} \\ -\sin\theta_{rot} & \cos\theta_{rot} \end{bmatrix} \begin{bmatrix} \cos\theta_b \\ \sin\theta_b \end{bmatrix} \tag{5.20}$$

And then they are combined. As an example we transform the peaks θ_b from ULA-B to A using $\theta_{rot} = -60°$ in Eq. 5.20 we obtain

$$\boxed{\theta_{b2a} = \tan^{-1}\left(\frac{x}{y}\right) - 90°}$$

Table 5.2 Azimuth coverage by rotation matrix method

Band	$\theta_a \leq 60$		$\theta_a > 60°$	
Test	$\lvert\theta_a - \theta_{b2a}\rvert < \delta$	$\lvert\theta_a - \theta_{c2a}\rvert < \delta$	$\theta_{b2a} > \theta_{c2a}$	$\theta_{c2a} > \theta_{b2a}$
Estimate $\hat{\theta}$	$-\theta_a$	θ_a	$-\theta_{c2a} - 60$	$\theta_{b2a} + 60$
Sign of $\hat{\theta}$	Negative	Positive	Negative	Positive

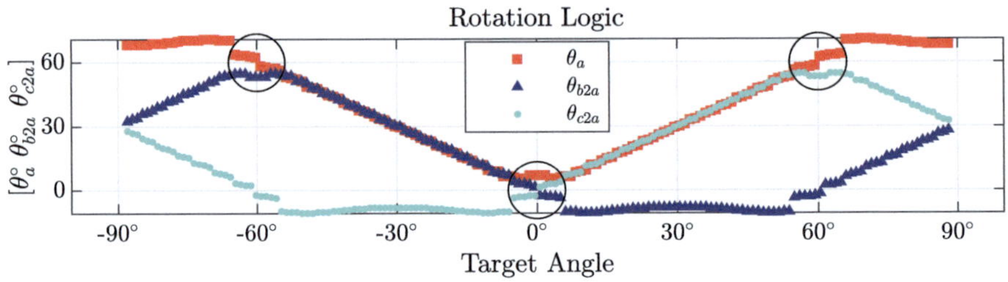

Fig. 5.9 Rotation of peaks for $J(\theta)$ Eq. 5.20

Similarly we obtain θ_{c2a} as using $\theta_{rot} = 60°$ and

$$\boxed{\theta_{c2a} = \tan^{-1}\left(\frac{x}{y}\right) + 30°}$$

In the case of ULA-C to A. Readers should note that our reference is based on the normal ULA-A as shown in Fig. 5.7.

The logic in this case is elementary with states (Table 5.2). This method yields far superior performance and can resolve the critical zones circled in Fig. 5.9.

5.6.5 *Performance*

Figure 5.10 summarizes the algorithm's overall performance. For testing and evaluation, we set $f_n = \frac{1}{10}$ and observed that its impact is nearly negligible. The pole position r was selected as 0.95, the inter-element spacing $\frac{d}{\lambda}$ was set to 0.5, and the radial spacing of Uniform Linear Arrays (ULAs) $\frac{R}{\lambda}$ was chosen to be 15.2. The Signal-to-Noise Ratio (SNR) for a pure tone with White Gaussian Noise (WGN) is defined as $20\log_{10}\left(\frac{A_s}{\sqrt{2}\sigma}\right)$ where A_s is the amplitude of the NB signal and σ is the standard deviation of the noise. The algorithm was evaluated across a range from –10 dB to +10 dB for two signal types, and the results are impressive, showing that σ is less than 1° above 0 dB. In the worst case, it remains below 1.5°, performing competitively with high-resolution algorithms. This beam-steering approach estimates the Direction of Arrival (DOA) using a Spatial Tuned Filter (STF), for which we have

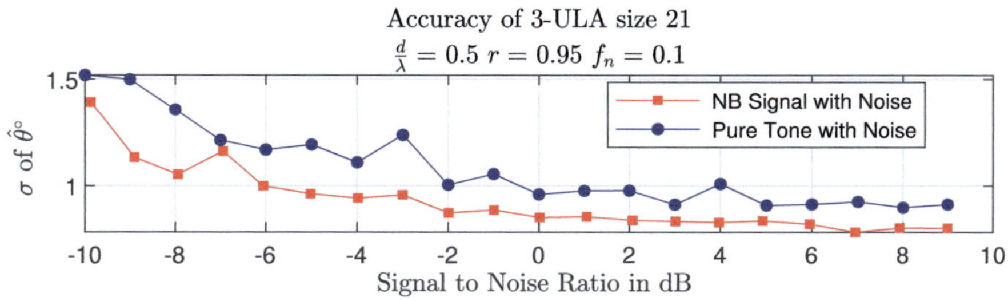

Fig. 5.10 Integrated beam steering performance with signal as in Eq. 5.17

derived the filter coefficients for a Finite Impulse Response (FIR) filter. The maxima of the energy spectrum, obtained by passing the signals from a ULA through the STF, correspond to the angles at which the signals arrive. We identify these peaks and the corresponding DOA values through gold-section univariate minimization without gradients. The results obtained are accurate across a range of SNR values.

5.7 Summary

The Spatial Tuned Filter (STF) beam-steering method accurately estimates the Direction of Arrival (DOA). This approach utilizes a Spatial Tuned Filter, obtaining the coefficients of a Uniform Linear Array (ULA) from those of an Infinite Impulse Response (IIR) filter. These coefficients serve as weights in the covariance matrix, while the weighting function is determined as a closed-form solution for each angle θ. The maxima of the energy spectrum generated by passing signals through a Uniform Linear Array (ULA) with the STF correspond to the angles at which the signals arrive. We identify these peaks and their corresponding DOA values using gold-section univariate minimization without gradients. The results are accurate across various Signal-to-Noise Ratio (SNR) levels. Overall, the performance of the STF method is comparable to that of subspace methods, demonstrating both robustness and a reduced requirement for the number of spatial sampling elements, m. The limitation of a single ULA with real coefficients, which used to restrict the spatial angle to a range from 0 to $\frac{\pi}{2}$, has now been extended to the full range by employing 3-ULA topology, along with a generic algorithm that applies to any method.

5.7.1 MEX File Generation

The C source files and MATLAB scripts used to generate MEX files in Chap. 4 are Located in two directories: `chap5\figures\stfMexCode` and `chap5\figures \stfBeamSteer\stfBeamSteer`. Each MATLAB `.m` file includes a `mex` compile directive that links the relevant C source code to produce a corresponding MEX file for use in MATLAB. A total of six MEX files are generated in this chapter. The following table presents the generated `.mex` files in the first column, the location of the C source files in the second column, and the MATLAB `.ms` Files containing the `mex` commands in the third column.

This chapter C files for MEX		
MEX File	Location of C Files	Command
abcUla.mexw64	chap5\figures\stfMexCode	myMexAbcUla.m
stfSweep.mexw64	chap5\figures\stfMexCode	myMexStfSweep.m
coef.mexw64	chap5\figures\stfMexCode	myMexCoef.m
map3ulaR.mexw64	chap5\figures\stfBeamSteer\stfBeamSteer	myMexMap3UlaR.m
stfSweepDoa.mexw64	chap5\figures\stfBeamSteer\stfBeamSteer	myMexStfSweepDoa.m
map3ulaS.mexw64	chap5\figures\stfBeamSteer\stfBeamSteer	myMexMap3UlaS.m

5.7.2 File Organization

This subsection lists program files related to the chapter *Beam Steering Techniques*. The table below shows these files and their respective directories. With directory names highlighted in yellow at the top of each column. These directories include `fig3Targets` , `figSweepBeam`, `figTriUlaStf`, `figFirIirBeam`, `fig SnrEror`, `figAdcock`, `figFanBeam`, `figHeteroThese`, `figCapon`. These programs support the implementation and analysis of beam steering algorithms Discussed in this chapter. The code is available separately in the repository and It is not embedded in the book.

This chapter program files				
fig3Targets	figSweepBeam	figTriUlaStf	figFirIirBeam	figSnrEror
abcUla.mexw64	abcUla.mexw64	abcUla.mexw64	coef.mexw64	abcUla.mexw64
ds2nfu.m	coef.mexw64	coef.mexw64	ds2nfu.m	ds2nfu.m
fig3Targets.eps	ds2nfu.m	data.xlsx	figFirIirBeam.eps	fig3Tgts.m
fig3Targets.m	figSweepBeam.eps	ds2nfu.m	figFirIirBeam.m	figRot.eps
logicFor3.m	figSweepBeam.m	figRangeExpand.m	Iir2Fir.m	figRot.m
map3ulaS.mexw64	figUlaSig.eps	figTriUlaStf.eps	labelSubplot.m	figSnrEror.eps
mergeLogic.m	labelSweep.m	figTriUlaStf.m		figSnrEror.m
stfSweep.mexw64	labelUla.m	labelABC.m		figSnrSweep.m
stfSweepDoa.mexw64	stfSweep.mexw64	map3ulaS.mexw64		map3ulaR.mexw64
theta3ToPhi.m	stfSweepDoa.mexw64	stfSweepDoa.mexw64		mergeLogic.m
ulaPlot.m			figCapon	rotUla.m
			abcUla.mexw64	snrFig.mat
figAdcock	figFanBeam	figHetero	ds2nfu.m	stfSweepDoa.mexw64
figAdcock.eps	ds2nfu.m	ds2nfu.m	figCapon.eps	tstPksFixed.m
figAdcock.m	figFanbeam.eps	figHetero.eps	figCapon.m	
figSqnt.eps	figFanbeam.m	figHetero.m	labelCapon.m	
polarDS2nfu.m			stfSweepDoa.mexw64	

References

1. B. Widrow, P. E. Mantey, L. J. Griffiths and B. B. Goode, *Adaptive antenna systems*, in Proceedings of the IEEE, vol. 55, no. 12, pp. 2143–2159, 1967
2. L. J. Griffiths, *Adaptive monopulse beamforming*, in Proceedings of the IEEE, vol. 64, no. 8, pp. 1260–1261, 1976.
3. L. J. Giffiths, *A simple adaptive algorithm for real-time processing in antenna arrays*, Roc. IEEE, vol. 57, pp. 1696–1704, 1969.
4. A. J. Berni, *Angle-of-Arrival Estimation Using an Adaptive Antenna Array*, in IEEE Transactions on Aerospace and Electronic Systems, vol. AES-11, no. 2, pp. 278–284, 1975.
5. T. B. Vu and M. Rathinam, *Direction finding with null steering at baseband using digital signal processors: a computer simulation*, 1988 IEEE AP-S. International Symposium, Antennas and Propagation, Syracuse, NY, USA, 1988, pp. 254–257 vol.1.
6. J. E. Evans, *Aperture Sampling Techniques for Precision Direction Finding*, in IEEE Transactions on Aerospace and Electronic Systems, vol. AES-15, no. 6, pp. 891–895, 1979.
7. L. C. -L. Yuan, *Ultra-High-Frequency Radiosonde Direction Finding*, in Proceedings of the IRE, vol. 34, no. 11, pp. 852–857, 1946.
8. R. Ma and X. Y. Zhang, *A Mechanically Rotating Antenna Used in Direction-Finding Systems on Unmanned Aerial Vehicles*, 2022 International Conference on Microwave and Millimeter Wave Technology (ICMMT), Harbin, China, 2022, pp.
9. N. K. Bose and C. R. Rao, eds., Chap 16, A. Paulraj, B. Ottersten, R. Roy, A. Swindlehurst, G. Xu and T. Kailath, *Subspace Methods for Directions-of-Arrival Estimation*, Handbook of Statistics, Vol. 10, 1993 Elsevier Science Publishers.
10. Merrill I. Skolnik, *Introduction to Radar Systems* Mc graw-Hill Publishing company, New York, 1990.
11. Paul. A. Lynn, Radar systems, Mc.Millan, 1994.
12. Nadav, Levanon, *Radar principles*, A Wiley Interscience publication, U.S.A, 1988.
13. S.A Hovanessian, *Radar system Design and Analysis* Artech House, INC, Norwood, 1984. London, 1983.
14. B. Widrow, *Adaptive filters I: Fundamentals*, Stanford Electronics Labs., Stanford, Calif., Rept. SEL-66-126 ('Tech. Rept. 6764-6), 1966.
15. J. S. Koford and G. F. Groner, *The use of an adaptive threshold element to design a linear optimal pattern classifier*, IEEE Trans. Informtion Theory, vol. IT-12, pp. 42–50, 1966.
16. P. Handel, P. Stoica and T. Soderstrom, *Capon method for doa estimation: accuracy and robustness aspects*, IEEE Winter Workshop on Nonlinear Digital Signal Processing, Tampere, Finland, 1993, pp. P7.1–P7.5.

17. P. Stoica, Zhisong Wang and J. Li, Robust Capon beamforming, Conference Record of the Thirty-Sixth Asilomar Conference on Signals, Systems and Computers, 2002., Pacific Grove, CA, USA, 2002, pp. 876–880 vol.1.
18. J. Capon; *High resolution frequency-wavenumber spectrum analysis*, Proc. IEEE, Vol. 57, No. 8, 1969.
19. S. Namba, E. Iso and S. Ueno, *Polarization of High-Frequency Waves and Their Direction Finding*, in Proceedings of the Institute of Radio Engineers, vol. 19, no. 11, p. 2000–2019, 1931.
20. F. E. Terman and J. M. Pettit, *The Compensated-Loop Direction Finder*, in Proceedings of the IRE, vol. 33, no. 5, pp. 307–318, 1945.
21. A. D. Bailey and W. C. McClure, *A Sum-and-Difference Interferometer System for HF Radio Direction Finding*, in IEEE Transactions on Aerospace and Navigational Electronics, vol. ANE-10, no. 1, pp. 65–72, 1963.
22. S. Sharenson, *Angle Estimation Accuracy with a Monopulse Radar in the Search Mode*, in IRE Transactions on Aerospace and Navigational Electronics, vol. ANE-9, no. 3, pp. 175–179, 1962.
23. R. Martin and L. Schwartzman, *A monopulse Cassegrainian antenna*, 1958 IRE International Convention Record, New York, NY, USA, 1960, pp. 96–102.
24. Ralph. O. Schmidt; *Multiple Signal Location and Signal Parameter Estimation* IEEE Trans. on Antennas and Propagation, Vol. AP-34, NO. 3 1986, pp 276–279.
25. Anthony J. Weiss and Benjamin Friedlander; *Direction Finding for Diversely Polarized Signals Using Polynomial Rooting* IEEE Trans. SP, 1993, 41, (5).
26. Kaluri V. Rangarao, Shridhar V., V. Prathyusha, T. Neela Pavani; *Estimating the Directions of Arrival of Narrow Band Signals using Spatial Tuned Filter* IEEE International Conference on Radar 2011, Chengdu, China, 24–27 2011, pp 619–622.
27. K. V. Rangarao and P. A. Janakiraman; *A New Algorithm for Frequency Estimation in the Presence of Phase Noise* Digital Signal Processing 4, 1994, Academic Press Inc., pp 198–203.

Chapter 6
Direction Finding for Wideband Signals—Case Studies

6.1 Wide Band Signals

There are various types of wideband signals that we encounter in everyday life. One example is the Frequency Modulated Continuous Wave (FMCW) signal [1], which is commonly used in radar applications [2, 3]. Additionally, the human voice [4–6], a naturally occurring wideband signal, is frequently encountered in diverse contexts. For spread spectrum signals, the gold-MUSIC algorithm is highly effective. It is crucial to pay special attention to wideband signals. In this chapter, we address the two domains.

6.1.1 FMCW Radar in Automotive Application

The increasing demand for self-driving cars and driver assistance is the motivation behind this work. The main objective is to comprehend a scene quickly and quantify it accurately. For scene viewing, FMCW radar is the sensor that has been utilized [7]. Section 6.2 gives the overview. In Sect. 6.2.2, the algorithm's context is explained, including how an object is modeled along with associated sensor parameters and digitized raw data from the sensor. Section 6.3 focuses on preprocessing the raw data to generate a cloud of targets, while Sect. 6.4 details an algorithm for clustering those targets. Section 6.4.1 delves into the nature of objects, and Sect. 6.5 provides a summary of the implementation. In Sect. 6.6, the scene matrix is described, along with typical scenarios. Section 6.6.5 describes the relative performance of this method with the standard procedure, and finally, conclusions are drawn.

V. R. Kaluri, *Direction Finding Algorithms for Practicing Engineers*,
https://doi.org/10.1007/978-3-032-06997-9_6

6.1.2 FMCW Radar Parameters

Each data set collected is associated with the parameters of the sensor [8] (radar). A quick understanding of these parameters is essential. Figure 6.1 illustrates the chirps produced by the radar and the sensor hardware. The scene observed by the sensor is shown in Fig. 6.1a. The sweep time is defined as $t_{\text{chirp}} = N\delta t$, where N is the number of samples per chirp, and δt is the sampling interval. For a typical system, the Intermediate Frequency (IF) ADC sampling rate is given by $f_s = \frac{1}{\delta t} = 4500$ KHz, with $M = 512$. This results in $t_{\text{chirp}} = \frac{512}{4500} \approx 114\,\mu$ seconds and a chirp slope of $\alpha = 26\,\frac{\text{MHz}}{\mu\text{s}}$. The time interval between two chirps is $\Delta t = t_{\text{chirp}} + t_b$, where t_b is the blanking time, defined as an integral multiple of t_{chirp}. We use a constant value for this purpose.

$$r_g = \left[\frac{c_M}{\alpha} \times \frac{f_s}{1000}\right] \times 0.5\,\frac{\text{meters}}{\text{Hz}} \tag{6.1}$$

as defined by Eq. 6.1, where $c_M \approx 300$ Mm/s. The constant r_g links data from the sensor domain to the data domain, as illustrated in Fig. 6.4b and c. Based on the typical values mentioned earlier, we find that $r_g \approx 26$. Various scenarios have been examined, and offline data were collected using this sensor shown in Fig. 6.4d. In

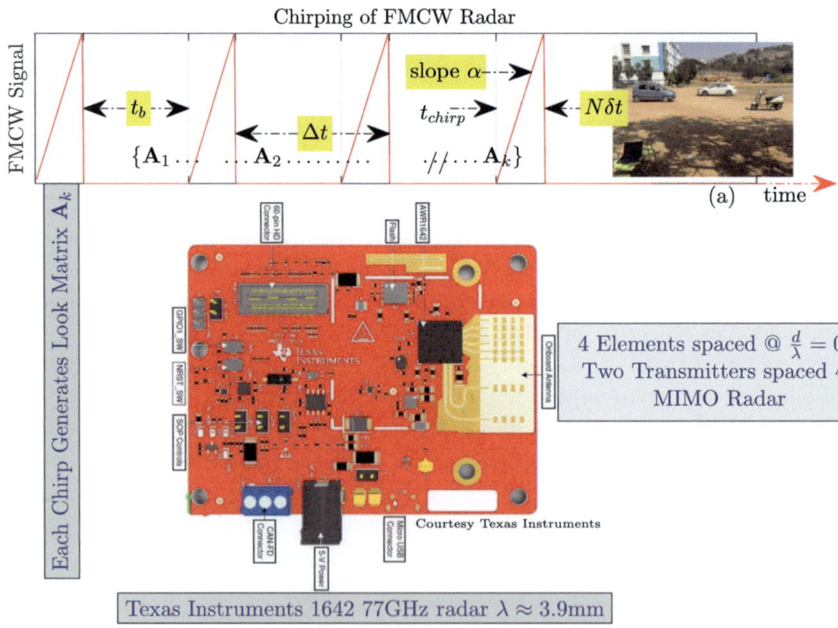

Fig. 6.1 Complex look matrix $\{\mathbf{A}_1, \mathbf{A}_2 \ldots \mathbf{A}_k\}$ for k chirps is *glance*

the coming days, it will be essential for mobile devices to utilize small-footprint software for object perception.

6.1.3 *Human Voice*

Extracting Formants or pitch [9–11] and Direction of Arrival(DOA) [12–16] has been addressed separately for decades for various applications. In recent years, the combined need [17, 18] has been in great demand in various applications, including surveillance, language processing, and music classification, among others. With advances in ML/DL, there is a greater demand and need for a solution. The choice of formant frequency for DOA has the advantage of better SNR conditions because most of the audio energy is concentrated around the formant.

A simple model [19–21] of voice production is given in Fig. 6.2. The voice tract is excited by e_k, which is inaccessible, and the voice tract model $H(z)$ is unknown. We use nonparametric methods to obtain the formant. A typical voice signal v_k of 1024 samples of duration 128 mS is shown in Fig. 6.2a, and the complex Fourier Spectrum V_n as defined in Eq. 6.2 is shown in Fig. 6.2b as $|V_n|$. The complex spectrum [22] is defined as

$$V_n = \sum_{k=0}^{N-1} v_k \times W^{nk} \text{ where } W = e^{-j\frac{2\pi}{N}} \tag{6.2}$$

Using this DFT, we cannot accurately represent the time series v_k because the frequency components change over time. If there is a prominent peak in the spectrum, but we don't know when it occurred, it is challenging to represent it accurately. Therefore, we need to incorporate the time dimension into the spectrum. Human formant band variations typically range from 100 to 1000 Hz, as illustrated in Fig. 6.2b.

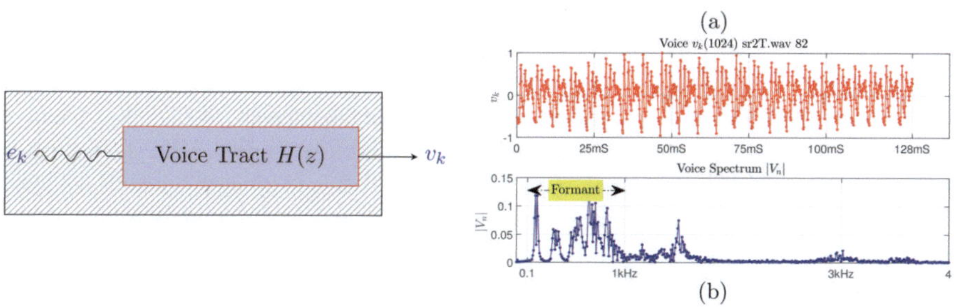

Fig. 6.2 Voice production model

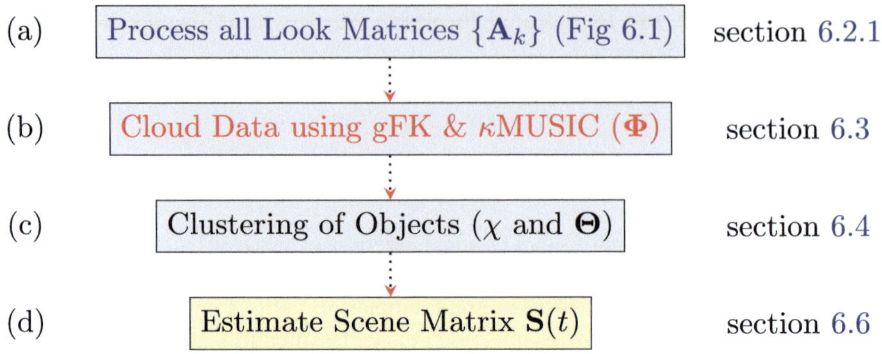

Fig. 6.3 Schematic of *perception engine* (a, b, c, d) Eq. 6.19

6.2 Perception Engine

The sensor for perception [14] is shown in Fig. 6.1. In Fig. 6.1a, a typical scene is depicted, while multiple chirps are shown in Fig. 6.1. The raw data for a single chirp is represented by Matrix **A**, as seen in Fig. 6.4a. An overview of generating r and φ for a particular Matrix **A** is shown in Fig. 6.4. This raw data, as shown in Fig. 6.3, is processed using methods [16, 23] for multiple chirps, say 10, to generate a cloud of data $\{r, \varphi\}$ for use in Fig. 6.3b. It's important to note that most objects give multiple reflections, and each reflection is annotated as a target, denoted by a solid red circle in Fig. 6.5. The perception engine operates over this cloud of data, as seen in Fig. 6.3c, to form clusters. These clusters are utilized to get a corresponding quantifiable scene matrix $\mathbf{S}(t)$, as shown in Fig. 6.3d. The algorithm scheme depicted in Fig. 6.3 includes four subfigures, each of which is labeled (a), (b), (c), (d).

6.2.1 Input Raw Data

Complex in-phase(I) and quadrature (Q) Raw Data Matrices $\{\mathbf{A}_1 \ldots \mathbf{A}_k\}$ used in Fig. 6.1 is depicted as table in Fig. 6.4d and graphically in Fig. 6.4a. This data is obtained in files along with r_g and M, as defined in 6.1.2, and labeled for each scenario to evaluate the perception engine. The snapshot is a row vector in matrix **A**, annotated as $\mathbf{s}^T$, and is shown as a table in Fig. 6.4, highlighted in yellow. The constituents of this row vector are illustrated in detail in the same figure. The essential components for generating a *cloud* (Fig. 6.5) are precise range and Direction of Arrival (DOA) algorithms [24] that are *Lean* and accurate. Various techniques for DOA estimation were presented in the previous chapters of this book [16, 25–31], with each approach designed to meet specific domain needs and requirements, and we choose κMUSIC.

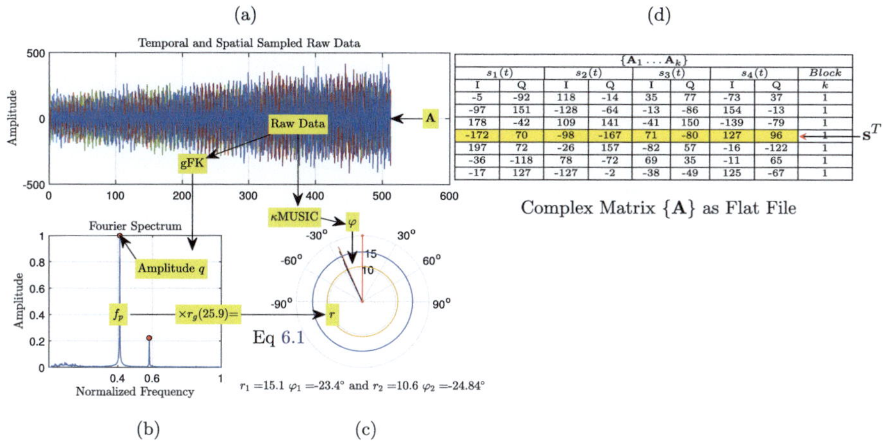

$\{\mathbf{A}_1 \dots \mathbf{A}_k\}$								
$s_1(t)$		$s_2(t)$		$s_3(t)$		$s_4(t)$		*Block*
I	Q	I	Q	I	Q	I	Q	k
-5	-92	118	-14	35	77	-73	37	1
-97	151	-128	-64	-13	-86	154	-13	1
178	-42	109	141	-41	150	-139	-79	1
-172	70	-98	-167	71	-80	127	96	1
197	72	-26	157	-82	57	-16	-122	1
-36	-118	78	-72	69	35	-11	65	1
-17	127	-127	-2	-38	-49	125	-67	1

Fig. 6.4 *Cloud* points $\phi_i = [\kappa\ r\ q\ \varphi\ x\ y]$ (Eq. 6.4) from raw data

6.2.2 *Modeling of Object*

When using radar, we designate any object we detect by its Radar Cross Section (RCS), measured in square meters (m^2) units. Objects [32] often reflect multiple times, with each reflection being called a target located at (r, φ) and labeled as κ. A *Cluster* of small red dots is the *targets* inside the *statistical* bounding box of size (σ_x, σ_y) for a given object, as shown in Fig. 6.5. These are *random* reflecting points from the object. The object shape could be *arbitrarily* defined by $\{\kappa, r, \varphi\}$ and *centroid* $\bar{x}, \bar{y}$. Based on the accuracies of range and DOA estimates, the radar detects several targets. These targets form a cluster in a vertical plane over k chirps. We model the object by its centroid and bounding box, along with the feature vector $\mathbf{s}_i$, which is depicted in Fig. 6.5.

6.3 Pre-processing of Raw Data

In FMCW radars, the traditional method for Range-Doppler (RD) processing involves estimating the Fourier spectrum of the return signals from multiple frequency sweeps (or chirps), as shown in Fig. 6.1. The *peak* frequency values (f_p) from the spectrum are then multiplied by r_g to generate a range set $\{r\}$, as depicted in Fig. 6.4b and c. To perform spatial sampling, multiple receiving elements are used, as described in references [33, 34]. These antenna elements are typically spaced equally at half wavelength λ and are designed to obtain the DOA $\{\varphi\}$.

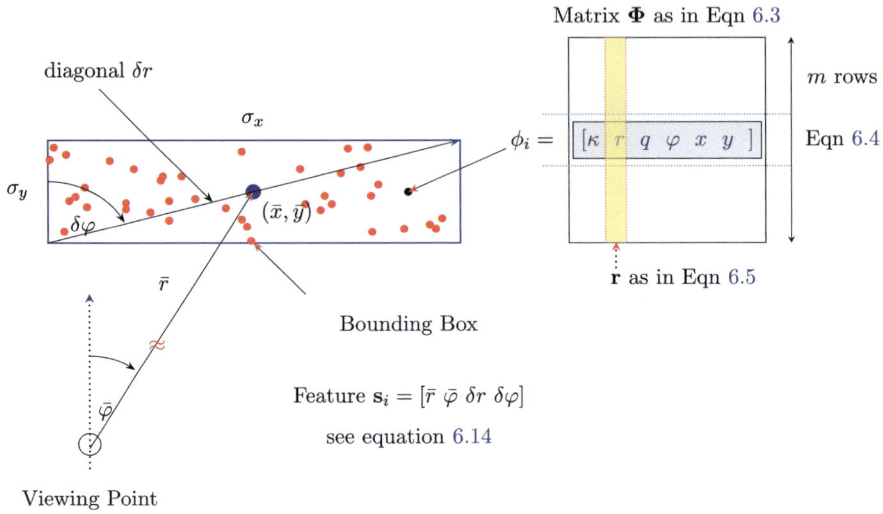

Fig. 6.5 Modeling of an object ($\approx$ indicates a long line $\bar{r}$ to object)

6.3.1 *Cloud Data*

Our approach focuses on *lean* computing and utilizes domain-specific methods such as κMUSIC and gold-Fourier-Kaluri (gFK) to generate a cloud of data. The combined method of gFK and κMUSIC is referred to as transformation $gFK\mu$, which is explained in detail in existing literature [16, 23]. As demonstrated in Fig. 6.4a, these *highly accurate* algorithms quickly provide range $\{r\}$ and $\{\varphi\}$ for the reflections from objects in the environment. The data matrix Φ *glance* matrix is obtained over k chirps.

$$\Phi = gFK\mu\,\{\mathbf{A}_1 \ldots \mathbf{A}_k\}\,. \tag{6.3}$$

Specialized algorithms are necessary to convert data matrix Φ into a *machine-perceivable* matrix $\mathbf{S}(t)$.

6.3.2 *Structure of Cloud Matrix* $\mathbf{\Phi}$

The *cloud matrix* Φ is composed of row vectors represented as red solid circles, with a specific vector denoted as ϕ_i, which is illustrated as a black solid circle in Eq. 6.4 and Fig. 6.5. In this context, κ signifies a target identifier within the chirp, r denotes the range of the target, and q indicates the quality, referring to the normalized signal strength (as shown in Fig. 6.4b) reflected from a specific point. Additionally, φ represents the direction of arrival (DOA), with $x = r\cos\varphi$ and $y = r\sin\varphi$ depicting the points in the vertical plane. Typically, there are k chirps, and N_t represents the number of selected targets. Consequently, the maximum number of rows in the matrix is calculated as $m = k \times N_t$. Thus, the size of the matrix Φ is $m \times 6$, as illustrated in the table in Fig. 6.5.

$$\phi_i = [\kappa \; r \; q \; \varphi \; x \; y] \tag{6.4}$$

Radial and Angular positions of the centroid are

$$\bar{r} = \sqrt{\bar{x}^2 + \bar{y}^2} \quad \bar{\varphi} = \tan^{-1}\left(\frac{\bar{x}}{\bar{y}}\right)$$

The objects Diagonal and Tilt are

$$\delta r = \sqrt{\sigma_x^2 + \sigma_y^2} \quad \delta\varphi = \tan^{-1}\left(\frac{\sigma_x}{\sigma_y}\right)$$

All angles are measured w.r.t. vertical axis, see Fig. 6.5.

6.4 Clustering of Targets

We use a threshold on q to pre-process Φ, which results in dropping rows to make it more compact and eliminate spurious targets. The vector $\mathbf{r}$ is defined as

$$\mathbf{r}^T = \{r_1 \; r_2 \ldots \; r_m\} \tag{6.5}$$

and is the second column of the matrix Φ. (as per Eq. 6.4). The vector $\mathbf{r}$ is sorted along with its indices to generate a new vector called $\mathbf{r}_s$ as in Eq. 6.6.

$$\mathbf{r}_s = \text{sort}(\mathbf{r}) \tag{6.6}$$

The matrix Φ can be sorted as Θ using the indices of $\mathbf{r}_s$. The table in Fig. 6.6 shows the second column of Θ, where $\mathbf{r}_s$ in yellow and blue is shown with $k = 10$ and $N_t = 5$. The Φ has a size of $50{\times}6$. The target identifier, denoted by κ, is always less than or equal to N_t. In this particular case $\mathbf{r}_s$ is partitioned into two segments. Each segment has its *mean* μ and *standard deviation* σ. As shown in Fig. 6.6a, each partition is separated by markers. It is important to note the original distribution of $\mathbf{r}$ has been segregated into two distributions. This is described in 6.4.2, which is a *Maximum-Likelihood* partitioning algorithm.

	Θ					
	κ	r	q	φ°	x	y
Θ_1	2	15.060	0.223	-23.444	-5.992	13.817
	2	15.060	0.226	-23.444	-5.992	13.817
	2	15.060	0.225	-23.367	-5.973	13.825
	2	15.060	0.223	-23.401	-5.981	13.821
	2	15.060	0.225	-23.293	-5.955	13.833
	2	15.060	0.221	-23.449	-5.993	13.816
	2	15.060	0.223	-23.415	-5.985	13.820
	2	15.060	0.223	-23.467	-5.997	13.814
	2	15.060	0.226	-23.355	-5.970	13.826
	2	15.060	0.223	-23.319	-5.961	13.830
Θ_2	1	10.629	1.000	-24.859	-4.468	9.644
	1	10.629	1.000	-24.829	-4.463	9.646
	1	10.629	1.000	-24.896	-4.474	9.641
	1	10.629	1.000	-24.806	-4.459	9.648
	1	10.629	1.000	-24.852	-4.467	9.645
	1	10.629	1.000	-24.859	-4.468	9.644
	1	10.629	1.000	-24.829	-4.463	9.646
	1	10.629	1.000	-24.822	-4.462	9.647
	1	10.629	1.000	-24.833	-4.464	9.646

$\{N(\mu_1, \sigma_1^2) + N(\mu_2, \sigma_2^2)\} = \mathbf{r}_s$ as in Eqn 6.6

(a)

(c)

Corner Reflector Distributed Objects

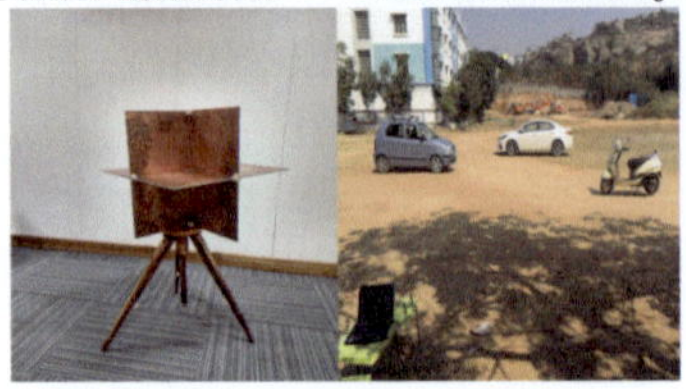

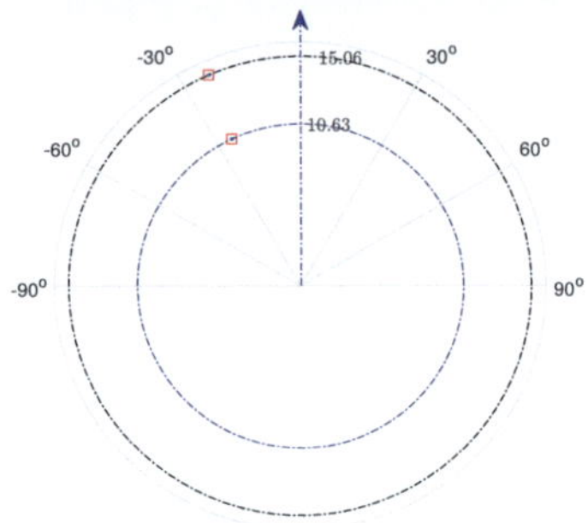

r_1 =15.06 φ_1 =-23.38° and r_2 =10.63 φ_2 =-24.83° $\delta\varphi$ = -1.45°

σ_r =2.03e-04 σ_φ° =5.96e-02 σ_r =5.13e-05 σ_φ° =2.67e-02

$N(\mu_1, \sigma_1^2)$ $N(\mu_2, \sigma_2^2)$ section 6.4.2

(b)

Fig. 6.6 Matrix Φ (Eq. 6.3) sorted as Θ on *r*

6.4.1 *Types of Objects*

In our daily lives, we encounter a wide range of objects that vary in shape and size. We can categorize these objects detected by radar as sharp or distributed objects. In Fig. 6.6c, there is a display of the objects utilized during the field tests. The corner reflector [35], depicted in left of Fig. 6.6c, and measuring 80 cm on each side, is a sharp object with a nearly pointed RCS. Moving forward, larger objects such as cars and scooters, which fall under the category of distributed objects as shown in right of Fig. 6.6c, were utilized. When dealing with distributed objects, selecting a specific point of range can be challenging. As the size of the object grows, the uncertainty surrounding the selection of sampling points on the object also increases. Therefore, we opt to represent the object with a centroid($\bar{x}$, $\bar{y}$), a statistical diagonal δr, and its orientation $\delta\varphi$ as depicted in Fig. 6.5.

6.4.2 *Partitioning Algorithm*

The Matrix Θ is partitioned using $\mathbf{r}_s$, as outlined in Eq. 6.6, resulting in the creation of an integer index matrix $\boldsymbol{\emptyset}$. The proposed partitioning method consists of several iterations, starting with $i = 1$. After each iteration i, we obtain a collection of clusters

$$\text{as } \{p_1, p_2, \ldots, p_i\} \text{ with each cluster } p_i \text{ has a distribution of } N(\mu_p, \sigma_p^2) \tag{6.7}$$

That has been formed, along with a remainder set P_i that needs to be further divided into additional clusters if possible. Each cluster p_i is defined as a set of values derived from the vector $\mathbf{r}_s$. The algorithm initializes with $P_0 = \mathbf{r}_s$ as stated in Eq. 6.6 and in column 2 of the table presented in Fig. 6.6a for $i = 1$. This initial set is then utilized in the iterative algorithm outlined in Eq. 6.8.

$$\begin{aligned} \forall r \in P_{i-1} \;\; p_i =& \{r \geq \sigma_{i-1}\} \text{ and} \\ P_i =& \{r < \sigma_{i-1}\}'' \end{aligned} \tag{6.8}$$

The choice of the *dynamic* threshold, σ_{i-1}(second moment of P_{i-1}) in Eq. 6.8 is *heuristic* [36].

$$\boxed{\begin{aligned} &\text{we note } P_{i-1} = p_i \cup P_i \text{ and } p_i \cap P_i = NULL \\ &\text{where } \sigma_{i-1} = \sqrt{\tfrac{\sum (r-\mu)^2}{n-1}} \;\; \forall r \in P_{i-1} \\ &\text{in which } n = \text{size } (P_{i-1}) \text{ and } \mu = E(P_{i-1}) \end{aligned}} \tag{6.9}$$

The recursive set of operations as given in Eqs. 6.8 and 6.9 is performed till either set p_i or P_i becomes a NULL set, in which i is an integer. In case p_i is NULL, the set p_i is replaced by P_i. The matrix Θ is partitioned as $\Theta(\chi)$ where

$$\chi = \begin{pmatrix} 1 & 10 \\ 11 & 19 \end{pmatrix} \text{ is an integer } index \text{ matrix} \tag{6.10}$$

Is of size $N_c \times 2$, in which N_c is the number of clusters formed as given in the table in Fig. 6.6.

6.4.3 *Computation of Scene Matrix*

Using the clustering algorithm, we obtain the matrix χ, as shown in Eq. 6.10. The matrix χ has several rows corresponding to the number of clusters and consists of two columns. Each row $\chi(i) = [s\ e]$ represents the range from row s to row e in the matrix Θ, as depicted in Fig. 6.5a. The ith cluster matrix is represented as $\Theta(\chi(i))$, allowing us to derive Θ_i as a subset and partition of Θ. It is important to note that

$\Theta_i \cap \Theta_{i+1} = \text{NULL}$, indicating that the clusters do not overlap. We denote the nth column vector in Θ_i as $\Theta_i(n)$. In this context, the x and y variables correspond to the 5th and 6th columns, respectively, as shown in Eq. 6.4 and Fig. 6.5a. We define $\{x\} = \Theta_i(5)$ and $\{y\} = \Theta_i(6)$. The centroid coordinates of the object in the vertical plane, denoted as $(\bar{x}, \bar{y})$, are then computed as follows:

$$\bar{x} = E(\{x\}) \text{ and } \bar{y} = E(\{y\}) \tag{6.11}$$

The bounding box dimensions of the object are computed as

$$\sigma_x = \sqrt{\frac{\sum_{i=0}^{n}(x_i - \bar{x})^2}{n-1}} \text{ and } \sigma_y = \sqrt{\frac{\sum_{i=0}^{n}(y_i - \bar{y})^2}{n-1}} \tag{6.12}$$

where n is size of $\{x\}$ or $\{y\}$. Using object centroid coordinates and the bounding box dimensions, we get ith row $\mathbf{s}_i$ entries in the scene matrix $\mathbf{S}(t)$ as Feature Vector $\mathbf{s}_i = [\bar{r}\ \bar{\varphi}\ \delta r\ \delta\varphi]$.

6.5 Implementation Summary

The algorithm, as shown in Eq. 6.13, has been implemented as standalone code written in C++ and is also available as MEX code to run under MATLAB control for evaluation purposes. The code includes standard MUSIC for comparison.

$$\boxed{\{\mathbf{A}\} \longrightarrow \Phi \longrightarrow \Theta \longrightarrow \chi \longrightarrow \mathbf{S}(t)} \tag{6.13}$$

The C code comprises approximately 10,000 lines and is organized into 16 modules, as shown in Fig. 6.7b. The corresponding header files are displayed in Fig. 6.7a. The algorithm implementation begins by reading a flat file that contains raw data, presented as a table in Fig. 6.4d.

$$\mathbf{S}(t) = \begin{pmatrix} \bar{r} & \bar{\varphi} & \delta r & \delta\varphi \\ \hline 15.060 & -23.431 & 0.021 & 66.607 \\ \hline 10.629 & -24.853 & 0.006 & 65.192 \end{pmatrix} \tag{6.14}$$

This process involves a series of matrices $\{\mathbf{A}_1, \ldots, \mathbf{A}_k\}$ that are processed according to Eq. 6.3, along with a configuration file that specifies the radar parameters, as outlined in Sect. 6.1.2. The procedure utilizes gFK and κMUSIC to generate a data cloud matrix known as the *glance* matrix Φ. This matrix is then analyzed using a clustering algorithm to obtain Θ, which is partitioned as $\Theta(\chi(i))$, where χ is defined in Eq. 6.10. The results are illustrated in Fig. 6.6. All the rows (i) of the scene matrix

$\mathbf{S}(t)$ is generated from Θ for all i values. You can run this code as a standalone *fmcwRadar.exe* on Windows or as a DLL *getRgD.mexw64* in the MATLAB environment.

$$\mathbf{S}(t) = \left(\begin{array}{cccc} \bar{r} & \bar{\varphi} & \delta r & \delta\varphi \\ \hdashline 15.688 & -10.657 & 0.226 & 23.365 \\ \hdashline 8.867 & -22.943 & 0.151 & 21.447 \\ 6.938 & 14.763 & 0.056 & 75.148 \end{array} \right) \tag{6.15}$$

6.5.1 Execution Time

The *fmcwRadar.exe* code is a standalone executable file, measuring 938 KB in size. It was developed using Microsoft Visual Studio Community 2022 (64-bit), version 17.5.3. To estimate its execution time, we ran the code on an Intel Core i7-10510U CPU, which operates at 1.80 GHz with a clock speed of 2304 MHz, featuring four cores and eight logical processors. The system is a Lenovo ThinkPad X1 Carbon Gen 8, model number 20U9-BU. The complex matrix $\mathbf{A}$ for a chirp has dimensions of 512×4. After conducting several runs, the average execution time is summarized in the table shown in Fig. 6.7. Fetching $\mathbf{A}$ takes approximately 2 ms. As expected,

(a) Header Files (b) Source Files

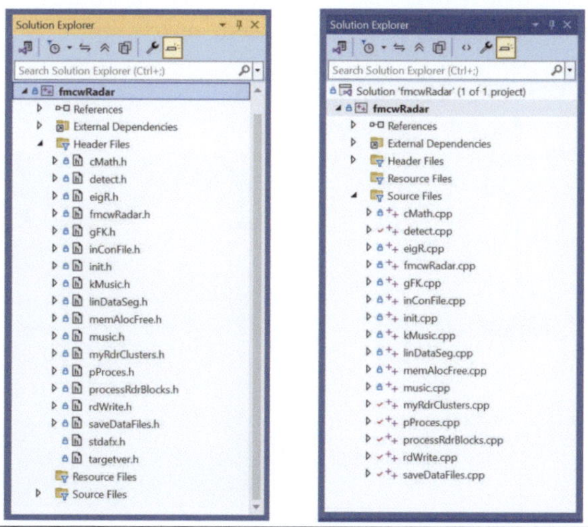

Process	$\{\mathbf{A}\}$	$\{\mathbf{A}\}\rightarrow\mathbf{\Phi}$	$\mathbf{\Phi} \rightarrow \chi \rightarrow \mathbf{\Theta} \rightarrow \mathbf{S}(t)$
Time in mSec	2	12	0.1

Fig. 6.7 Header and C++ files for FMCW radar solution

the most significant portion of the execution time is dedicated to the formation of the cloud matrix Φ, which, with $k = 10$ chirps and with number of targets $N_t = 5$, takes 12 ms. In comparison, creating the scene matrix only requires 0.1 ms. If this is implemented as an application on any contemporary mobile device or system-on-chip (SoC), it is likely to achieve similar performance.

6.6 Scene Matrix

We utilized the techniques outlined in Sect. 6.4.1 for two different scenarios. The scene matrix was calculated for both static and dynamic cases, including sharp objects, and the resulting data was reported. The number of rows in the matrix corresponds to the estimated number of objects. At the same time, $\bar{r}$ and $\bar{\varphi}$ represent the radial and angular position of the object's centroid in the vertical plane. Additionally, δr indicates the diagonal of the object and $\delta\varphi$ represents its orientation as shown in Fig. 6.5.

6.6.1 *Sharp Objects*

To ensure thorough testing, a scene matrix has been generated for two sharp objects positioned at close angles, as depicted in Fig. 6.8b. Despite their physical size (see Fig. 6.6ca) being that of an 80 cm cube, these objects have been designed to appear as point objects. Figure 6.8b is the actual scene while Fig. 6.8a is the *machine perceived*. It is essential to note that visual scenes such as Fig. 6.8b are used *only* for testing and evaluation of the algorithm and code. In the scene matrix above, we can see the row

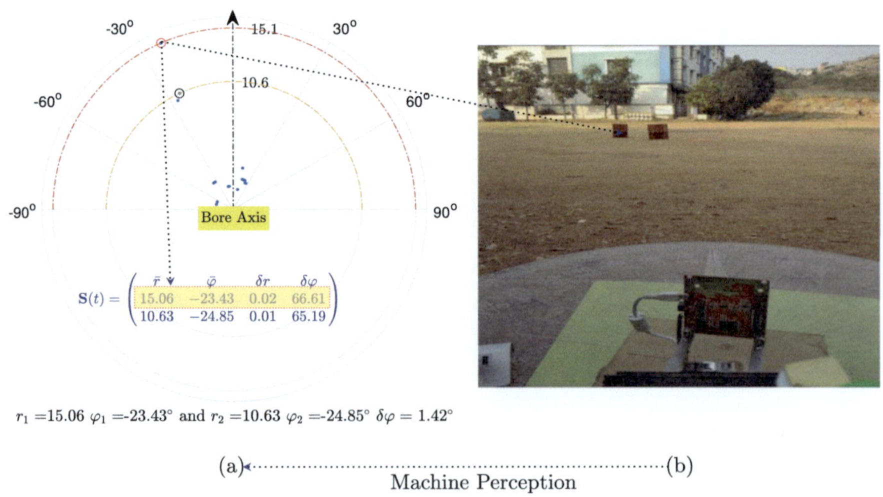

Fig. 6.8 Perception of closely placed ($\approx$ 1.4°) two point objects

feature vector $\mathbf{s}_i$ of the farthest corner reflector. From the scene matrix we observe that there are two objects positioned at 15 m and 10.6 m, at *close* angles of $-23.45°$ and $-24.856°$. These two objects are located very closely to each other at a separation of $\approx 1.4°$. This separation corresponds to an arc length of $1.4° \times \frac{\pi}{180} \times 10.63$, which is ≈ 26 cm. This suggests that the two objects are overlapping, as indicated by the radar. Upon closer observation, we can determine that the two objects appear to be virtually point objects with the same tilt of $\approx 66°$. The diagonal dimensions of δr of 2 cm and 0.6 cm are consistent with corner reflectors, which are expected to have these properties. Additionally, the diagonal distance is the *electrical distance* based on the material properties.

$$\mathbf{S}(t) = \begin{pmatrix} \bar{r} & \bar{\varphi} & \delta r & \delta\varphi \\ \hline 15.055 & 6.964 & 1.319 & 81.507 \\ \hline 8.619 & -7.751 & 0.137 & 41.417 \\ 0.970 & 15.639 & 0.004 & 70.821 \end{pmatrix} \tag{6.16}$$

6.6.2 Distributed Objects

Figure 6.9b depicts the three distributed objects, and Fig. 6.9a shows the matrix $\mathbf{S}(t)$ and the corresponding machine visualization, which is also demonstrated in Eq. 6.15. Additionally, the figure depicts an object and its corresponding parameters within the scene matrix. We see from the matrix's first row that the farthest object is 15.7 m

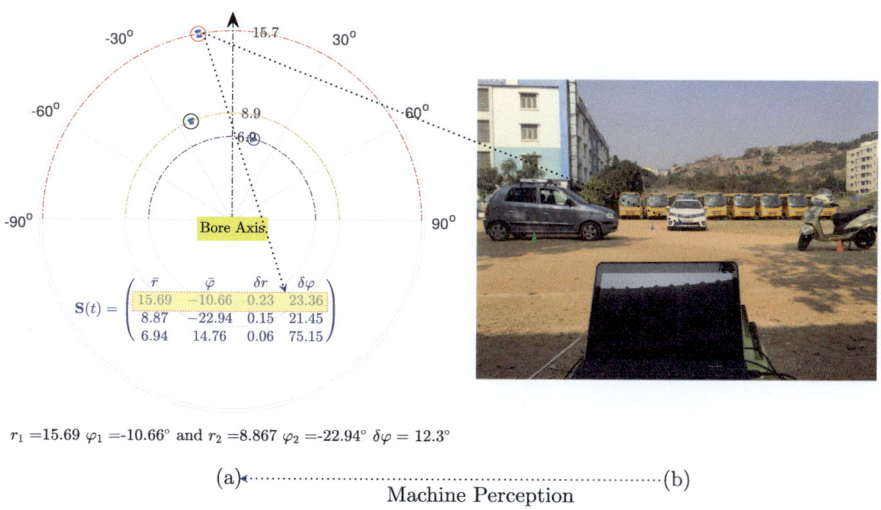

Fig. 6.9 Perception of distributed objects two cars and scooter

at an angle $-10.66°$ *wrt* normal axis of the radar. A diagonal (δr) of 0.23 m the tilt ($\delta\varphi$) of 23.36° depicts it is in extended mode, *(i.e.)*, the fore and aft axis of the car is parallel to *bore axis* of the radar, as can be seen in Fig. 6.9a.

6.6.3 Orientation of Object

During this evaluation, the car's orientation was changed, and the review took place on a different day. As shown in Fig. 6.10b, it is visible that the background buses are missing. By observing the scene matrix, we can determine that the farthest object is 15 m away and the centroid is at 7° angle from the bore axis. The statistical diagonal, δr, measures 1.32 m. It is important to note that the tilt, $\delta\varphi$, is now at 81.5°. We can see that the fore and aft axes of the car are perpendicular to the bore axis. The micro-strip antenna on the board has a 3dB beam width of ±35° in H-plane and ±15° in E-plane concerning the bore axis, as stated in reference [8]. It is essential to note that the third object, a scooter, is not visible to radar because it is outside the beam. This can be seen in Fig. 6.10a.

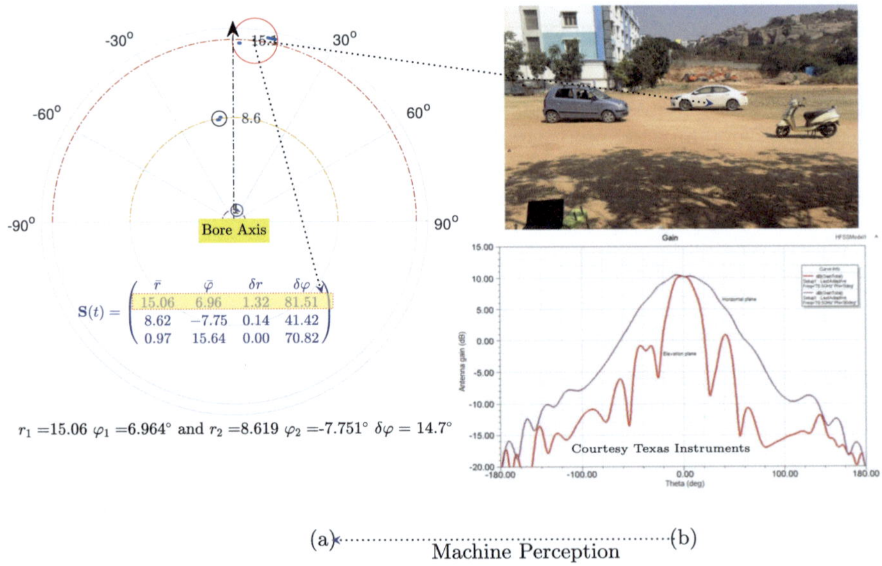

Fig. 6.10 Perception of distributed objects two cars and scooter

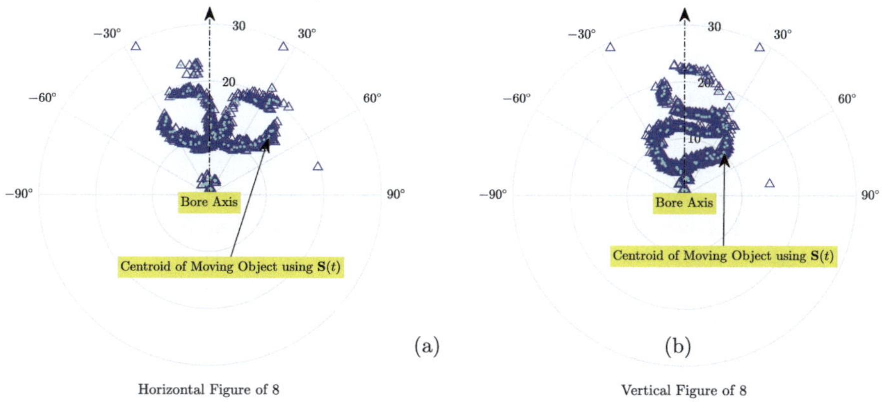

Fig. 6.11 Moving object in a figure-eight pattern with two orientations

6.6.4 Dynamic Scenario

A distributed object, such as a car, is programmed to move in a figure-eight pattern with two orientations, and the collected data is stored. The process is executed using the standalone code *fmcwRadar.exe*, as described in Eq. 6.13. The scene matrix $\mathbf{S}(t)$ is computed at regular intervals, leading to the graphical representations shown in Fig. 6.11a and b. In these figures, the bright dots within the blue bands represent the centroid of the object, which is derived from $\mathbf{S}(t)$. The time trace of the matrix Φ is illustrated by the blue band. However, tracking the object is not within the scope of the current book.

6.6.5 Relative Performance

Standard MUSIC is used for comparison with the existing method and is presented in Chap. 4, Sect. 4.5. Results were obtained in well-calibrated laboratory conditions and shown in Fig. 4.26. They have excellent linearity & accuracy. κMUSIC takes $\approx$ 23μSec, on same machine standard MUSIC takes $\approx$ 254 μSec, for $M = 128$. We have compared the results with standard MUSIC, which is computationally expensive (needs *eigen* values and vectors) and has other limitations. Current algorithm κMUSIC is $approx$ 11 times faster than MUSIC. The angular accuracies ($\sigma_\theta = 0.15°$ and $\sigma_r = 0.2$ mm) are of the order of a fraction of a degree. The proposed method exhibited the same superior performance as described in 6.5.1 when evaluated against all objects, as in 6.6, compared to the standard MUSIC.

6.7 Direction of Human Voice (DOV)

Locating a person by analyzing the direction of their voice [38] and studying the formant frequencies is a fascinating challenge. A person's formant changes over time, creating a wide-spectrum signal, whereas most direction-finding methods typically require a narrow-band signal. Moreover, the ratio of interelement distance to wavelength ($\frac{d}{\lambda}$) varies over time. We track the formant using Discrete Fourier Transform (DFT) and Wavelets. We employ a new streamlined *easy* MUltiple SIgnal Characterization (MUSIC) method to determine the direction. Our research focuses on capturing the formant range and determining the direction using this new approach. This formant stream and Direction of Arrival (DOA) provide crucial data for machine learning. We have chosen the $\frac{d}{\lambda}$ parameter to be between 0.1 and 0.3, with the interelement spacing at a practical distance for this audio formant frequency. Before conducting accurate data testing, we simulated the array using authentic voices, which presented a significant challenge.

6.7.1 Spectral Peaks

We begin by filtering the signal v_k shown in Fig. 6.2a, to create a new time series, $\tilde{v}_k$, which contains only the formant band. To accomplish this, we apply the Discrete Fourier Transform (DFT) to the signal v_k as in Eq. 6.2 and the spectrum $|V_n|$ is shown in 6.2b. During this process, we set all components outside the formant band range (100 to 1000 Hz) to zero, making $\tilde{V}_n$ conjugate symmetric. Finally, we perform the Discrete Fourier Transform (DFT) on this conjugate-symmetric complex sequence to obtain a real sequence $\tilde{v}_k$ of length 1024.

6.7.2 Detection and Decimation

Detection is performed by computing the energy in this filtered 1024 sequence. If there is insufficient energy, we will read the next data block. We decimate this 1024 sequence by a factor of 2, resulting in a new time series, $\tilde{v}_k$, with a length of 512. We designate the amplitude spectrum of this time series as $|\tilde{V}_n|$. Figure 6.12 depicts both the amplitude spectrum $|\tilde{V}_n|$ and the decimated sequence $\tilde{v}_k$.

6.7.3 Dominant Peaks of $|\tilde{V}_n|$

One of the crucial steps in generating the formant involves estimating the dominant peaks of the amplitude spectrum $|\tilde{V}_n|$. This is a critical aspect of the algorithm. We

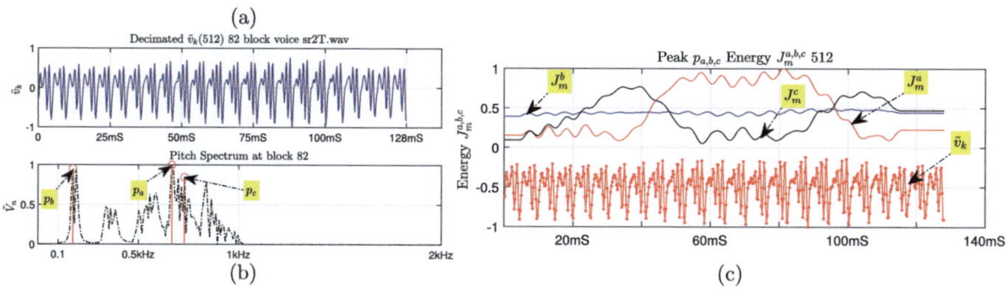

Fig. 6.12 Decimated v_k and band limited spectrum V_n and energy of the peaks p_a, p_b, p_c

identify peaks and their bin locations as

$$\{p_n\} = \text{ peaks } (|\tilde{V}_n|) \text{ where } n \text{ is the bin number} \tag{6.17}$$

We need to perform one more step *peaks of peaks*

$$\{P_n\} = \text{ peaks } (\{p_n\}) \text{ where } n \text{ is the bin number} \tag{6.18}$$

The final candidate peak set is $\hat{p}_n$, a subset of the union of p_n and P_n ($\hat{p}_n \subseteq p_n \cup P_n$). This process involves using the distance measure between peaks to eliminate redundant and unwanted peaks. Only three candidate peaks are selected as potential contributors to the formant frequency. These three peaks are illustrated in Fig. 6.12b and represented as $\hat{p}_n = \{p_a, p_b, p_c\}$ in a stem plot with a red color. Here, a, b, c are the bin numbers of the peaks. The normalized frequencies are calculated as

$$\hat{p}_n = \{f_a = \frac{a}{N}, f_b = \frac{b}{N}, f_c = \frac{c}{N}\} \tag{6.19}$$

where N is the length of the sequence $\tilde{v}_k$.

6.8 Time Varying Peaks and Wavelets

Up to this point, we have assumed the process v_k to be stationary, which is not true. To account for this and capture the time-varying nature, we must resort to wavelet methods and select the appropriate peak or a combination of them. This is achieved using short duration of data and computing the Fourier Objective Function. We define the Fourier Objective Function [23] $J_m^F(f_a)$ over a short time moving window w, which consists of 16 samples out of 512 samples.

$$A_m = \sum_{i=0}^{w-1} \left[(\tilde{v}_{(m+i)} \times \cos(2\pi f_a i) \right] \tag{6.20}$$

$$B_m = \sum_{i=0}^{w-1} \left[(\tilde{v}_{(m+i)} \times \sin(2\pi f_a i) \right] \tag{6.21}$$

In the Eqs. 6.20 and 6.21, f_a represents the normalized peak frequency obtained from Eq. 6.19, and the index m varies from 0 to $N-1$.

$$J_m^F(f_a) = \frac{\sqrt{A_m^2 + B_m^2}}{N} = J_m^a \tag{6.22}$$

In Eq. 6.22, we concise $J_m^F(f_a)$ as J_m^a represents the energy of the peak p_a as a function of time, depicted in Fig. 6.12c, where N is the number of samples in the time series $\{\tilde{v}_k\}$. Acknowledging the computational load involved in Eq. 6.22 is essential.

6.9 Uniform Linear Array

The most challenging aspect is to ensure that the ULA data closely resembles reality for testing before attempting a Proof of Concept (POC) on a simple microphone array. A 360° continuous delay [30] is available for this purpose. In diagram 6.9a, the audio source is located at a distance of R, and the outputs at each microphone are phase shifted by $\varphi = \left[2\pi\frac{d}{\lambda}\right]\sin\theta$ between any two consecutive elements. The phase shift for a given Direction of Arrival (DOA) θ is achieved using Eq. 6.23 or a cascade of All-Pass Filters [30]. As mentioned in the diagram 6.9a, the real matrix $\mathbf{V}$ is obtained by repeatedly performing phase shifts. It has rows of length $\tilde{v}_k$ (512) and columns equal to the number of elements in the uniform linear array (ULA) (Fig. 6.13).

$$\tilde{v}_k^{\varphi} = r\tilde{v}_{k-1}^{\varphi} - r\tilde{v}_k + \tilde{v}_{k-1} \text{ 1st Order APF} \tag{6.23}$$

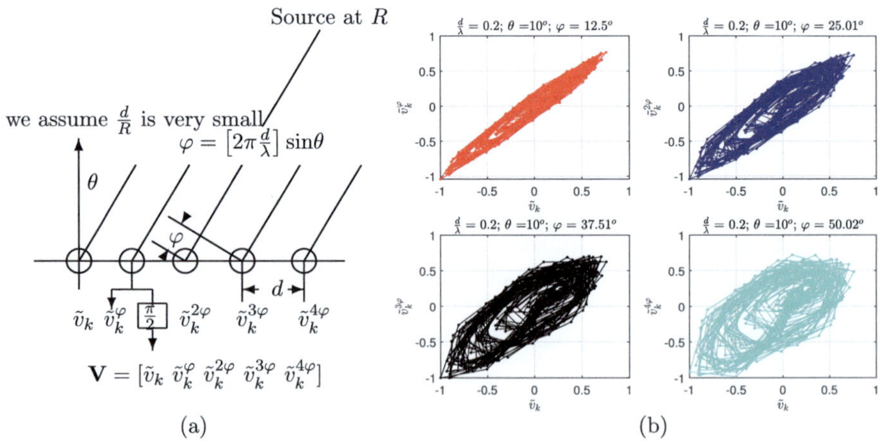

Fig. 6.13 Uniform linear array 5 microphones $d = 10\,\text{cm}$ phase shift between ULA elements

where $\tilde{v}_k$ is the decimated signal for a desired phase shift φ at a normalized frequency $f_n = \frac{F_0}{f_s}$ we can chose the r value as

$$r = \frac{\tan(\frac{\varphi}{2})}{\tan(\frac{\varphi}{2})\cos 2\pi f_n - \sin 2\pi f_n}. \tag{6.24}$$

Figure 6.9b displays the phase shifts between elements as Lissajous figures. Notably, in these figures, the ellipse's minor axis increases with the phase.

6.10 Direction of Arrival

We can utilize any of the formant frequencies to determine direction. In this application, we focused on the dominant frequency F_0, specifically the peak p_a. The time series $\{\tilde{v}_k\}$ is processed through a second-order autoregressive process, as described in Eq. 6.25. This process serves as a narrowband filter.

$$x_k^{i\varphi} = rpx_{k-1}^{i\varphi} - r^2 x_{k-2}^{i\varphi} + g(\tilde{v}_k^{i\varphi} - \tilde{v}_{k-2}^{i\varphi}) \tag{6.25}$$

note $i\varphi$ is superscript not exponent

where r is set to 0.9 and $p = 2r\cos(2\pi F_0)$, with $g = \frac{1-r^2}{2}$. This configuration allows the spectral content to concentrate around F_0 while maintaining unity gain. The equation (referenced as Eq. 6.25) is applied for $i = 0$ to 4. For $i = 0$, the superscript is omitted, resulting in x_k and $\tilde{v}_k$. The amplitude spectrum x_k is illustrated as $|X_n|$ in Fig. 6.14b, where the narrowband spectrum $|\tilde{V}_n|$ is superimposed. Additionally, the narrowband signal time series x_k is shown in Fig. 6.14a.

Fig. 6.14 Narrow band signal

6.10.1 Snapshots

The snapshot vector is given as

$$\mathbf{x}_k^T = [x_k \; x_k^{\varphi} \; x_k^{2\varphi} \; x_k^{3\varphi} \; x_k^{4\varphi}] \tag{6.26}$$

In traditional MUSIC for DOA, we require the in-phase (I) and quadrature (Q) components of the signal, as depicted in the ULA diagram in Fig. 6.9a. In practice, these components are not readily available. However, a Hilbert Transform or numerical method (see [37]) or the process described in [30] can be employed to achieve a $\frac{\pi}{2}$ shift. This poses a significant challenge as the size of the complex look matrix would be 512×5, necessitating further processing. We present an alternative approach *easy*-MUSIC to alleviate this complexity. For quick understanding we create a matrix $\mathbf{X}$ as

$$\mathbf{X}^T = [\mathbf{x}_1 \ldots \mathbf{x}_k \ldots \mathbf{x}_N] \tag{6.27}$$

The matrix $\mathbf{X}$ contains columns as time series $\{x_k\}$, $\{x_k^{\varphi}\}$, $\{x_k^{2\varphi}\}$, $\{x_k^{3\varphi}\}$, $\{x_k^{4\varphi}\}$ giving a 512×5 *real* matrix.

6.10.2 *easy*-MUSIC

In this novel approach [38], we compute the Discrete Fourier Transform (DFT) of the columns of the real matrix $\mathbf{X}$ as defined in Eq. 6.27 using the Fast Fourier Transform (FFT). Each column represents a time series $x_k^{i\varphi}$ of processed data from a sensor in the ULA, as described in Eq. 6.25. This results in a complex matrix denoted as $\mathbf{Z}$ (Fig. 6.15a). We exploit that the matrix columns $\mathbf{X}$ represent narrow-band signals. With this in mind, we select specific row vectors from matrix $\mathbf{Z}$ centered around frequency f_a or bin number a, as defined in Eq. 6.19. This partitioned complex matrix, designated as $\mathbf{Y}$, is shown in a picture in Fig. 6.15a. Typically, the size of this complex data matrix would be approximately $n \times m$, with a range chosen from $a - \frac{n}{2}$ to $a + \frac{n}{2}$. This compact complex matrix $\mathbf{Y}$ is further processed by the *gold*-MUSIC algorithm. The value of n is as small as 20 instead of $N = 512$. In this method, we have compacted the matrix and provided the I and Q components demanded by gMUSIC as easy MUSIC.

6.10.2.1 *gold*-MUSIC

In this section, we will review the concepts of the MUSIC spectrum as utilized in [28]. Let's assume there are m sensors in an intelligent array with n snapshots from the ULA sensor. The $\mathbf{Y}$ matrix, as described in Eq. 6.15a, represents the $n \times m$ matrix of snapshots in the spectral domain. The $\mathbf{Y}$ matrix contains complex values representing

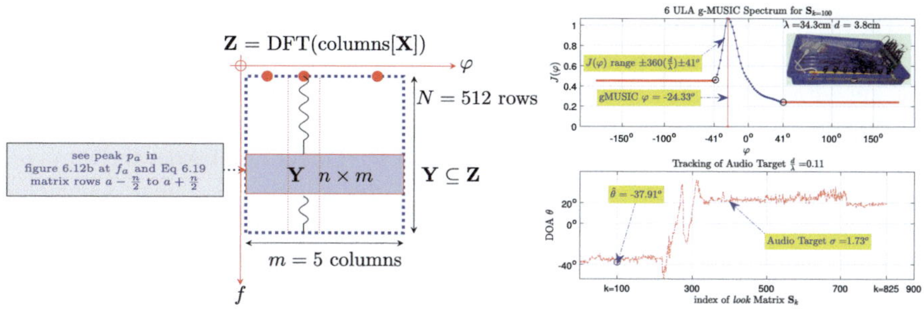

(a) (b)

Fig. 6.15 Proof of concept using *easy*-MUSIC

the in-phase and quadrature components since $\mathbf{X}$ is real. The covariance matrix can be given by

$$\mathbf{S} = \mathbf{Y}^H \mathbf{Y} \tag{6.28}$$

where ^{H} denotes Hermitian. The eigenanalysis of $\mathbf{S}$ yields the eigenvalues $\mathbf{L}$ and the corresponding eigenvectors $\mathbf{E}$. It has been shown that $\mathbf{L}$ will contain only positive real values as $\mathbf{S}$ is positive definite. If there are $D < m$ independent signals, $m - D$ of the eigenvalues will ideally be zero under no noise condition, but will be close to zero depending on the *signal-to-noise ratio* (SNR). After sorting the eigenvalues in $\mathbf{L}$ in ascending order, the $m \times (m - D)$ matrix $\mathbf{E}_N$, the matrix of the $m - D$ eigenvectors corresponding to the $m - D$ lowest eigenvalues, is found. $\mathbf{E}_N$ contains the noise eigenvectors. $\mathbf{E}$ can be written as$\mathbf{E} = \{\mathbf{E}_N | \mathbf{E}_S\}$, where $\mathbf{E}_S$ are the signal eigenvectors. The noise eigenmatrix $\mathbf{E}_N$ can be written as

$$\mathbf{E}_N = \{\mathbf{v}_1, \mathbf{v}_2 \ldots \mathbf{v}_{m-D}\}$$

Considering each eigenvector $\mathbf{v}_i$ as a transversal filter. It can be written as $h_i(\varphi) = \mathbf{v}_i(\varphi)$. Using this, an objective function is defined as

$$J(\varphi) = \frac{1}{h_t(\varphi)} \text{ where } h_t(\varphi) = \sum_{i=1}^{m-D} |h_i(\varphi)| \tag{6.29}$$

Gold univariate minimization is employed to exactly scale the peaks of $J(\varphi)$. The phase and DOA are related through a non-linear relation as

$$\theta = \sin^{-1}\left(\frac{\varphi}{2\pi\frac{d}{\lambda}}\right) \tag{6.30}$$

The factor $\frac{d}{\lambda}$ plays a crucial role in determining the valid range of φ(see Fig. 6.15b) since the argument in Eq. 6.30 must be less than or equal to one. The function $J(\varphi)$, also known as the MUSIC spectrum, is computed using Eq. 6.29. Figure 6.14d depicts the function $J(\theta)$ using Eq. 6.30. The accurate peak of $J(\varphi)$ (phase φ) is obtained using the gold-MUSIC method, and the value of the Direction of Arrival (DOA) (θ) is obtained using this peak phase. In Fig. 6.14d, the equation $\frac{d}{\lambda} = F_0 \frac{d}{c}$ is depicted on the x-axis, where c is the velocity of sound. It displays the DOA error e_k, which represents variations resulting from changes in formant frequency. The impact on the direction of arrival (DOA) estimate is denoted as e_k. When $\frac{d}{\lambda} < 0.1$, errors are more noticeable from the σ value.

6.10.3 Proof of Concept

A simple setup of an array of microphones (product model would be MEMS array) was created to illustrate the concept, as shown in the inset of Fig. 6.15b. A data acquisition system controlled by MATLAB was utilized, with a limitation of 6 channels. After data acquisition, narrow-band filtering was applied using a fixed filter at 1000 Hz. With a spacing of $d = 3.8$ cm, we obtained a $\frac{d}{\lambda} = 0.11$ velocity of sound, which is 343 m/sec. In Fig. 6.15b, we can observe that when $\frac{d}{\lambda} < 0.5$, the phase range decreases while the DOA range remains at $\pm\frac{\pi}{2}$. The target's movement from left to right was used to estimate the DOA.

The concept is implemented in C++, linked with MATLAB, and then compiled into a MATLAB MEX file, as shown in Fig. 6.16. The figure includes a screenshot of

```
  clc; clear all; close all;
% Kaluri V Ranga Rao, Belle Mead
  ula = 6;MintwoPowerM=10;D=1; wavfile = 'sr2T.wav'; F=3;
  bpf =[100 1000];doa2 = -35; waveletWindow = 64; indx = 1;
for k=0:100
  % extract block of data
  % from wavfile
  [u,s,flag,fs,A,dbyL,uwav,pitch,At] = xTrktNb(wavfile,k,MintwoPowerM,...
  ula,doa2,bpf);
% energy detection flag
  if ( flag > 0 )
  %... get 3 formant frequencies
    [x,sp,z,pC,bins,pg] = voice2pitch(u,F,k,waveletWindow);
p = real(pC);
  %... direction DOA using gold MUSIC
    [muSpk doa En SNR] = gMusik(D,dbyL,A'); sz = size(A);
    if ( k==82) % take a snap shot at 82 block
       if (length(bins) > 1) labelPitchE(u,p,fs); end; pause;
    end;
  end;
%.. end of for loop
  end; % @copyright protected kaluri@ieee.org
```

Fig. 6.16 Embedded C in MATLAB

the C++ solution. Additionally, three mex commands displayed in colored boxes are visible in Fig. 6.16. The code contains approximately 5000 lines. In this section, we discuss two types of wideband signals: an FMCW radar signal and a voice signal. Neither is classified as a narrowband signal. Both types require different approaches to determine the signal's direction.

6.11 Summary

The algorithm used in Frequency Modulated Continuous Wave (FMCW) radar analyzes the phase information of a narrowband signal from each antenna element. It employs the *gold*-Fourier-Kaluri (gFK) technique to accurately extract the narrowband signal, also known as the phasor. The κMUSIC method uses these phase and amplitude values to determine the Direction of Arrival (DOA), fulfilling the specific requirements of FMCW radar and outperforming traditional MUSIC methods. Additionally, all reflections from a target are captured and modeled as clusters. The concept is based on classical rigid body mechanics, focusing on the motion of the centroid and its surrounding area. Our current algorithm, called κMUSIC, runs approximately 11 times faster than the original MUSIC algorithm. In this context, the whole scene is viewed as a set of distributed objects, forming what we call a scene matrix, represented as $\mathbf{S}(t)$. This matrix serves as input for our machine learning model, particularly in automotive applications. For voice signals, the dominant signal is captured and its direction estimated using *easy*-MUSIC, which processes only real signals.

6.11.1 MEX File Generation

The C files used to generate the MEX files in this chapter are located in two leading directories:

This chapter C files for MEX		
MEX file	Location of C files	Command
gMusik.mexw64	chap6\ figures\ dOfVoice\ dOfVoice	mexGmusik.m
voice2pitch.mexw64	chap6\ figures\ dOfVoice\ dOfVoice	mexVoice2Pitch.m
xTrktNb.mexw64	chap6\ figures\ dOfVoice\ dOfVoice	mexXtRktNb.m
getScene.mexw64	chap6\ figures\ fmcwRadar\ fmcwRadar	myMexGetScene.m
LatexFileMatrix.mexw64	chap6\ figures\ fmcwRadar\ fmcwRadar	myMexLatexFileMatrix.m
getRgDcLuster.mexw64	chap6\ figures\ fmcwRadar\ fmcwRadar	myMexGetRgDcLuster.m
initR.mexw64	chap6\ figures\ fmcwRadar\ fmcwRadar	myMexInitR.m

`chap6\figures\dOfVoice\dOfVoice` and `chap6\figures\fmcwRadar\fmcwRadar`. In each directory, specific MATLAB `.m` files are used to compile the corresponding C source code into platform-specific MEX files using the `mex` command. In the first directory, the files `mexGmusik.m`, `mexVoice2Pitch.m`, and mexXtRktNb.m generate the MEX files gMusik.mexw64, voice2pitch.mexw64, and xTrktNb.mexw64, respectively. In the second directory, the files myMexGetScene.m, myMexLatexFileMatrix.m, myMexGetRgDcLuster.m, and myMexInitR.m produce the MEX files getScene.mexw64, LatexFileMatrix.mexw64, getRgDcLuster.mexw64, and initR.mexw64, respectively. Each MATLAB script contains a call to the mex function, which compiles the associated C file into a MEX binary, enabling efficient integration and execution within the MATLAB environment.

6.11.2 File Organization

This subsection provides a list of program files associated with the previous chapter, *Wideband Signals and Machine Learning Applications*. The files are organized into 12 directories, presented in two tables, each containing six directories. Each directory name is highlighted in yellow at the top of its respective column for easy identification. Table A includes the directories figLookMatMicAry, figBpfPeaks, figCarFront, figCarSide, figNBsig, and figRgPhiGfk along with the files in it. Table B includes the directories figVoice, figOf8H, figSharpObject, figPerception, figOf8V, and figWaveId along with the files in it.

This chapter program files Table A

figLookMatMicAry	figBpfPeaks	figCarFront	figCarSide	figNBsig	figRgPhiGfk
del.mat	ds2nfu.m	C.csv	beamTi1642.jpg	del.mat	closeDoa.txt
ds2nfu.m	figBpfPeaks.m	CarFrontScene.tex	C.csv	ds2nfu.m	data.mat
figLookMatMicAry.m	gMusik.mexw64	D.csv	CarSideScene.tex	eMusic.m	ds2nfu.m
gMusik.mexw64	labelBpf.m	DataCarFront.txt	D.csv	figNBsig.m	figRgPhiGfk.eps
label211.m	labelPitchE.m	figCarFront.eps	DataCarSide.txt	gMusik.mexw64	figRgPhiGfk.m
lookMat.tex	obj.csv	figCarFront.m	figCarSide.eps	labelFigMu.m	figRgPhiPolar.eps
obj.csv	peaksEnergy.m	getScene.mexw64	figCarSide.m	labelNB.m	getRgDcLuster.mexw64
ula1.mat	sr2T.wav	initR-del.mexw64	getScene.mexw64	obj.csv	initR.mexw64
ula10.mat	voice2pitch.mexw64	kMuGmu.csv	kMuGmu.csv	Spk.m	label211.m
ula11.mat	xTrktNb.mexw64	labelPolarClouds.m	labelPolarClouds.m	sr2T.wav	label223.m
ula12.mat		LatexFileMatrix.mexw64	LatexFileMatrix.mexw64	voice2pitch.mexw64	label224.m
ula13.mat	figLookMatMicAry	polarDS2nfu.m	phase.csv	xTrktNb.mexw64	labelPolarClouds.m
ula14.mat	ula4.mat	rcon.txt	polarDS2nfu.m		LatexFileMatrix.mexw64
ula15.mat	ula5.mat	unsort.csv	rangeSpk.csv		plotObjects.m
ula2.mat	ula6.mat		rcon.txt		polarDS2nfu.m
ula3.mat	ula7.mat		unsort.csv		rawDataTable.tex
	ula8.mat				rcon.txt
	ula9.mat				rgDoa.m
	ulaAu6.jpg				rgPhiTable.tex

These directories contain the algorithms and generate figures essential for understanding the concepts discussed in this chapter. The figures are largely self-explanatory and serve to illustrate the algorithms presented in the text visually. The implementations rely on MATLAB-executable C-code (MEX files) for efficient processing and display. The code itself is provided separately in the repository and is not embedded in this document.

This chapter program files Table B					
figVoice	figOf8H	figSharpObject	figPerception	figOf8V	figUlaPhase
ds2nfu.m	C.csv	C.csv	ds2nfu.m	C.csv	figUlaPhase.m
figVoice.eps	D.csv	closeDoa.txt	dsxy2figxy.m	D.csv	gMusik.mexw64
figVoice.m	figOf8H.eps	D.csv	figChirp.eps	figOf8V.eps	labelUlaPhase.m
gMusik.mexw64	figOf8H.m	figSharpObject.eps	figChirp.m	figOf8V.m	obj.csv
labelVoice.m	figOf8H.txt	figSharpObject.m	figPerception.tex	figOf8V.txt	sr2T.wav
obj.csv	getScene.mexw64	getScene.mexw64	labelChirp.m	getScene.mexw64	ulaLp.tex
Spk.m	kMuGmu.csv	kMuGmu.csv	scene.jpg	kMuGmu.csv	voice2pitch.mexw64
sr2T.wav	phase.csv	labelPolarClouds.m	xLabel.m	phase.csv	xTrktNb.mexw64
voice2pitch.mexw64	polarDS2nfu.m	LatexFileMatrix.mexw64		polarDS2nfu.m	
xTrktNb.mexw64	polarLabel.m	polarDS2nfu.m		polarLabel.m	
	rangeSpk.csv	rcon.txt		rangeSpk.csv	
	rcon.txt	SharpObjectScene.tex		rcon.txt	
	unsort.csv	unsort.csv		unsort.csv	

Disclaimer

References

1. H. Rohling and C. Moller, *Radar waveform for automotive radar systems and applications*, 2008 IEEE Radar Conference, Rome, Italy, 2008, pp. 1–4.
2. M. D. Richter, M. Schneider, P. Wenig and R. Weigel, *77 GHz automotive digital beamforming radar with SiGe chipset*, German Microwave Conference Digest of Papers, Berlin, Germany, 2010, pp. 210–213.
3. Z. Tong, R. Renter and M. Fujimoto, *Fast chirp FMCW radar in automotive applications*, IET International Radar Conference 2015, Hangzhou, 2015, pp. 1–4.
4. N. Chandolikar, C. Joshi, P. Roy, A. Gawas and M. Vishwakarma, *Voice Recognition: A Comprehensive Survey*, 2022 International Mobile and Embedded Technology Conference (MECON), Noida, India, 2022, pp. 45–51.
5. M. Sigmund, *Comparison of Different Kinds of Long-Time Spectra of Voice Estimated by Modified Linear Prediction to Distinguish Speakers*, 2019 International Conference on Speech Technology and Human-Computer Dialogue (SpeD), Timisoara, Romania, 2019, pp. 1–6.
6. Z. K. Abdul and A. K. Al-Talabani, *Mel Frequency Cepstral Coefficient and its Applications: A Review*, in IEEE Access, vol. 10, pp. 122136–122158, 2022.
7. *The Impact of Cognition on Radar Technology—Radar, Sonar and Navigation* A. Farina (editor), Antonio De Maio (editor), Simon S. Haykin, Scitech Publishing 2018.

8. Texas Instruments User Guide *AWR1642 Evaluation Module Single-Chip mmWave Sensing Solution User's Guide* (Rev. C) May 2020, page 13.
9. H. T. Tan and M. Dong, *Analyzing the Relationship between Formants and Pitch for Singing Voice*, 2011 International Conference on Asian Language Processing, Penang, Malaysia, 2011, pp. 248–252.
10. M. G. Christensen and A. Jakobsson, *Multi-pitch estimation, Synthesis Lectures on Speech and Audio Processing*, vol. 5, no. 1, pp. 1–160, 2009.
11. Daniel Gabriel *et al, Design and assessment of multiple-sound source localization using microphone arrays*, pp 199–204, 2019 IEEE/SICE International Symposium on System Integration (SII).
12. M. Viberg, B. Ottenten and T. Kailath, *Direction-of-arrival estimation and detection using weighted subspace fitting*, Twenty-Third Asilomar Conference on Signals, Systems and Computers, 1989, Pacific Grove, CA,USA, 1989, pp.
13. Kaluri V. Rangarao and Shridhar V. Narasimhan *gold-MUSIC: A variation on MUSIC to accurately determine peaks of the spectrum*, IEEE Trans Antenna and Propagation Vol 61 issue 4, April 2013 pp 2263–2268, http://ieeexplore.ieee.org/document/6376104/.
14. Kaluri V. Rangarao, Atul Negi, *A Perception Engine in Automotive FMCW Radar*, 2023 IEEE International Workshop on Technologies for Defense and Security (TechDefense), Rome, Italy, 2023, pp. 234–239, https://ieeexplore.ieee.org/document/10380840.
15. Kaluri V. Rangarao, *et al., Estimating the Directions of Arrival of Narrow Band Signals using Spatial Tuned Filter* in Proc of RADAR-2011 at Chengudu, pp 319–22, http://ieeexplore.ieee.org/document/6159541/
16. Kaluri V. Rangarao, and Balaji Kanigicherla, *DOA Estimation via kMUSIC in FMCW Radar Application*, 2018 14th IEEE International Conference on Signal Processing (ICSP), Beijing, China, 2018, pp. 903–908. https://events.vtools.ieee.org/m/175360 https://ieeexplore.ieee.org/document/8652394
17. Yuntao Wu et al *Joint Pitch and DOA Estimation Using the ESPRIT Method*, Trans IEEE/ACM Transactions on Audio, Speech, and Language Processing, Vol. 23, NO. 1, January 2015.
18. J. R. Jensen, M. G. Christensen, and S. H. Jensen, *Joint DOA and fundamental frequency estimation methods based on 2-d filtering*, in Proc. European Signal Processing Conf., Aug. 2010, pp. 2091–2095.
19. J. A. Moorer, *Signal processing aspects of computer music: A survey*, in Proceedings of the IEEE, vol. 65, no. 8, pp. 1108–1137, 1977.
20. A. K. Krishnamurthy, *Glottal source estimation using a sum-of-exponentials model*, in IEEE Transactions on Signal Processing, vol. 40, no. 3, pp. 682–686, 1992.
21. S. Narusawa, N. Minematsu, K. Hirose and H. Fujisaki, *A method for automatic extraction of model parameters from fundamental frequency contours of speech*, 2002 IEEE International Conference on Acoustics, Speech, and Signal Processing, Orlando, FL, USA, 2002, pp. I-509–I-512.
22. Kaluri Venkata Rangarao and Ranjan K. Mallik, *Digital Signal Processing : A Practitioner's Approach*, ISBN: 978-0-470-01769-2 November 2005 John Wiley.
23. Kaluri V. Rangarao, and Venugopal A, *gold-Fourier Kaluri Method for Estimating Vortex Shedding Frequency*, in Proc IEEE R10 2016 Symposium (TENSYMP), pp 379–383, Bali, Indonesia, http://ieeexplore.ieee.org/document/7519436/
24. W. Ross; *Fundamental Problems In Radio Direction-Finding at High Frequencies(3-30Mc/s)*, (1947).
25. R. L. Smith-Rose and H. G. Hopkins; *Radio Direction-Finding On Wavelengths Between 6 and 10 meters(Frequencies 50 to 30 Mc./Sec.)*, (1938).
26. Ralph O. Schmidt; *Multiple Emitter Location and Signal Parameter Estimation*, IEEE Transactions on Antennas and Propagation, Vol. AP-34, No. 3, March 1986.
27. A. J. Weiss and B. Friedlander, *Direction finding for diversely polarized signals using polynomial rooting*, [1991] Conference Record of the Twenty-Fifth Asilomar Conference on Signals, Systems & Computers, Pacific Grove, CA, USA, 1991, pp. 287–289 vol.1.

28. Kaluri V. Rangarao and Shridhar V. Narasimhan *gold-MUSIC: A variation on MUSIC to accurately determine peaks of the spectrum*, IEEE Trans Antenna and Propagation Vol 61 issue 4, April 2013 pp 2263–2268, http://ieeexplore.ieee.org/document/6376104/
29. Kaluri V. Rangarao et al *Estimating the Directions of Arrival of Narrow Band Signals using Spatial Tuned Filter*, IEEE International Conference on Radar Oct 24–27 2011, Chengdu, CHINA, http://ieeexplore.ieee.org/document/6159541/
30. Kaluri V. Rangarao and Shridhar V. *An Accurate Numerical Method for Estimating the Delay Between Two Omni-Directional Receiving Elements*, IEEE 30th Digital Avionics Systems Conference 2011, Seattle, Washington, U.S.A., October 2011, pp 8C3-4–8C3-7, http://ieeexplore.ieee.org/document/6096146/
31. Ranjan.K. Mallik, K V Rangarao and U.M.S. Murty, *DOA estimation by least squares approach, Electronics Letters*, vol. 34, no. 12, pp. 1187–1189, June 11 1998, http://ieeexplore.ieee.org/document/702362/
32. Rob Carrikre and Randolph L. Moses *High Resolution Radar Target Modeling Using a Modified Prony Estimator* IEEE Trans Antenna and Propagation, Vol. 40, No. I, January 1992.
33. Yuan-Hung Hsiao *et al., A 77-GHz 2T6R Transceiver With Injection-Lock Frequency Sextupler Using 65-nm CMOS for Automotive Radar System Application* IEEE Trans on MTT, Vol. 64, No. 10, Oct 2016 pp 3031–48.
34. Jrgen Hasch *et al., Millimeter-Wave Technology for Automotive Radar Sensors in the 77 GHz Frequency Band* IEEE Trans on MTT, Vol. 60, No. 3, Mar 2012 pp 845–860.
35. Garthwaite, M. C., Nancarrow, S., Hislop, A., Thankappan, M., Dawson, J. H., Lawrie, S. *The Design of Radar Corner Reflectors for the Australian Geophysical Observing System* Record 2015/03 GeoCat 82751 www.ga.gov.au.
36. Harry L. Van Trees; *Detection, Estimation, and Modulation Theory, Part 1* John Wiley & Sons.
37. K. V. Rangarao, *et al*, *A robust BFSK signal demodulator using Orthogonal Decomposer*, 2013 IEEE/AIAA 32nd Digital Avionics Systems Conference (DASC), East Syracuse, NY, USA, 2013, pp. 3D4-1–3D4-5.
38. Kaluri. V. Rangarao and A. Negi, *Formant Based Direction of Voice for Smart Microphone Array*, 2024 IEEE International Workshop on Technologies for Defense and Security (TechDefense), Naples, Italy, 2024, pp. 363–367.

Index

V. R. Kaluri, *Direction Finding Algorithms for Practicing Engineers*,
https://doi.org/10.1007/978-3-032-06997-9

MIX
Papier aus verantwortungsvollen Quellen
Paper from responsible sources
FSC® C105338

If you have any concerns about our products,
you can contact us on
ProductSafety@springernature.com

In case Publisher is established outside the EU,
the EU authorized representative is:
Springer Nature Customer Service Center GmbH
Europaplatz 3, 69115 Heidelberg, Germany

Printed by Libri Plureos GmbH
in Hamburg, Germany